SPOTLIGHT on
LITERACY

READ ALOUDS,
PLAYS, POEMS, AND
CHORAL READINGS

Margaret H. Lippert
Anthologist

As part of the Macmillan / McGraw-Hill's effort to help make a difference to the environment, this anthology has been printed on recycled paper.

10% post-consumer content

**Macmillan
McGraw-Hill**

New York • Farmington

Macmillan/McGraw-Hill

A Division of The **McGraw·Hill** *Companies*

Macmillan/McGraw-Hill
1221 Avenue of the Americas
New York, New York 10020

Printed in the United States of America

ISBN 0-02-183202-1/6

1 2 3 4 5 6 7 8 9   P O H   02   01   00   99   98   97

CONTENTS

READ ALOUDS

= *available on audiocassettes*

PLAYS, POEMS, CHORAL READINGS

WRITE YOUR OWN

POETRY

8

CHORAL READINGS

INTRODUCTION

by Margaret H. Lippert

Long before I wrote stories, I listened for stories. Listening for them is something more acute than listening to them. I suppose it's an early form of participation in what goes on. Listening children know stories are there. When their elders sit and begin, children are just waiting and hoping for one to come out, like a mouse from its hole.

EUDORA WELTY[1]

This book is stuffed with mice. Your students are waiting.

You are part of a long tradition of storytellers and story readers. Stories belong to us all. From ancient times, people have been entertained and nourished by stories. All of us in our own families and culture have, like Eudora Welty, been entranced by the tales that have been told to us from the time we first started to listen. From these stories, we learned about listening and speaking and then about reading—connecting the images and messages of stories with print and with books.

The power of stories draws us to ideas and thoughts and feelings that we want and need to explore. Through stories we learn about the experiences of others and come to understand ourselves better. The best stories take us from where we are and lead us, word by word, image by image, into places known and unknown, familiar and new, comfortable and exciting.

Reading aloud opens students to a new way of learning— listening. Many of us, and many of our students, are unaccustomed to listening carefully. We tune out much of what goes on around us. We need to remember the power of listening and help our students do the same.

Reading aloud can grip students in a listening vise—because they want to know what will happen next, they listen with fully focused attention. Since students can understand a much larger vocabulary than they can read themselves, when we read aloud we expose them to more sophisticated concepts and content than they could read independently. People of traditional cultures knew this—they passed on knowledge through their stories.

As you read aloud, you give your students stories and something of yourself. You build a community in your classroom that links you and your students to one another, to the story, and to the thinking and feeling of the author and the culture from which that story springs. Your students stretch and grow, discovering the pathways and journeys of others and, in the process, making discoveries of their own.

A READ-ALOUD CELEBRATION

Each Read Aloud in this collection relates in some way—theme, style, author, content—to a selection in the Macmillan/McGraw-Hill Reading/Language Arts student anthologies. Many of the Read Alouds are traditional tales, stories that were handed down from one generation to another within a particular culture. Traditional stories include folk tales, fairy tales, myths, legends, tall tales, and fables. In addition to traditional literature, classics and contemporary literature are represented.

In order to root this collection in the traditional oral heritage from which stories spring, I interviewed people who grew up in storytelling cultures and taped them telling stories so that you and your students would have access to their wisdom and to their stories. Some of these gifted storytellers are included on the SONGS AND STORIES AUDIOCASSETTES that are offered with the series.

The information about the contributors and the indexes at the end of the collection provide important information for you to share with your students about the origins of the tales and of the tellers.

It is preferable, though not absolutely necessary, to skim through a story before you read it aloud. That way you will know where the story is headed, and you can adjust your reading style to the mood and rhythm of the story.

As you read, take your time and read with involvement and intensity. Your students will need time to construct story images and to process ideas as the story moves along. To help you judge the time you will need to allow for each story reading, the range of times it took several different teachers to read each story aloud to a group of students is included in the CONTENTS.

Sometimes questions will arise in response to a story. When this happens, I often ask students if they can answer the questions that have been raised. I have done this countless times, and, no matter how difficult the question, no student has ever said, "I don't know." Within the story's context, they do know, and they help one another explore the answers to their own questions.

Now I often ask after reading or telling a story, "Was there any part of the story that was unclear to you?" or "What did you wonder about as you listened to the story?" There are always many questions. And frequently there are many answers to a question. The harder the question, the more ideas and responses the question seems to generate. For example, after hearing me tell *Yeh-Shen*,[2] which is a Chinese version of the Cinderella story, one third grader asked, "Why did the stepmother kill the fish?" Seven children offered seven different explanations. Some of the responses were as follows: "Maybe she didn't like the fish." "One of the reasons could be that she wanted the meat from the fish. Or that she didn't want the girl [Yeh-Shen] to be friends with the fish." "I think she was just plain mean."

The students listened to the story. They struggled with parts that were unclear or unexplained, and they integrated all of their previous knowledge with the information generated in the story. They also developed plausible explanations to justify the actions of the characters and the events in the story.

In an atmosphere where questions are encouraged, hard questions are more likely to rise to the surface so they can be explored. Every question is a new starting point. Through ALL their questions, students seek meaning and struggle collaboratively to find answers to their own puzzling questions about the stories. What a wonderful model for seeking responses to the puzzling questions that confront them in their lives.

"I DO AND I UNDERSTAND"

There is an ancient Chinese proverb: "I hear and I forget. I see and I remember. I do and I understand."

By reading these stories aloud, you make them part of the oral tradition. Just listening to these stories will enrich the imaginations of your students, offering them new ideas and insights. But if your students re-create a favorite story in another form, it will become theirs in an even deeper way. "Doing" the stories leads to further understanding and appreciation of them.

Your students may wish to retell the story as a group in their own words, or to illustrate or depict the story in paintings, collages, or dioramas. They may enjoy spontaneously reenacting the story without props or scenery, or perhaps with the simplest of these. They may choose to write their favorite or least favorite part of the story, or their own version of the story either in whole or in part. If they do any of these things, either prompted by you or motivated on their own, they will know the story more intimately. The better they know the story, the more comfortable they will feel with it, and the better they will like it. The more they like it, the more they will want to share it, perhaps even outside the classroom, with family or friends. Thus the oral tradition continues.

ONWARD TO STORYTELLING

As a storyteller and story lover, I would be remiss if I did not encourage you to try telling, without the text, a tale or two. Telling a story is fun. It also models for students the possibility that they, too, can recall, retell, and enjoy stories whenever they wish. If you've told stories before, you know the flexibility and closeness engendered by direct contact with listeners, without an intervening page. If you haven't, you could begin with a short, familiar tale.

13

You don't need to memorize the words to enjoy telling stories. In fact, memorizing the words may distract you from the images and sequence of the tale itself. I simply picture the story as it takes place, then describe it to my listeners as I "see" it. This is the same skill you use when relating an anecdote that happened to you or when telling a joke. As a teacher, you already know how to hold the attention of your class. Storytelling is one small step beyond explaining a concept or describing an assignment.

The author-storyteller-artist Ashley Bryan has a favorite African proverb: "He who learns, teaches!" Learn the craft of storytelling along with your students. Allow them to watch you struggle and try and learn. Make mistakes and work through your mistakes. Allow them also to watch you as you succeed and soar on the wings of new stories. This will teach them about your love of story and language, and about how much you are willing to risk for them.

ENDINGS AND BEGINNINGS

From here, it is up to you. The stories are yours now. Read them, enjoy them, pass them along. By sharing these stories with your students, you will preserve them for at least one more generation.

Since this is a book of stories, I'd like to end this introduction with a story, or to be more accurate, a part of a Russian folk tale that is my favorite story. The oldest man in the village, encouraging a young boy to tell his first story to the expectant listeners around the fire, says:

> *A story is a letter that comes to us from yesterday. Each person who tells it adds his word to the message and sends it on to tomorrow. So begin.*
>
> from "The Tale of the Tales"[3]

[1] Eudora Welty, *One Writer's Beginnings* (Cambridge, MA: Harvard University Press, 1983), p. 16.

[2] Ai-Ling Louie, *Yeh-Shen: A Cinderella Story from China* (New York: Philomel Books, 1982).

[3] George and Helen Papashvily, "The Tale of the Tales," *Yes and No Stories: A Book of Georgian Folk Tales* (New York: Harper & Brothers, 1946).

I can promise that once you begin the daily experience of reading aloud to children, it will become one of the best parts of your day and the children's day, minutes and hours that will be treasured for years to come.

JIM TRELEASE
from *The Read-Aloud Handbook*

Papa Who Wakes Up Tired In The Dark

a vignette by Sandra Cisneros

Your abuelito is dead, Papa says early one morning in my room. *Está muerto,* and then as if he just heard the news himself, crumples like a coat and cries, my brave Papa cries. I have never seen my Papa cry and don't know what to do.

I know he will have to go away, that he will take a plane to Mexico, all the uncles and aunts will be there, and they will have a black and white photo taken in front of the tomb with flowers shaped like spears in a white vase because this is how they send the dead away in that country.

Because I am the oldest, my father has told me first, and now it is my turn to tell the others. I will have to explain why we can't play. I will have to tell them to be quiet today.

My Papa, his thick hands and thick shoes, who wakes up tired in the dark, who combs his hair with water, drinks his coffee, and is gone before we wake, today is sitting on my bed.

And I think if my own Papa died what would I do. I hold my Papa in my arms. I hold and hold and hold him.

HERACLES

a Greek myth retold by Margaret H. Lippert

The story of Heracles (her′ ə klēz), who is often called by his Roman name Hercules, has been told and retold for more than two thousand years. According to the ancient Greeks, Heracles was the son of the great god Zeus (züs), king of all the gods. However, the mother of Heracles was not a goddess. She was a mortal, or human being. Heracles was born a man with the godlike strength of his father.

From the time he was an infant, Heracles could do remarkable things. When he was eight months old, he strangled two sea serpents.

When Heracles grew up, an angry goddess made him temporarily insane and caused him to kill his wife and three sons. To work through his grief, Heracles agreed to do twelve labors for his cousin King Eurystheus (ū rēs′ thē əs). The King was jealous of Heracles because he was so strong. He ordered Heracles to do more and more dangerous labors, hoping that Heracles would be killed. Over eight years, Heracles completed ten of the labors successfully. Now he is about to be given the eleventh labor.

King Eurystheus looked up. The mighty hero stood before him. Heracles was back, again. And again he had performed his task. King Eurystheus was filled with rage. "I will get rid of this man forever," he thought.

"Heracles," he began, "you have killed ferocious beasts. You have overcome gruesome monsters. But you have not yet visited the land of the gods themselves. I have heard that the gods have a beautiful garden, planted around a tree which bears golden apples. I wish to have three of these golden apples to give to my daughter. Your eleventh labor is this: bring me three golden apples from the garden of the gods."

Heracles lowered his head. He knew that Eurystheus was desperate. No mortal had ever been to the garden of the gods, which lay at the far western edge of the world. Furthermore, it was said that the golden apples which grew there could be picked only by the gods themselves. If a mortal plucked one, he or she would die. Heracles was silent. He knew he must accomplish this labor, as he had accomplished all the others before it. But he was filled with dread.

Heracles set out with his lion skin over his shoulders and his bow and arrows at his side. He traveled over land and sea. At last he came to the far western edge of the world and approached the garden of the gods.

The singing of birds, beginning so softly that it could hardly be heard, became more distinct as he got closer. The sweet smell of flowers in bloom grew stronger. In front of him loomed a high stone wall. Behind the wall was the garden. Heracles walked along the wall until he came to an open gate.

The first sight of the garden took his breath away. Flowers of every color lined grassy walkways. Trees with ripe fruit arched over the paths. In the center of the garden grew a tree lovelier than the rest. Its branches were bending under the weight of golden apples.

"I am standing where no human has ever been," Heracles thought, "seeing what humans were not meant to see. I want to turn back, but I cannot. I must complete my labor, though I do not know how to begin."

A low hiss broke through his thoughts. "What can that be?" he wondered, turning toward the tree hung with golden apples. At the base of the tree he saw a huge dragon head, then another, and another . . . dozens and dozens, more than Heracles could count. The hundred-headed dragon, which was chained to the tree to guard the golden apples, had become aware of the presence of a stranger. It roused itself to protect the treasure. Heracles drew back behind the wall to plan his next move.

At that moment, his eye was caught by a sight more wondrous than the garden, and more frightening than the dragon. A giant stood in the distance, outside the stone wall. His knees were as high as Heracles' head. Without looking up, Heracles turned to run. But he heard no heavy footsteps behind him. Heracles looked back and was astonished to see that the giant had not moved.

Heracles shaded his eyes against the sun to see why the towering giant had not come after him. He was amazed to see that the giant was supporting the inverted bowl of the sky on his head and uplifted hands.

"That must be the god Atlas," thought Heracles. "I heard he was ordered by Zeus to hold up the sky forever." An idea began to take form in Heracles' mind. "I will die if I pick the golden apples. Only a god can do so and live. Atlas is a god. Perhaps I can persuade him to help me."

Heracles walked toward Atlas. He cupped his hands around his mouth to make his voice louder. Lifting his head, he looked up at Atlas and shouted, "Atlas, I am Heracles."

"What business have you here?" challenged Atlas.

"I have been sent by King Eurystheus to get three golden apples for his daughter," responded Heracles politely. "I will take your burden from you for a moment if you will pick them for me."

Atlas could not believe his good fortune. He looked down, almost toppling the whole sky. Below him stood a man. He was a big man, eight feet tall, with muscular shoulders and a back almost as broad as it was long. His arms were massive, and his hands looked strong enough to overcome man and beast. Yet in spite of his extraordinary size and build, Atlas did not think that the man beneath him could hold the sky. He did not think that any human being could be strong

19

enough to do that. However, no one had ever offered to take his burden, even for a moment. So Atlas could not resist Heracles' offer.

Atlas looked over the wall into the garden and saw that the hundred-headed dragon had wakened and was alerted to danger. "I will be happy to pick the apples for you, Heracles," he said, "if you will kill the dragon."

The hundred-headed dragon did not frighten Heracles. He had killed beasts and monsters much more dangerous than the dragon. He stepped into the garden through the gate and crouched on the grass. He carefully fitted a poisoned arrow to his bow and took aim. Dozens of hissing heads with open mouths stretched out toward him, but because the dragon was chained to the tree Heracles was out of its reach. The dragon shrieked with helpless rage. Streaks of flame shot toward Heracles from the open mouths. Heracles took aim at the closest head and loosed his arrow, which sank deep into the neck. The dragon's hundred heads roared with agony as the poison took effect. Then the writhing body slipped down to the ground and lay motionless.

Heracles returned to Atlas and stood at his feet. Atlas had witnessed the death of the dreaded dragon. Without another word, he carefully leaned over and transferred the weight of the sky to the shoulders of Heracles.

Heracles could not believe what was demanded of his body. Only the sheer force of his will kept him pressing his hands up against the overpowering weight of the sky. His legs began to buckle, and he knew that his strength would soon give out. He struggled to steady his arms, and pain ripped through his shoulders. Salty sweat pouring down his forehead stung his eyes, but forcing them open he called frantically. "Atlas, have you picked the apples? Bring them to me."

Atlas was enjoying his unexpected freedom. He stretched and looked around. He had never really noticed how beautiful this garden was, how sweet the flowers, how lovely the songs of the birds, how luscious the fruit. He stepped over the wall and helped himself to three golden apples. Then he returned to Heracles.

"Heracles," he taunted, "what a fine job you are doing. I have the apples, and I believe I will deliver them to King Eurystheus myself. Then I will return to take up my burden again."

Heracles knew that Atlas had no intention of returning. He knew that if Atlas left, he would be imprisoned until the end of time under the unbearable weight of the sky. He was in so much pain that he could barely think, but through his distress came a glimmer of a thought.

"Atlas," he gasped, "I will be glad to share this burden with you. However, I cannot survive unless I place a pad on my shoulders. Take the sky until I can fold my lion skin to cushion the weight."

Atlas was deceived. He put down the apples and reached up to take the sky for a moment. Heracles relaxed his shoulders, and the full weight of the sky rested once again on the head and upstretched hands of the mighty Atlas. Heracles picked up the apples and ran as fast as his aching body could go.

Heracles returned to King Eurystheus with the golden apples safely hidden in his tunic. When the king saw him approaching, empty-handed, he was delighted. "Heracles, my cousin, have you failed? Where are the golden apples I ordered you to bring back for my daughter?"

Without a word, Heracles drew forth the apples and held them out to the king. Eurystheus glanced down at them and was overcome with fear. Surely the gods would punish anyone in possession of their golden apples. Suddenly he wished he had never requested them for his daughter. He was afraid to present them to her. "Take them, Heracles," he said. "They are yours."

Heracles was too wise to keep the lovely shining apples. He returned them to the shrine of a goddess, so that she could take them back to their rightful place in the garden of the gods.

For the twelfth labor, King Eurystheus ordered Heracles to go to the land of the dead and bring back the fierce three-headed dog that guarded the underworld. No human had ever returned from there alive. But after challenging the king of the dead and capturing the vicious dog, Heracles came back.

The twelve labors prepared Heracles for a life full of further adventure and glory. At his death, he was lifted by the gods to join them in their palace on the top of Mount Olympus. Heracles was the only mortal ever to be so honored.

LA BAMBA

a story by Gary Soto

Manuel was the fourth of seven children and looked like a lot of kids in his neighborhood: black hair, brown face, and skinny legs scuffed from summer play. But summer was giving way to fall: the trees were turning red, the lawns brown, and the pomegranate trees were heavy with fruit. Manuel walked to school in the frosty morning, kicking leaves and thinking of tomorrow's talent show. He was still amazed that he had volunteered. He was going to pretend to sing Ritchie Valens's "La Bamba" before the entire school.

Why did I raise my hand? he asked himself, but in his heart he knew the answer. He yearned for the limelight. He wanted applause as loud as a thunderstorm, and to hear his friends say, "Man, that was bad!" And he wanted to impress the girls, especially Petra Lopez, the second-prettiest girl in his class. The prettiest was already taken by his friend Ernie. Manuel knew he should be reasonable, since he himself was not great-looking, just average.

Manuel kicked through the fresh-fallen leaves. When he got to school he realized he had forgotten his math workbook. If his teacher found out, he would have to stay after school and miss practice for the talent show. But fortunately for him, they did drills that morning.

During lunch Manuel hung around with Benny, who was also in the talent show. Benny was going to play the trumpet in spite of the fat lip he had gotten playing football.

"How do I look?" Manuel asked. He cleared his throat and started moving his lips in pantomime. No words came out, just a hiss that sounded like a snake. Manuel tried to look emotional, flailing his arms on the high notes and opening his eyes and mouth as wide as he could when he came to *"Para bailar la baaaaammmba."*

After Manuel finished, Benny said it looked all right, but suggested Manuel dance while he sang. Manuel thought for a moment and decided it was a good idea.

"Yeah, just think you're like Michael Jackson or someone like that," Benny suggested. "But don't get carried away."

During rehearsal, Mr. Roybal, nervous about his debut as the school's talent coordinator, cursed under his breath when the lever that controlled the speed of the record player jammed.

"Darn," he growled, trying to force the lever. "What's wrong with you?"

"Is it broken?" Manuel asked, bending over for a closer look. It looked all right to him.

Mr. Roybal assured Manuel that he would have a good record player at the talent show, even if it meant bringing his own stereo from home.

Manuel sat in a folding chair, twirling his record on his thumb. He watched a skit about personal hygiene, a mother-and-daughter violin duo, five first-grade girls jumping rope, a karate kid breaking boards, three girls singing "Like a Virgin," and a skit about the pilgrims. If the record player hadn't been broken, he would have gone after the karate kid, an easy act to follow, he told himself.

As he twirled his forty-five record, Manuel thought they had a great talent show. The entire school would be amazed. His mother and father would be proud, and his brothers and sisters would be jealous and pout. It would be a night to remember.

Benny walked onto the stage, raised his trumpet to his mouth, and waited for his cue. Mr. Roybal raised his hand like a symphony conductor and let it fall dramatically. Benny inhaled and blew so loud that Manuel dropped his record, which rolled across the cafeteria floor until it hit a wall. Manuel raced after it, picked it up, and wiped it clean.

"Boy, I'm glad it didn't break," he said with a sigh.

That night Manuel had to do the dishes and a lot of homework, so he could only practice in the shower. In bed he prayed that he wouldn't mess up. He prayed that it wouldn't be like when he was a first-grader. For Science Week he had wired together a C battery and a bulb, and told everyone he had discovered how a flashlight worked. He was so pleased with himself that he practiced for hours pressing the wire to the battery, making the bulb wink a dim, orangish light. He showed it to so many kids in his neighborhood that when it was time to show his class how a flashlight worked, the battery was dead. He pressed the wire to the battery, but the bulb didn't respond. He pressed until his thumb hurt and some kids in the back started snickering.

But Manuel fell asleep confident that nothing would go wrong this time.

The next morning his father and mother beamed at him. They were proud that he was going to be in the talent show.

"I wish you would tell us what you're doing," his mother said. His father, a pharmacist who wore a blue smock with his name on a plastic rectangle, looked up from the newspaper and sided with his wife. "Yes, what are you doing in the talent show?"

"You'll see," Manuel said with his mouth full of Cheerios.

The day whizzed by, and so did his afternoon chores and dinner. Suddenly he was dressed in his best clothes and standing next to Benny backstage, listening to the commotion as the cafeteria filled with school kids and parents. The lights dimmed, and Mr. Roybal, sweaty in a tight suit and a necktie with a large knot, wet his lips and parted the stage curtains.

"Good evening, everyone," the kids behind the curtain heard him say. "Good evening to you," some of the smart-alecky kids said back to him.

"Tonight we bring you the best John Burroughs Elementary has to offer, and I'm sure that you'll be both pleased and amazed that our little school houses so much talent. And now, without further ado, let's get on with the show." He turned and, with a swish of his hand, commanded, "Part the curtain." The curtains parted in jerks. A girl dressed as a toothbrush and a boy dressed as a dirty gray tooth walked onto the stage and sang:

Brush, brush, brush
Floss, floss, floss
Gargle the germs away—hey! hey! hey!

After they finished singing, they turned to Mr. Roybal, who dropped his hand. The toothbrush dashed around the stage after the dirty tooth, which was laughing and having a great time until it slipped and nearly rolled off the stage.

Mr. Roybal jumped out and caught it just in time. "Are you OK?"

The dirty tooth answered, "Ask my dentist," which drew laughter and applause from the audience.

The violin duo played next, and except for one time when the girl got lost, they sounded fine. People applauded, and some even stood up. Then the first-grade girls maneuvered onto the stage while jumping rope. They were all smiles and bouncing ponytails as a hundred cameras flashed at once. Mothers "aahed" and fathers sat up proudly.

The karate kid was next. He did a few kicks, yells, and chops, and finally, when his father held up a board, punched it in two. The audience clapped and looked at each other, wide-eyed with respect. The boy bowed to the audience, and father and son ran off the stage.

Manuel remained behind the stage shivering with fear. He mouthed the words to "La Bamba" and swayed from left to right. Why did he raise his hand and volunteer? Why couldn't he have just sat there like the rest of the kids and not said anything? While the karate kid was on stage, Mr. Roybal, more sweaty than before, took Manuel's forty-five record and placed it on the new record player.

"You ready?" Mr. Roybal asked.

"Yeah . . ."

Mr. Roybal walked back on stage and announced that Manuel Gomez, a fifth-grader in Mrs. Knight's class, was going to pantomime Ritchie Valens's classic hit "La Bamba."

The cafeteria roared with applause. Manuel was nervous but loved the noisy crowd. He pictured his mother and father applauding loudly and his brothers and sisters also clapping, though not as energetically.

Manuel walked on stage and the song started immediately. Glassy-eyed from the shock of being in front of so many people,

Manuel moved his lips and swayed in a made-up dance step. He couldn't see his parents, but he could see his brother Mario, who was a year younger, thumb-wrestling with a friend. Mario was wearing Manuel's favorite shirt; he would deal with Mario later. He saw some other kids get up and head for the drinking fountain, and a baby sitting in the middle of an aisle sucking her thumb and watching him intently.

What am I doing here? thought Manuel. This is no fun at all. Everyone was just sitting there. Some people were moving to the beat, but most were just watching him, like they would a monkey at the zoo.

But when Manuel did a fancy dance step, there was a burst of applause and some girls screamed. Manuel tried another dance step. He heard more applause and screams and started getting into the groove as he shivered and shaked like Michael Jackson around the stage. But the record got stuck, and he had to sing

Para bailar la bamba
Para bailar la bamba
Para bailar la bamba
Para bailar la bamba

again and again.

Manuel couldn't believe his bad luck. The audience began to laugh and stand up in their chairs. Manuel remembered how the forty-five record had dropped from his hand and rolled across the cafeteria floor. It probably got scratched, he thought, and now it was stuck, and he was stuck dancing and moving his lips to the same words over and over. He had never been so embarrassed. He would have to ask his parents to move the family out of town.

After Mr. Roybal ripped the needle across the record, Manuel slowed his dance steps to a halt. He didn't know what to do except bow to the audience, which applauded wildly, and scoot off the stage, on the verge of tears. This was worse than the homemade flashlight. At least no one laughed then, they just snickered.

Manuel stood alone, trying hard to hold back the tears as Benny, center stage, played his trumpet. Manuel was jealous because he sounded great, then mad as he recalled that it was

Benny's loud trumpet playing that made the forty-five record fly out of his hands. But when the entire cast lined up for a curtain call, Manuel received a burst of applause that was so loud it shook the walls of the cafeteria. Later, as he mingled with the kids and parents, everyone patted him on the shoulder and told him, "Way to go. You were really funny."

Funny? Manuel thought. Did he do something funny?

Funny. Crazy. Hilarious. These were the words people said to him. He was confused, but beyond caring. All he knew was that people were paying attention to him, and his brothers and sisters looked at him with a mixture of jealousy and awe. He was going to pull Mario aside and punch him in the arm for wearing his shirt, but he cooled it. He was enjoying the limelight. A teacher brought him cookies and punch, and the popular kids who had never before given him the time of day now clustered around him. Ricardo, the editor of the school bulletin, asked him how he made the needle stick.

"It just happened," Manuel said, crunching on a star-shaped cookie.

At home that night his father, eager to undo the buttons on his shirt and ease into his La-Z-Boy recliner, asked Manuel the same thing, how he managed to make the song stick on the words *"Para bailar la bamba."*

Manuel thought quickly and reached for scientific jargon he had read in magazines. "Easy, Dad. I used laser tracking with high optics and low functional decibels per channel." His proud but confused father told him to be quiet and go to bed.

"Ah, *que niños tan truchas,*" he said as he walked to the kitchen for a glass of milk. "I don't know how you kids nowadays get so smart."

Manuel, feeling happy, went to his bedroom, undressed, and slipped into his pajamas. He looked in the mirror and began to pantomime "La Bamba," but stopped because he was tired of the song. He crawled into bed. The sheets were as cold as the moon that stood over the peach tree in their backyard.

He was relieved that the day was over. Next year, when they asked for volunteers for the talent show, he wouldn't raise his hand. Probably.

The Boy Who Became a Deer

a Hopi story from Arizona told by student Roy Masayesva to Byrd Baylor

This happened long ago.

Coyote found a baby sleeping under a bush. He asked his grandmother what to do with it. She said, "Just take it to the deer. They will know how to raise that child."

Coyote did that. He carried the baby in his mouth to the place where deer live. A mother deer took the baby and gave it milk and it lived with the deer and grew up like a deer, running with them and hiding with them in the hills.

But there was a woman in the village who kept saying, "I need a boy."

She heard about the boy who lived with the deer so she went and got him and brought him to her village.

At that time he was five or six years old, still very young.

The other children stayed close to the village on top of the *mesa*. But this boy was always wandering away. It seemed like he wanted

to go back to the hills. Day after day the woman had to walk around looking for him and sometimes that made her cross.

The day came that she was busy weaving a plaque and she forgot to keep her eye on the boy. It was afternoon when she went up to the second roof of the village and looked off in all directions.

Here's what she saw. The boy was sliding on a sunbeam from one of the high roofs down to the ground.

So the woman ran back and told her husband, "He's not a human boy. He can slide on the rays of the sun."

Her husband knew that it must be true that the boy was not human. Thinking of it, they were both sad.

The boy did not come back that night though they called and looked for him.

Five days passed. Then a group of men from the village happened to go back into the hills for wood. They saw a herd of deer running past them. This boy ran with them and he made his own sound when he ran because he wore little bells tied around his ankles.

Several times after that people from the village caught a glimpse of the boy. He was always running with the deer. They heard his bells ringing.

The woman missed the boy even though she knew he was not human. So the people of the village decided to catch him for her.

All the men gathered and started the journey together. They went toward the hills where the deer live.

They found the herd of deer and sure enough the boy was with them. The men made a circle around the deer. One by one, they let each deer run out of the circle. But they would not let the boy run out. They kept him in the circle and they moved closer and closer. That is how they caught him.

They took the boy back to the village. A medicine man told them what they had to do if they wanted to make him into a human boy, not a deer.

This is what the medicine man told them to do. They must put the boy into a house which was so dark that no light from outside could get in. Any cracks in the stone walls of that house were to be plastered with more mud.

The medicine man said that no one must look in until the end of the fourth day after the sun had set. The parents would have to leave enough food in there for the boy to eat for four days because it was very important that no one open the door even a crack.

The medicine man said that if everyone did exactly as he told them, then they would have a human child, not a deer.

Everything went well through the third day. Every day they heard the sound of bells tinkling inside that dark house.

On the morning of the fourth day the woman again listened outside. She heard no bells.

She was very excited now. She wanted her boy back more than ever and since she did not hear the bells she thought surely she did not have to wait until night to open the door.

She opened the door just enough to peep in, just a little way. But the second the door opened she heard the jingle of the deer bells begin again.

The woman's husband said, "We might as well give him back to the deer."

They knew they had ruined the medicine man's cure by not doing exactly what he said. There was no hope now.

So they opened the door all the way and let the deerboy out of the house. They sprinkled cornmeal on him for a blessing as he went bounding toward the hills.

People say that ever since then, whenever danger comes to the deer, the boy is with them, shaking and dancing and jingling his bells.

Many people tell of hearing him.

Now that boy has become a *kachina* and you can see him sometimes dancing down in the *kiva* in night dances. He is dressed with antlers on his head and he is beautiful, shaking and dancing like a deer.

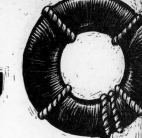

A NIGHT to REMEMBER

from the book by Walter Lord

The "unsinkable" Titanic *was the largest and most glamorous ship in the world. On April 10, 1912, she left Southampton, England, on her maiden voyage to New York. Just before 11:40 P.M. on the frigid night of April 14, she struck an iceberg in the North Atlantic Ocean.*

The iceberg tore a hole in the Titanic, *and she began taking on water. There was confusion, disbelief, denial. But within 20 minutes, it was clear to Captain Smith that his ship, and every person on her, was in grave danger. He knew, as did none of the passengers and few of the crew, that the* Titanic's *20 lifeboats had space for 1,178 people; there were 2,207 on board. [At the end of the excerpt is the list of passengers mentioned in the selection. Those saved are underlined.]*

At 12:05 A.M., Captain Smith ordered that the lifeboats be uncovered, then loaded, women and children first. Many passengers were hesitant to trade the bright decks of the Titanic *for a dark rowboat. But gradually they were persuaded to do so, and at 12:45, the first lifeboat, with 19 or 20 people aboard, was lowered into the ocean.*

*At 12:15, Captain Smith had ordered wireless operator Phillips to telegraph the international signal for help—*CQD. *But the wireless operator on the* Californian, *a ship only 10 miles away, had gone off duty at 11:30* P.M. *and never received the distress call.*

All this time, the crew was struggling below to pump water out of the engine rooms.

Boiler room No. 5 was the only place where everything seemed under control. After the fires were drawn, Lead Fireman Barrett sent most of the stokers up to their boat stations. He and a few others stayed behind to help Engineers Harvey and Shepherd with the pumps.

At Harvey's orders he lifted the iron manhole cover off the floor plates on the starboard side, so Harvey could get at the valves to adjust the pumps.

The boiler room was now clouding up with steam from the water used to wet down the furnaces. In the dim light of their own private Turkish bath, the men worked on . . . vague shapes moving about through the mist.

Then Shepherd, hurrying across the room, fell into the manhole and broke his leg. Harvey, Barrett, and Fireman George Kemish rushed over. They lifted him up and carried him to the pump room, a closed-off space at one end of the boiler room.

No time to do more than make him comfortable . . . then back into the clouds of steam. Soon orders came down from the bridge for all hands to report to boat stations. As the men went up, Shepherd still lay in the pump room; Barrett and Harvey kept working with the valves. Another 15 minutes and both men were beginning to cheer up—the room was still dry, the rhythm of the pumps was fast and smooth.

Suddenly the sea came roaring through the space between the boilers at the forward end of the room. The whole bulkhead between No. 5 and No. 6 collapsed.

Harvey shouted to Barrett to make for the escape ladder. Barrett scrambled up, the foam surging around his feet. Harvey himself turned toward the pump room where Shepherd lay. He was still heading there when he disappeared under the torrent of rising water.

The silence in the Marconi shack was broken only by the rasping spark of the wireless, as Phillips rapped out his call for help and took down the answers that bounced back. Bride was still struggling into his clothes, between dashes to the bridge.

So far the news was encouraging. First to reply was the North German Lloyd steamer *Frankfort*. At 12:18 she sent a crisp "OK . . . Stand by"—but no position. In another minute acknowledgements were pouring in—the Canadian Pacific's *Mt. Temple* . . . the Allan liner *Virginian* . . . the Russian passenger steamer *Birma*.

The night crackled with signals. Ships out of direct contact got the word from those within range . . . The news spread in ever-widening circles. Cape Race heard it directly and relayed it inland. On the roof of Wanamaker's department store in New York, a young wireless operator named David Sarnoff caught a faint signal and also passed it on. The whole world was snapping to agonized attention.

Close at hand, the Cunarder *Carpathia* steamed southward in complete ignorance. Her single wireless operator, Harold Thomas Cottam, was on the bridge when Phillips sent his CQD. Now Cottam was back at his set and thought he'd be helpful. Did the *Titanic* know, he casually asked, that there were some private messages waiting for her from Cape Race?

It was 12:25 when Phillips tapped back an answer that brushed aside the *Carpathia*'s courteous gesture: "Come at once. We have struck a berg. It's a CQD, old man. Position 41.46 N 50.14 W."

A moment of appalled silence . . . then Cottam asked whether to tell his captain. Phillips: "Yes, quick." Another five minutes and welcome news—the *Carpathia* was only 58 miles away and "coming hard."

At 12:34 it was the *Frankfort* again—she was 150 miles away. Phillips asked, "Are you coming to our assistance?" *Frankfort:* "What is the matter with you?" Phillips: "Tell your captain to come to our help. We are on the ice."

33

Captain Smith now dropped into the shack for a first-hand picture. The *Olympic*, the *Titanic*'s huge sister ship, was just chiming in. She was 500 miles away; but her set was powerful, she could handle a major rescue job, and there was a strong bond between the two liners. Phillips kept in close touch, while urging on the ships that were nearer.

"What call are you sending?" Smith asked.

"CQD," Phillips answered noncommittally.

Bride had a bright idea. While CQD was the traditional distress call, an international convention had just agreed to use instead the letters SOS—they were easy for the rankest amateur to pick up. So Bride suggested, "Send SOS; it's the new call, and it may be your last chance to send it."

Phillips laughed at the joke and switched the call. The clock in the wireless shack said 12:45 A.M. when the *Titanic* sent the first SOS in history.

None of the ships contacted seemed as promising as the light that winked ten miles off the *Titanic*'s port bow. Through his binoculars Fourth Officer Boxhall saw clearly that it was a steamer. Once, as he tried to get in touch with the Morse lamp, he felt he saw an answer. But he could make nothing of it and finally decided it must be her mast light flickering.

Stronger measures were necessary. As soon as Quartermaster Rowe reached the bridge, Captain Smith asked if he brought the rockets. Rowe produced them, and the Captain ordered, "Fire one, and fire one every five or six minutes."

At 12:45 a blinding flash seared the night. The first rocket shot up from the starboard side of the bridge. Up . . . up it soared, far above the lacework of masts and rigging. Then with a distant, muffled report it burst, and a shower of bright white stars floated slowly down toward the sea. In the blue-white light Fifth Officer Lowe remembered catching a glimpse of Bruce Ismay's startled face.

Ten miles away, Apprentice James Gibson stood on the bridge of the *Californian*. The strange ship that came up from the east had not moved for an hour, and Gibson studied her with interest. With glasses he could make out her side lights and a glare of lights on her afterdeck. At one point he thought she was trying to signal the *Californian* with her Morse lamp. He tried to answer with his own lamp, but soon gave up. He decided the stranger's masthead light was merely flickering.

Second Officer Herbert Stone, pacing the *Californian*'s bridge, also kept his eye on this strange steamer. At 12:45 he saw a sudden flash of white light burst over her. Strange, he thought, that a ship would fire rockets at night.

Second class passenger Lawrence Beesley considered himself the rankest landlubber, but even he knew what rockets meant. The *Titanic* needed help—needed it so badly she was calling on any ship near enough to see.

The others on the Boat Deck understood too. There was no more joking or lingering. In fact, there was hardly time to say good-by.

"It's all right, little girl," called Dan Marvin to his new bride; "you go and I'll stay a while." He blew her a kiss as she entered the boat.

"I'll see you later," Adolf Dyker smiled as he helped Mrs. Dyker across the gunwale.

"Be brave; no matter what happens, be brave," Dr. W. T. Minahan told Mrs. Minahan as he stepped back with the other men.

Mr. Turrell Cavendish said nothing to Mrs. Cavendish. Just a kiss . . . a long look . . . another kiss . . . and he disappeared into the crowd.

Mark Fortune took his wife's valuables, as he and his son Charles saw off Mrs. Fortune and their three daughters. "I'll take care of them; we're going in the next boat," he explained. "Charles, take care of Father," one of the girls called back to her brother.

"Walter, you must come with me," begged Mrs. Walter D. Douglas.

"No," Mr. Douglas replied, turning away, "I must be a gentleman."

"Try and get off with Major Butt and Mr. Moore," came a final bit of wifely advice; "They are big, strong fellows and will surely make it."

Some of the wives still refused to go. Mr. and Mrs. Edgar Meyer of New York felt so self-conscious arguing about it in public that they went down to their cabin. There, they decided to part on account of their baby.

Arthur Ryerson had to lay down the law to Mrs. Ryerson: "You must obey orders. When they say 'Women and children to the boats,' you *must* go when your turn comes. I'll stay here with Jack Thayer. We'll be all right."

Alexander T. Compton, Jr., was just as firm when his mother announced she would stay rather than leave him behind: "Don't be foolish, Mother. You and Sister go in the boat—I'll look out for myself."

Mr. and Mrs. Lucien Smith were having the same kind of argument. Seeing Captain Smith standing near with a megaphone, Mrs. Smith had an inspiration. She went up to him, explained she was all alone in the world, and asked if her husband could go along with her. The old Captain ignored her, lifted his megaphone and shouted, "Women and children first!"

At this point Mr. Smith broke in: "Never mind, Captain, about that; I'll see she gets in the boat." Turning to his wife, he spoke very slowly: "I never expected to ask you to obey, but this is one time you must. It is only a matter of form to have women and children first. The ship is thoroughly equipped and everyone on her will be saved."

Mrs. Smith asked him if he was being completely truthful. Mr. Smith gave a firm, decisive, "Yes." So they kissed good-by, and as the boat dropped to the sea, he called from the deck, "Keep your hands in your pockets; it is very cold weather."

Sometimes it took more than gentle deception. Mrs. Emil Taussig was clinging to her husband when No. 8 started down with her daughter. Mrs. Taussig turned and cried, "Ruth!" The brief distraction proved enough: two men tore her from Mr. Taussig and dropped her into the lowering boat.

A seaman yanked Mrs. Charlotte Collyer by the arm, another by her waist, and they dragged her from her husband Harvey. As she kicked to get free, she heard him call, "Go, Lottie! For God's sake, be brave and go! I'll get a seat in another boat!"

When Salini Yazbeck saw she had to go alone, she began yelling and crying to rejoin Mr. Yazbeck, but the boat dropped to the sea while she tried in vain to get out.

No amount of persuasion and force could move Mrs. Hudson J. Allison of Montreal. A little apart from the rest, she huddled close to Mr. Allison, while their small daughter Lorraine tugged at her skirt.

Mrs. Isidor Straus also refused to go: "I've always stayed with my husband; so why should I leave him now?"

They had indeed come a long way together: the ashes of the Confederacy . . . the small china business in Philadelphia . . . building Macy's into a national institution . . . Congress . . . and now the happy twilight that crowned successful life—advisory boards, charities, hobbies, travel. This winter they had been to Cap Martin, and the *Titanic*'s maiden voyage seemed a pleasant way to finish the trip.

Tonight the Strauses came on deck with the others, and at first Mrs. Straus seemed uncertain what to do. At one point she handed some small jewelry to her maid Ellen Bird, then took it back again. Later she crossed the Boat Deck and almost entered No. 8—then turned around and rejoined Mr. Straus. Now her mind was made up: "We have been living together for many years. Where you go, I go."

Archibald Gracie, Hugh Woolner, other friends tried in vain to make her go. Then Woolner turned to Mr. Straus: "I'm sure nobody would object to an old gentleman like you getting in . . ."

"I will not go before the other men," he said, and that was that. Then he and Mrs. Straus sat down together on a pair of deck chairs.

LIST OF PASSENGERS MENTIONED IN THE EXCERPT

This list was taken from the White Star Line's final list of lost and saved, dated May 9, 1912. Those saved are <u>underlined</u>.

FIRST CLASS PASSENGERS

Mr. Hudson J. Allison
<u>Mrs. Hudson J. Allison
    and maid</u>
Miss Lorraine Allison
<u>Master T. Allison
    and nurse</u>

Major Archibald W. Butt

Mr. Turrell Cavendish
<u>Mrs. Turrell Cavendish
    and maid</u>

<u>Mrs. A. T. Compton
Miss S. P. Compton</u>
Mr. Alexander T. Compton, Jr.

Mr. Walter D. Douglas
<u>Mrs. Walter D. Douglas
    and maid</u>

Mr. Mark Fortune
<u>Mrs. Mark Fortune
Miss Ethel Fortune
Miss Alice Fortune
Miss Mabel Fortune</u>
Mr. Charles Fortune

<u>Colonel Archibald
Gracie</u>

<u>Mr. J. Bruce Ismay
    and manservant</u>

Mr. Dan W. Marvin
<u>Mrs. Dan W. Marvin</u>

Mr. Edgar J. Meyer
<u>Mrs. Edgar J. Meyer</u>

Dr. W. T. Minahan
<u>Mrs. W. E. Minahan
Miss Daisy Minahan</u>

Mr. Clarence Moore
    and manservant

Mr. Arthur Ryerson
<u>Mrs. Arthur Ryerson
    and maid
Miss Emily Ryerson
Miss Susan Ryerson
Master Jack Ryerson</u>

Mr. Lucien P. Smith
<u>Mrs. Lucien P. Smith</u>

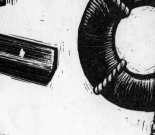

Mr. Isidor Straus
    and manservant
Mrs. Isidor Straus
    and maid

Mr. Emil Taussig
Mrs. Emil Taussig
Miss Ruth Taussig

Mr. Jack B. Thayer
Mrs. Jack B. Thayer
    and maid
Mr. J. B. Thayer, Jr.

Mr. Hugh Woolner

SECOND CLASS PASSENGERS

Mr. Lawrence Beesley

Mr. Harvey Collyer
Mrs. Charlotte Collyer
Miss Marjorie Collyer

THIRD CLASS PASSENGERS

Adolf Dyker
Elizabeth Dyker

Antoni Yazbeck
Salini Yazbeck

CREW MEMBERS

Walter Lord did not include in his book a list of crew members
lost and saved.

THE POWER OF THE LITTLE PEOPLE

a Seneca story from the northeastern United States
told by Jesse J. Cornplanter

An Indian boy about the age of seven was out hunting little birds. He had his little bow and arrow to shoot what he may see, as it was the custom in those days, to teach their growing boys all the sports of the hunt and chase as a major part of their early training,—it was their school-time.

This little boy was wandering on, when he finally came to a river to see if he could see some water-fowl to shoot. He had no sooner reached the edge of the water, when he heard a swishing noise to the direction of up-stream. Looking up, he was surprised to see a tiny canoe shoot around the bend of the stream at a rapid speed. In the canoe were two of the tiniest little men that the boy ever had seen. They came right up to where the boy stood and stopped. Both had a tiny bow and a quiver of arrows.

They both greeted the boy, then one of them asked him thus, "How would you like to trade your bow and arrows with one of us?"

Then the boy thought how foolish it would be to do so, as their bows and arrows were much smaller than his; so he said, "How foolish it would be to do so,—why, yours are so much smaller than mine."

Then one of them took a bow and strung it and taking an arrow he shot it straight up, the arrow disappeared into the sky and did not come down at all. Saying at the same time, "That may be true, but all

40

great things on earth are not always the biggest; you may live to learn that." Then they took their canoe-paddles and with one stroke disappeared around the bend of the river.

The boy was surprised; so he went back to his home, where he was staying with his grandmother. He told her all about what happened. Then his grandmother scolded her grand-son, saying: "You made a big mistake by your refusal to accept the trade. Had you taken one of their bows and arrows, you could take any game that you desired, as they are magic. Hereafter never be too hasty in judging people as you see them, for you never know who or what they may be."

That is one legend, then there are others. There are three different tribes of these "Djo-geh-onh," each living according to their type. There are the tribe who dwell underneath the rocks and caverns. It is their work to watch constantly the "White Buffaloes" that dwell underground,—if they came out above, they would cause much suffering to mankind. Then there are the tribe who live among the plants. It is they that cause the green things to come up in spring; they paint the flowers their colors and paint the fruit when the time comes; they also painted the corn all the different tints. And the third tribe are the ones who dwell along the streams and are called "Stone Throwers." They can throw big rocks long distance, uproot big trees, and are very powerful in every way, but are very friendly to the earth-children.

The story of the
Shipwrecked Sailor

a tale of ancient Egypt retold by Roger Lancelyn Green

When Pharaoh Amen-em-het ruled Egypt in about the year 2000 B.C. he brought peace and prosperity to a country that had been torn by civil war and rebellion for nearly two hundred years. During his reign adventurers and traders went on many expeditions to the south—either up the Nile through Nubia and even as far as Ethiopia, or along the Red Sea and out into the Indian Ocean to the mysterious land of Punt, whence they brought back jewels and spices and other treasures.

The Royal Court, whether it was in residence at Thebes or Memphis, was thronged with ships' captains and the leaders of expeditions, each with a tale to tell—and each anxious to win a commission from Pharaoh to command some royal venture on the strength of his past achievements.

One day such a wanderer stopped the Grand Vizier in the palace courtyard at Thebes, and said to him, 'My lord, harken to me a while. I come with costly gifts for Pharaoh, nor shall his counsellors such as yourself be forgotten. Listen, and I will tell you of such adventures as have not been told: Pharaoh himself—life, health, strength be to him!—will reward you for bringing to his presence a man with such adventures to tell. I have been to a magic island in the sea far to the south—far beyond Nubia, to the south even of Ethiopia. I beg of you to tell Pharaoh that I am here and would tell my tale to him.'

The Grand Vizier was accustomed to such appeals, and he looked doubtfully at the wanderer and said, 'It seems to me that you speak foolishly and have only vain things to tell. Many men such as you think that a tall story will win them a commission from Pharaoh—but when they tell their tale they condemn themselves out of their own mouths. If what you have to tell is one of these, be sure that I shall have you thrown out of the palace. But if it is of sufficient interest, I may bring you before Pharaoh. Therefore speak on at your own risk, or else remain silent and trouble me no more.'

'I have such a tale to tell,' answered the wanderer, 'that I will risk your anger with an easy mind. When you have heard it, you will beg me to come before Pharaoh and tell it to him—even to the good god Pharaoh Amen-em-het who rules the world. Listen, then.

'I was on my way to the mines of Pharaoh in a great ship rowed by a hundred and fifty sailors who had seen heaven and earth and whose hearts were stronger than lions. We rowed and sailed for many days down the Red Sea and out into the ocean beyond.

'The captain and the steersman swore that they knew the signs of the weather and that the wind would not be strong but would waft us gently on our way. Nevertheless before long a tempest arose suddenly and drove us towards the land. As we drew near the shore the waves were eight cubits in height and they broke over the ship and dashed it upon the rocks. I seized a piece of wood and flung myself into the sea just as the ship ran aground: a moment later it was smashed to pieces and every man perished.

'But a great wave raised the board to which I clung high over the sharp rocks and cast me far up the shore, on level sand, and I was able to crawl into the shelter of the trees out of reach of the cruel, angry sea.

'When day dawned the tempest passed away and the warm sun shone out. I rose up to see where I was, giving thanks to the gods for my delivery when all the rest had perished. I was on an island with no other human being to be a companion to me. But such an island as no man has seen! The broad leaves of the thicket where I lay formed a roof over my head to shield me from the burning midday sun. When I grew hungry and looked about for food, I found all ready for me within easy reach: figs and grapes, all manner of good herbs, berries and grain, melons of all kinds, fishes and birds for the taking.

'At first I satisfied my hunger on the fruits around me. And on the third day I dug a pit and kindled a fire in it on which I made first of all a burnt offering to the gods, and then cooked meat and fish for myself.

'As I sat there comfortably after an excellent meal I suddenly heard a noise like thunder. Nearly beside myself with terror, I flung myself on the ground, thinking that it was some great tidal wave come to engulf the island: for the trees were lashing as if at the breath of the tempest and the earth shook beneath me.

'But no wave came, and at last I cautiously raised my head and looked about me. Never shall I forget the horror of that moment. Moving towards me I saw a serpent thirty cubits long with a beard of more than two cubits. Its body was covered with golden scales and the scales round its eyes shaded off into blue as pure as lapis lazuli.

'The serpent coiled up its whole length in front of where I lay with my face on the ground, reared its head high above me, and said: "What has brought you, what has brought you here, little one? Say, what has brought you to my island? If you do not tell me at once I will show you what it is to be burnt with fire, what is it to be burnt utterly to nothing and become a thing invisible. Speak quickly, I am waiting to hear what I have not heard before, some new thing!"

'Then the serpent took me in his huge jaws and carried me away to his cave, and put me down there without hurting me. Yes, though he had held me in his sharp teeth he had not bitten me at all: I was still whole.

'Then he said again, "What has brought you, what has brought you here, little one? Say what has brought you to this island in the midst of the sea with the waves breaking on all sides of it?"

'At this I managed to speak, crouching before him and bowing my face to the ground as if before Pharaoh himself.

' "I sailed by command of Amen-em-het, Pharaoh of Egypt, in a great ship one hundred and fifty cubits in length to bring treasure from the mines of the south. But a great tempest broke upon us and dashed the ship upon the rocks so that all who sailed in her perished except for myself. As for me, I seized a piece of wood and was lifted on it over the rocks and cast upon this island by a mighty wave, and I have been here for three days. So behold me, your suppliant, brought hither by a wave of the sea."

'Then the serpent said to me, "Fear not, fear not, little one, nor let your face show sadness. Since you have come to my island in this way, when all your companions perished, it is because some god has preserved and sent you. For surely Amen-Ra has set you thus upon this island of the blessed where nothing is lacking, which is filled with all good things. And now I will tell you of the future: here in this isle shall you remain while one month adds itself to another until four months have passed. Then a ship shall come, a ship of Egypt, and it shall carry you home in safety, and at length you shall die in your own city and be laid to rest in the tomb which you have prepared.

' "And now I will tell you of this island. For it is pleasant to hear strange things after fear has been taken away from you—and you will indeed have a tale to tell when you return home and kneel before Pharaoh, your lord and master. Know then that I dwell here with my brethren and my children about me; we are seventy-five serpents in all, children and kindred. And but one stranger has even come amongst us: a lovely girl who appeared strangely and on whom the fire of heaven fell and who was turned into ashes. As for you, I do not think that heaven holds any thunderbolts for one who has lived through such dangers. It is revealed to me that, if you dwell here in patience, you shall return in the fullness of time and hold your wife and children in your arms once more."

'Then I bowed before him, thanking him for his words of comfort, and said, "All that I have told you is true, and if what you have said to me happens indeed, I shall come before Pharaoh and tell him about you, and speak to him of your greatness. And I will bring as offerings to you sacred oils and perfumes, and such incense as is offered to the gods in their temples. Moreover I shall tell him of all the wonders of this isle, and I shall sacrifice asses to you, and

Pharaoh shall send out a ship filled with the riches of Egypt as presents to your majesty."

'The king serpent laughed at my words, saying, "Truly you are not rich in perfumes—for here in this island I have more than in all the land of Punt. Only the sacred oil which you promise me is scarce here—yet you will never bring it, for when you are gone this island will vanish away and you shall never more see it. Yet doubtless the gods will reveal it in time to come to some other wanderer."

'So I dwelt happily in that enchanted island, and the four months seemed all too short. When they drew to a close I saw a ship sailing over the smooth sea towards me, and I climbed into a high tree to see better what manner of men sailed in it. And when I perceived that they were men of Egypt, I hastened to the home of the serpent king and told him. But he knew already more than I did myself, and said to me, "Farewell, brave wanderer. Return in safety to your home and may my blessing go with you."

'Then I bowed before him and thanked him, and he gave me gifts of precious perfumes—of cassia and sweet woods, of kohl and cypress, of incense, of ivory and of other precious things. And when I had set these upon the ship and the sailors would have landed, the island seemed to move away from them, floating on the sea. Then night fell suddenly, and when the moon shone out there was no island in sight but only the open waves.

'So we sailed north and in the second month we came to Egypt, and I have made haste to cross the desert from the sea to Thebes. Therefore, I pray you, lead me before Pharaoh, for I long to tell him of my adventures and lay at his feet the gifts of the King of the Serpents, and beg that he will make me commander of a royal ship to sail once more into the ocean that washes the shores of Punt.'

When the wanderer's tale was ended, the Grand Vizier laughed heartily, crying, 'Whether or not I believe your adventures, you have told a tale such as delights the heart of Pharaoh—life, health, strength be to him! Therefore come with me at once, and be sure of a rich reward: to you who tell the tale, and to me who brings before him the teller of the tale.'

So the wanderer passed into the presence of the good god Pharaoh Amen-em-het, and Pharaoh delighted in the story of the shipwrecked sailor so much that his chief scribe Ameni-amen-aa was set to write it down upon a roll of papyrus where it may be read to this very day.

The Great Bear

a Micmac story from Nova Scotia by Maria Leach

When the old Micmac Indians used to look up in the sky in late spring, they saw the big bear crawl out of her cave and start across the heavens. All summer she runs across the northern sky with seven hunters after her.

The cave is the beautiful little arched constellation called Corona Borealis. The four stars of the Dipper represent the bear. The three stars in the handle are the first three hunters: Robin, Chickadee, Moosebird. Four more hunters follow them but cannot keep up. We can see them all summer, but they drop out of sight below the horizon in the fall.

Robin is the first hunter (his star has a reddish tinge). Not far behind comes Chickadee, carrying his little pot to cook the meat. (This is the double star in the middle of the handle; the little star Alcor is the pot.) The third hunter is Moosebird, who is never very far behind successful hunters.

Pigeon is the next hunter, and after him comes Bluejay (whose star is blue). Next comes the big owl (the star Arcturus in Boötes) and below him little Saw-whet (the tiny Acadian owl).

The two owls are the first to drop out of the chase—Saw-whet because he is too small to keep up with the hunters, the big owl (Arcturus) because he is too heavy. Pigeon and Bluejay get lost and give up; they drop below the horizon also.

But Robin and Chickadee follow the bear, and Moosebird follows the hunters. Robin kills the bear with an arrow, and she slowly falls over on her back. Her blood spatters Robin's breast, staining it red forever. The blood drips down to earth on the Nova Scotia maples. That is why they turn to gorgeous red every fall.

Chickadee and Robin cook the meat in the little pot, and Moosebird arrives, just as he does today in the Canadian woods right after some hunter has killed a moose or a bear or some other animal. Even though he is late and did not help, Robin and Chickadee share their meat with him. All good Micmacs have always shared their food with those who have none.

The old dead bear lies on her back all winter, but her spirit returns to the cave to sleep the winter through. And a new bear, reborn, comes forth every spring to flee before the hunters and re-enact this drama forever and forever.

The Fitting of the Slipper

a story by William J. Brooke

"PLEASE," implored the Prince, stepping back in some distress, "this is not fitting."

"Not yet, but it will in a minute," she muttered between clenched teeth.

"No, I mean it is not right."

She looked at the slipper in confusion for a moment. Then she took it off her right foot and began jamming it onto her left. "You might have said something sooner," she grumbled. "Your Highness," she added, remembering that she hoped to marry the Prince and must not snap at him until after the wedding.

She wore the daintiest little socklets, creamy white lawns with tiny red flowers strewn across them. They would have been enchanting but for the red that blossomed between the

49

flowers as she tried to put herself in the royal shoe by any means available.

"I thank you for trying," the Prince began to say as he gestured for his Lord Chamberlain to retrieve the slipper.

She swung her foot away from him on the pretense of getting a better angle of entry. "No trouble, no trouble, just I've been on my feet all day and they're a bit swollen." She shoved a finger behind her heel and tried to force her way in.

The Prince stared, appalled. "This cannot go on," he sighed to his Lord Chamberlain, who knelt at the woman's feet.

"It can! It can!" she said, redoubling her efforts as she saw her chances slipping away. "It's almost on now." Four toes had found a lodging place and she seemed perfectly determined to abandon the last to make its own way in the world.

"No! No!" He pushed forward and grabbed the slipper from her. A smear of red appeared on his snowy-white garments. "I am on a mission of romance. I am seeking love and finding naught but greed and grotesque self-mutilation."

She pursed up her mouth like a prune and said, "Well, I never heard of shoe size being a sound basis for matrimony, but if Your Highness chooses to place his future on that footing, I don't suppose he can blame anyone for trying to cut a few corners."

"Silence, woman," the Lord Chamberlain snapped automatically, but he looked as if he probably agreed with her.

"You do not understand," the Prince sighed. He stood open-mouthed, as if looking for words, then shook his head. "You did not see her. You do not know the feeling of . . . Oh, what is the use?"

The Lord Chamberlain tried to take control. "If Your Highness will step outside, we have three more houses to visit in this street."

"No! No more! No more feet, no more blood, no more women who wish only to crush me beneath their heels! I cannot bear it!"

And with that he clutched the bloody slipper to his bosom and swept out the door.

Only it was the wrong door, and he found himself in a dark little hallway instead of on the street where the royal retinue waited. The door behind him started to open again and he knew it would be the Lord Chamberlain.

"You are not to open that door on pain of . . ." The only punishment he could think of at the moment was decapitation, and that seemed excessive. ". . . Of my severe displeasure," he finished, rather lamely. The door closed again and he was alone.

Before anything else could happen, he slipped down the hall and through another door. He was not sure where he was going or what he wanted, but he knew that he wanted to be away from what was behind him. He closed the door and dropped a bar into place. He listened for any movement, but there was none. He was alone.

For a moment the Prince was so thrilled to be by himself that he paid no attention to his surroundings. He took a deep breath and listened. There was nothing. No one asking, "Is Your Highness ready to meet with your ministers?" No one imploring, "If Your Highness would only listen to my suit . . ." No one hinting, "Would Your Highness care to dine now?" Strange that it always sounded as if he were being asked his pleasure when in fact he was being told to do this or that right away. For being a Highness and a Majesty, he was always being bossed around by someone or other. The only time he was left alone was when he went to the bathroom. And even then it wasn't long before there would be a discreet knock and "Does Your Majesty wish to review the troops now?" Sometimes he would imagine himself replying, "Why, certainly, My Majesty always likes to review the troops with his pants around his ankles. It is a little hard to walk but it sets a good example for the recruits." But he knew he would never say anything remotely like that. And whenever he got that sort of thought, he would blush and say to himself, "This is not fitting." Then he would hurry up and be more obedient than ever.

For he knew he should be grateful for his wealth and position and that he owed it all to the love and goodwill of his people, and it was his responsibility and blah blah blah.

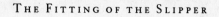

Sometimes he felt that a very wicked Prince lived inside him and would leap out and take over if he gave it the least chance. But he had never given it that chance. Until now.

For a while he just listened to the quiet. It was dark and shadowy with only a little fire at the far end of the room and he could not see very much. But he could hear lots of lovely silence, and when he put out his hand he could feel the rough wood of the door. It felt wonderful to him, all uneven and knotted and slivery, and it squirmed with lovely deep-red shadows in the flicker of the fire. He could feel the glass slipper in his other hand. *That* was what he was used to in his life, everything smooth and silky and featureless. He held it up and looked at its crystalline transparency, beautiful and perfect and boring. In sheer delight, he ran his hand across the rough landscape of the door.

And gave a howl as a big splinter slid into his palm.

He stuck the glass slipper under one arm and tried to ease the pain with his other hand. Then he froze and caught his breath again to listen.

Something had moved at the far end of the room. Near the fire, but in the shadows. In fact, one of the shadows itself.

He peered as hard as he could, but the harder he looked, the less he saw. When he moved his eyes, blue images of the fire danced in the dark. Even when he shut his eyes, the blue fire flitted about until he wasn't sure whether his eyes were open or closed.

He held his breath as tight as he could. But he noticed now that the breath he held was full of smells. They were kitchen smells, and to anyone who had grown up in a snug little cottage, they would have been comforting and comfortable smells. To someone like the Prince, though, who had grown up perfumed and scented and protected, they smelled like a wild beast in its lair.

He found himself wishing he had at least one of his guards or even a fawning courtier with him. Stories he had been told as a child came back to him, tales of witches and demons and unspeakable stews boiling on heathen hearths.

He had not thought of those stories in many years. They had been told him by an old peasant woman who had been his wet nurse when he was tiny. The infant Prince cried whenever she left him, and the Royal Nurse could not abide a squawling child, even if it was a Princeling. So the old woman had been allowed to stay until the child was old enough to learn that neither listening to silly stories nor crying was part of his responsibilities toward his people. One day he noticed he had not seen the old woman for a while. Eventually he forgot to notice when he never saw her again. He had outgrown her stories and her warm, soft hugs and her wet kisses.

Now he wondered how he had forgotten her. Her memory made the room a lovely warm haven again. Even the smells seemed to belong to her, and they comforted him like the low murmur of music from a distant place.

Suddenly a bent and twisted shadow stepped in front of the fire. The Prince gasped and grabbed for the door and gave out another howl when the splinter slid in a little deeper. The shadow pushed something into the fire. There was a little burst of light as a twig caught and then the shadow turned and thrust it at him, bright-blazing and shadow-twisting.

The Prince fell back against the door in absolute terror. He could see nothing past the light but a filthy hand, a coarse sleeve, and the dark bent shape beyond.

They were frozen like that for a moment of silence. Then the shape gave a low sigh in a rough, woman's voice. "Aaow. You am come then. I can't believe you really come."

There was something familiar about the voice, and the Prince straightened up to try to see. The shape abruptly dropped to its knees and the light lowered. "Your 'Ighness! I'm forgettin' me place! 'Ere is me all dirty an' bent over with scrubbin' an' stickin' the fire right in yer face like I 'ad any right at all. Please say yer fergivin' of me!"

The Prince stared down over the flame, at the wild, tangled hair and dirt-laden face, as if searching a dark thicket for a wounded boar. But instead of a ravening beast, that face held eyes bright and darting as twin harts startled by the hunt. He

was still frightened, but it was different now. And she sounded somehow familiar. . . .

The silence stretched out, with him looking thoughtfully down at her and her looking up at him with a question and a hope that belied dirt and rags. Then he blinked and pulled himself together.

"I believe that you have the most awful grammar that I have ever heard," he finally said.

She didn't reply but slowly lowered her eyes from his.

"I do not mean that as an insult. It is actually quite interesting to me. Everyone makes such a point of being precisely correct with me, it is rather refreshing to hear someone jabbering away." She stiffened at that. "Well, I do not really mean 'jabbering,' just . . ."

Her eyes, which had veiled themselves, suddenly widened with concern. "Yer 'urt! Why din't you tell me?" She was staring at the blood on his clothes.

"Oh, that is not my blood," he said. "That came from this." He held out the slipper. She looked hard at the glass shoe and then raised eyes filled with some terrible emotion.

He found it impossible to meet those pain-filled eyes, so he held out his hand. "I do have a slight injury, however—a splinter from your door."

She took his hand without a word and led him to the fire. She pulled a rough chair close to it and seated him, respectfully but firmly. Then she knelt before him, studying his hand in the firelight. She glanced up to see that he was ready, then seized the splinter and pulled it out.

It actually hurt rather a lot, but he was determined not to show it. "Thank you, my good woman." He wasn't sure if she was a woman or a girl. Even close to the fire, the layers of dirt and ragged clothes hid her almost completely.

He started to rise, but she took his hand again and examined it. "Not all out," she pronounced, and hurried away to a dark corner where she sorted through the contents of a box with a great clanking of metal and wood.

"Actually, it feels much better and perhaps I will wait for the Court Surgeon." But she was back then with a long, sharp darning needle, which caught the light like a dagger. She thrust its point into the fire and waited silently for it to heat up. The Prince felt distinctly ill at ease.

There was a faint scraping in the hall outside and a low tap on the door. The voice of the Lord Chamberlain sounded deliberately unconcerned, as though pretending that nothing was out of the ordinary. "Is Your Majesty ready to proceed to the next house?"

The Prince looked nervously at the needle, which was beginning to glow red at its tip, and at the girl whose shoulders tightened at the voice. He wondered what the Lord Chamberlain would think if he knew he was closeted with a strange serving girl who was about to apply a red-hot point to the royal person. The thought almost made him giggle.

"Perhaps Your Highness does not realize the lateness . . ."

"My Highness is perfectly capable of telling time. Even now I am looking at a clock above the mantel. I shall come out when I am ready."

"Very good, Your Majesty." After a moment, the steps scraped away down the hall again.

She looked at him warily. "We got no clock in 'ere."

He looked abashed. "I know. It was a lie."

"You lie a lot, then, do ya?"

"Never! I just . . . It wasn't me, it was . . ."

"Was what?"

Something made him blurt it out before he could think. "The Wicked Prince who lives inside me and tries to get out." He held his breath. He had never told anyone about the Wicked Prince.

She didn't laugh. "The Wicked Prince 'oo tries to get out. Well, I guess 'e succeeded this time, din't 'e? Don't seem to 'ave done much damage. Maybe you should let 'im out more often. Maybe 'e woun't be so wicked if 'e just got a breath o' fresh air every onc't in a while." She smiled. And her smile cut right through the dirt like a spray of clear, crisp spring water and made him smile back.

"Let's see if we can't cut 'im some air 'oles right now." She wiped the glowing needle on a rag and brandished it in the air with a piratical grin.

The Prince lost his smile. "Perhaps I should be going. There is a great deal of . . ."

She didn't answer, but knelt before him, grabbed his hand, and turned her back to him so that his arm was immobilized under her own, pressed against her side. It took only a moment, she was so quick, and he was left with the curious feeling of being completely defenseless and completely protected at the same time. She plunged the needle in swiftly and deftly. He tried not to think of the pain, and after a moment he didn't. His face was very close to her shoulder and all along the inside of his arm he was touching her. He could feel roundness and softness beneath the coarse fabrics. He could smell her smell, which was the scent that rises from under the earth after rainfall. And in the play of the firelight on her cheek he felt he could see beneath the dirt to some kind of shining essence that . . .

"I said, 'All finished.'"

He realized it was not the first time she had spoken. Yet she had not moved from where he half leaned against her, just waited for his pleasure. He sat back, embarrassed, and she turned and seated herself on the floor beside the fire.

"Not too bad? Yer 'and," she added when he showed no sign of comprehension.

"Oh! Oh, that. Fine. No pain at all. I am sorry that I am a little dreamy, but I was thinking of my old Nurse Reba. You make me think of her."

"Well, I don't know if I want to remind you of any old nurse."

"Not that you are old. I mean, I do not know if you are old. I mean, what is your name?"

She smiled to show that there was no offense. "Ella, Yer 'Ighness."

56

"Ella," he repeated. "A good . . . plain name. Fitting for a . . ."

"A good, plain girl?" she suggested.

"A good and faithful servant," he finished, trying to make it sound like a hearty compliment.

"Actually, I'm more in the line of poor relation than yer outright 'ouse'old servant."

"Ah, I see. A cousin of the house whose own family fell on hard times?"

She looked sadly at the walls around her. "This 'ouse is the 'ouse of me father."

The Prince couldn't take it in. "Your father? You are the daughter of this house? But this is a substantial house, so why are you . . ." He gestured mutely at their surroundings.

"Me mother died when I was a tiny one. Me father married agin an' 'ad two more daughters an' no more 'appiness afore 'e went to join me mother. Since then, this room 'as been me 'ome."

The Prince didn't know what to say. He felt deeply ashamed that he had ever felt ill-treated in his royal position.

Ella felt his pity and hastened to add, "It 'asn't been as bad as 'ow it might seem. There's good in anything if you know where to look for it."

The Prince felt deeply uncomfortable. He decided it was time to return to his duties. He tried to find something cheerful to say. "I am quite sure you are right. And we thank you for your good service to your Prince. Now we must be going, for there is much of importance to be done."

He started for the door, but she was in front of him suddenly, eyes flashing. " 'Much of importance to be done.' More customers to try on, ya mean."

"What!" he exclaimed, drawing himself up into a state of outraged dignity. "How dare you judge your betters! You should remember your place!"

She fell instantly into a deep and clumsy curtsy. "Fergive me, Yer 'Ighness. I just want the best for you."

He was sorry for her, but determined to be dignified. "It is all right, my girl. It was really our fault for encouraging you in a way we should never have done. You have your Prince's gratitude and his kind thoughts."

She held her face in shadow and spoke low. "I just wanted you to know as 'ow I wasn't just what I seemed."

"Of course. Thank you and farewell." He strode to the door.

He was starting to lift the bar when he was stopped by a gentle rap at the door. He sighed resignedly and said, "Yes, my Lord Chamberlain?"

But it was the voice of the older woman who had greeted them at the door. "If Your Highness please, my other daughter is still waiting to try her fortune. Or if Your Highness wishes to stay by the fire awhile, I wonder if you might send Cinderella out so she can get to her chores."

The Prince looked at Ella. She had slunk back into the corner by the fire, merging into the shadows from which she had appeared. "Cinderella?" he called through the door. She raised her eyes to him then, but he could not read them in the dark.

"Yes," called back the woman. "Cinderella, our kitchen maid." She laughed. "Unless Your Highness was figuring to try the slipper on her as well."

The Prince hurled the bar into a corner and threw the door open. The woman fell into a deep curtsy at his wrathful expression. "Your Highness!" she gasped, not at all sure what she had done.

"Yes," he said after a moment. "You are quite right. Please rise." She did so, uncertainly. "It was my intention to try the fit of the slipper on all the ladies of respectable houses. So of course I shall try it on Ella. If there is time, I shall do the same for your other daughter."

The woman was speechless for a moment. "Ella! A lady?"

The Prince silenced her with a look. "She has treated us as a lady should treat her liege and as others have not. Await us without." He closed the door on the woman's white, startled face.

The Prince was furious but also delighted. It was the sort of thing the Wicked Prince would have urged him to and yet it seemed entirely in keeping with royal behavior. He might find a way to reconcile himself yet.

He turned to the shadow that was frozen by the fire. "All right, my girl, come over here and try this . . ." He stopped in surprise as she burst past him and tried to get out the door. He reached past her and slammed it.

"No, no!" she cried, fleeing into shadow. "Please, my Prince, don't make me do it!"

"Come, girl, do not be silly. Stop it! The sooner you do it, the sooner we are done. Come, that is a good girl."

She came to him slowly, unwillingly.

"If Yer 'Ighness insists . . ."

"I do. I command it."

"Then I must tell Yer 'Ighness somethin' afore I try on that shoe."

"What is it, girl?"

"It's my shoe."

The Prince blinked. "What?"

"It's my shoe. It fell off o' me when I was runnin' . . ."

"What! Listen, girl, I am doing this out of the goodness of my heart, and you are wasting my time. Just put your foot . . ."

" 'Me birthright for yer name,' " she said, and his breath caught in his throat. " 'If I stay another moment, I'll lose everything.' "

"How do you know that?" he gasped out. He grabbed her shoulders and shook her. "I have told no one except my father our last words to each other. How do you know them?"

She broke away from him and stood up proudly. "I know 'cause I was there!"

"But you . . . you . . . Look at you!"

She did not lower her eyes. "I clean up better than you'd expect."

"But you jabber away like a trained bird and dart about like a ferret! *She* spoke so precisely and moved with a stateliness that shamed the court!"

"You try 'avin' a conversation without usin' any 'H' words an' see 'ow precise you sound. An' if you want stateliness, just you 'op up onto a pair o' glass 'eels. Believe me, it's either stately or fall down in them things."

59

"Your gown! Your coach! Whence came they?"

"Well, whence they come was a friend o' mine. A person o' some power, I might add. An' don't ask to meet 'er, 'cause she operates on 'er own schedule and only shows up when I need 'er. An' she's the one as decides when that is, 'owever much me own opinion may disagree."

The Prince sat in the chair and began to rub his temples. "You do not understand what I am feeling. You cannot be the person. And yet you know things you could not know if you were not."

She stood behind him. "Why can't I be 'er?"

"You would not ask if you had seen her."

She began to rub his neck and shoulders. "Tell me about 'er."

He knew it was an unpardonable liberty, both her touch and her request, but the warmth and the shadowy darkness and the smells gave him a sense that ordinary rules had been suspended.

And her closeness.

"She was beauty beyond beauty. She moved like a spirit slipping the bonds of earth. She was light in my eyes and light in my arms. Each moment with her was molten gold, slipping away all the faster the harder I clutched to hold it. And with the stroke of twelve, the dream was broken and I fell back to earth. I do not expect you to understand."

She massaged his neck in silence while they stared into the fire. Her hands were rough and firm and knowing. He felt unfathomable content.

"You was so tall an' so 'andsome," she said from the darkness at his back. "When we danced, you 'eld me like a big dog with a egg in 'is mouth, like if you chose you could of crushed me in a second. Which you couldn't of, you know." And she gave his neck a teasing little slap. "But it was good to be treated fragile, even if I wasn't. You was so strong an' gentle. The music was playin' just for us, an' there was colors everywhere but I couldn't see nothin' but you. It was the best night I'll ever 'ave."

Her hands were still upon his shoulders. They waited in silence. Finally he spoke into the fire.

60

"If you feel that way, try on the slipper."

She let her hands drop. "No. You'd 'ave to marry me, an' that ain't what you want."

He turned in the chair and took her hands. "If the slipper fits, I want you."

"No. You don't want the slipper to fit nobody."

"That is mad. Why do you think I am going through the whole kingdom on my knees to every woman who wants to try her foot at winning a prince?"

She smiled. "It's actually yer Lord Chamberlain 'oo is on 'is knees."

"Figuratively on my knees. Why am I doing it? Tell me."

She shrugged. "To prove that no one is fitting." He started to object, but she silenced him. "You don't know that, but it's true. If you found 'er, she might turn out to be real.

"You felt sorry for me, but I feel sorry for you. Our night was like a beautiful dream for me, too, but I can wake up an' get on with it. I've got me little kitchen an' me work and I can be 'appy. And if me stepmother someday needs to make a connection with a rich 'ouse, she'll clean me up an' marry me off to some stupid, ugly oaf of a merchant's son. And I'll be 'appy 'cause I'll keep me 'ouse tidy an' me kitchen cozy and afore I goes to sleep, I'll think a secret thought about me Prince. And I'll sleep smilin'.

"But I can see *you* in twenty year. You'll be King an' they'll 'ave married you off to someone or other 'oo you only see at dinnertime. An' you'll drink too much wine an' shed a tear for what might 'ave been. An' you could 'ave been a good King, but you won't be, 'cause you won't want to get down an' dirty yourself in what's real an' common. You'll just be thinkin' about yer dream Princess. It'll be sad but it'll be better than if you found 'er an' married 'er an' discovered that 'er breath smelt bad in the mornin' just like real people."

He had sat down again as she talked. "What's wrong with wanting to live a dream?" he mused into the fire.

"In a dream, you got to play by its rules, an' there's more nightmares than sweet dreams in my experience. In real life, you

61

got a chance to make yer own rules, especially if yer a prince to start off with." She stroked his hair. "Forget yer dream Princess. Be the King you can be. Think kindly of me now an' then, but don't let me 'old ya back. There's a beauty in what's real, too."

He sat silent a moment. She gave him a little push to get him moving. He stood and slowly moved to the door.

"Don't forget this." She picked up the slipper, saw it was stained, and dipped it in a bucket of water and dried it on her skirts. "Good as new. Drink me a toast out of it now and agin. Onc't a year. No more."

He nodded, took it, and turned to the door. He put his hand on the latch, then leaned his head against the rough wood. "I have to know," he said.

She gave a sigh. "Are ya sure?"

"Yes. As sure as I am of anything." He turned and knelt to place the slipper before her.

She started to lift her foot, then set it down. "There's one thing you ought to know afore I try it on."

"And that is?"

She rolled her eyes up for a minute, then looked back to him. "It may not fit."

From his kneeling position, he slowly slumped down into a sprawl on the floor. He cradled his head in his hands. "What are you doing to me?"

"Just tryin' to be honest with ya."

"But you knew our last words. It *must* have been you."

"Everybody in the kingdom knows your last words."

"That's impossible! I told no one but my father. He would never have repeated it to anyone."

"Yer sure nobody could 'ave over'eard?"

"There was no one else there!"

She counted off on her fingers. "Nobody 'cept for six guards, three table servants, two butlers an' one old falconer 'oo pretended 'e needed the King's advice about where to tie the pigeons for the next 'unt just so's 'e could 'ear the story for 'isself. Twelve people. Eleven versions of the story was all over

62

the kingdom within twenty-four hours, an' the twelfth was a day late only 'cause one of the guards had laryngitis."

The Prince knit his brow. "I never noticed them."

She nodded. "You wouldn't 'ave paid them much mind."

"And that is how you knew what I said."

"No, I knew 'cause I was there. I'm just sayin' you 'aven't been quite as secret as you thought."

"Then why will the slipper not fit you?"

"Might not fit," she corrected. "Because it was got by magic. See, the person I mentioned 'oo got me me gown and all was me fairy godmother. She did the coach out of a punkin an' the 'orses out o' mice an' so on. So I don't know if me foot really fit in that glass shoe or if that was more of 'er doin'."

He rose from the floor and stood before her, looking deep into her eyes. He spoke softly.

"That is the most ridiculous story I have ever heard."

She nodded. "I guess I'd 'ave to agree with ya. Bein' true is no excuse for bein' ridiculous."

He laughed. "But I do not care." He thought a moment. "I don't care. I have felt more in the last hour with you than I have felt in all the rest of my life. Except for one night. And I can live with that one night as a golden, receding memory if I know that I can have every day with you. I love you, Cinderella."

She was troubled even as she felt the stirring of hope. "I don't like that name."

"But it is a part of your life and I must have it. I want to know all of you." He smiled with a contentment he had never known. "Marry me, Cinderella."

She burst into tears then. "No, no! It can't be. Look at me! Listen to me!"

"That's all I want to do. That and hold you forever." He longed to touch her, but he waited.

She dried her tears on a sleeve and tried to laugh, but it was a desperate sort of attempt. "I'll say yes, 'cause there's no way I could say no." He stepped toward her. "But first—I'll try on the slipper."

He stepped away from her and his brow was furrowed. "You don't have to do that. I don't care."

"Not now, maybe. But in five years or ten years, you'd start regrettin' it. An' regret is the only thing that love can't cure. So gimme that slipper. What's the worst that could 'appen?"

Hollow-eyed, he looked at her. "It might fit," he whispered.

She started at that, but looked him straight in the face and said, "Give it to me."

He set the slipper in front of her, then straightened. She touched her hand to his face and knelt to the fitting.

They stood, then, face to face. And there was so much hope and joy and fear and pain that neither one could have said which of them was feeling what.

"Look," she said.

He tried not to, but he couldn't help it.

The slipper didn't fit.

It didn't near fit.

He raised his eyes to hers and saw the hope in them change to a terrible fear.

"It isn't fitting," he said. "It is not fitting." She cringed. The Wicked Prince was out for good.

"It isn't fitting that a Princess dance on her wedding night in shoes that do not fit her."

Her face was crumpling. He could do nothing but go on.

"I shall have to summon the royal glassblower."

Her eyes flashed the question at him.

"To make you shoes that fit. The shoe must fit the foot. It's madness to try to make the foot fit the shoe."

She kicked it off and stepped close, and they stood a moment, savoring together the bittersweet of the last instant of aloneness they would ever know.

Then he swept her up into his arms, so strong yet gentle, as if he feared to crush her, which he couldn't have.

And the first step of all the many they took together smashed the glass slipper past all fitting.

Three Strong Women

a tall tale from Japan
by Claus Stamm

Long ago, in Japan, there lived a famous wrestler. One day he decided to make his way to the capital city to wrestle before the Emperor.

He strode down the road on legs thick as the trunks of small trees. He had been walking for seven hours and could walk for seven more without getting tired. The time was autumn.

The wrestler hummed to himself, "Zun-zun-zun," in time with the long swing of his legs. Wind blew through his thin brown robe, and he wore no sword at his side. He needed no sword, even in the darkest and loneliest places, and few tailors would have been able to make warm clothes for a man so broad and tall. He felt strong, healthy, and rather conceited.

65

He thought: "They call me Forever-Mountain because I am a good wrestler. I'm a fine, brave man and far too modest ever to say so . . ."

Just then he saw a girl who must have come up from the nearby river, for she steadied a bucket on her head. Her hands on the bucket were small, and there was a dimple on each thumb. She was a round little girl with red cheeks and a nose like a friendly button. Her eyes looked as though she were thinking of ten thousand funny stories at once. She clambered up onto the road and walked ahead of the wrestler.

"If I don't tickle that fat girl, I shall regret it all my life," said the wrestler to himself. "She will squeak and I shall laugh and laugh. If she drops her bucket, I can run and fill it again and carry it home for her."

He tiptoed up and poked her lightly in the ribs.

"Kochokochokocho!" he said, a fine, ticklish sound in Japanese.

The girl gave a satisfying squeal, giggled, and brought one arm down so that the wrestler's hand was caught between it and her body.

"Ho-ho-ho! You've caught me! I can't move at all!" said the wrestler.

"I know," said the jolly girl.

He felt that it was very good-tempered of her to take a joke so well, and started to pull his hand free. Somehow, he could not.

He tried again, using a little more strength.

"Now, now—let me go, little girl," he said. "I am a powerful man. If I pull hard I might hurt you."

"Pull," said the girl. "I admire powerful men."

She began to walk, and though the wrestler tugged and pulled until his feet dug great furrows in the ground, he had to follow.

Ten minutes later, still tugging while trudging helplessly after her, he was glad that the road was lonely and no one was there to see.

"Please let me go," he pleaded. "I am the famous wrestler Forever-Mountain. I must go show my strength before the Emperor"—he burst out weeping from shame and confusion—"and you're hurting my hand!"

The girl steadied the bucket on her head with her free hand and dimpled sympathetically over her shoulder. "You poor, sweet little Forever-Mountain," she said. "Are you tired? Shall I carry you?"

"I do not want you to carry me. I want you to let me go. I want to forget I ever saw you. What do you want with me?" moaned the pitiful wrestler.

"I only want to help you," said the girl, now pulling him steadily up and up a narrow mountain path. "Oh, I am sure you'll have no more trouble than anyone else against the other wrestlers. You'll win, or else you'll lose, and you won't be too badly hurt either way. But aren't you afraid you might meet a really *strong* man someday?"

Forever-Mountain turned white. He stumbled. He was imagining being laughed at throughout Japan as "Hardly-Ever-Mountain."

She glanced back.

"You see? Tired already," she said. "I'll walk more slowly. Why don't you come along to my mother's house and let us make a strong man of you? The wrestling in the capital won't begin for three months. I know, because Grandmother thought she'd go. You'd be spending all that time in bad company and wasting what little power you have."

"All right. Three months. I'll come," said the wrestler. He felt he had nothing more to lose. Also, he feared that the girl might be angry if he refused, and place him in the top of a tree until he changed his mind.

"Fine," she said happily. "We are almost there."

She freed his hand. It was red and a little swollen. "But if you break your promise and run off, I'll have to chase you and carry you back."

Soon they arrived in a small valley where a simple farmhouse with a thatched roof stood.

"Grandmother is at home, but she is an old lady and she's probably sleeping." The girl shaded her eyes with one hand. "But Mother should be bringing our cow back from the field. There's Mother now!"

She waved. The woman coming around the corner of the house put down the cow she was carrying and waved back.

She smiled and came across the grass, walking with a lively bounce like her daughter's. Well, maybe her bounce was a little more solid, thought the wrestler.

"Excuse me," she said. "These mountain paths are full of stones. They hurt the cow's feet. And who is the nice young man, Maru-me?"

The girl explained. "And we have only three months!" she finished anxiously.

"Well, it's not long enough to do much, but it's not so short a time that we can't do something," said her mother, looking thoughtful. "But he does look terribly feeble. He'll need a lot of good things to eat. Maybe he can help Grandmother with some of the easy housework."

"That will be fine!" said the girl, and she called her grandmother—loudly, for the old lady was a little deaf.

"I'm coming!" came a creaky voice from inside the house, and a little old woman leaning on a stick tottered out of the door. As she came toward them she stumbled over the roots of a great oak tree.

"Heh! My eyes aren't what they used to be. That's the fourth time this month I've stumbled over that tree," she complained and, wrapping her skinny arms about its trunk, pulled it out of the ground.

"Oh, Grandmother! You should have let me pull it up for you," said Maru-me.

"Hm. I hope I didn't hurt my poor old back," muttered the old lady. She called out, "Daughter! Throw that tree away like a good girl, so no one will fall over it. But make sure it doesn't hit anybody."

"You can help Mother with the tree," Maru-me said to Forever-Mountain. "On second thought, you'd better not help. Just watch."

Her mother went to the tree, picked it up in her two hands, and threw it—clumsily and with a little gasp.

Up went the tree, sailing end over end, growing smaller and smaller as it flew. It landed with a faint crash far up the mountainside.

"Ah, how clumsy," she said. "I meant to throw it *over* the mountain. It's probably blocking the path now, and I'll have to move it tomorrow."

The wrestler was not listening. He had very quietly fainted.

"Oh! We must put him to bed," said Maru-me.

"Poor, feeble young man," said her mother.

"I hope we can do something for him. Here, let me carry him, he's light," said the grandmother. She slung him over her shoulder and carried him into the house, creaking along with her cane.

The next day they began the work of making Forever-Mountain over into what they thought a strong man should be. They gave him the simplest food to eat, and the toughest. Day by day they prepared his rice with less and less water, until no ordinary man could have chewed or digested it.

Every day he was made to do the work of five men, and every evening he wrestled with Grandmother. Maru-me and her mother agreed that Grandmother, being old and feeble, was the least likely to injure him accidentally. They hoped the exercise might be good for rheumatism.

He grew stronger and stronger but was hardly aware of it. Grandmother could still throw him easily into the air—and catch him again—without ever changing her sweet old smile.

He quite forgot that outside this valley he was one of the greatest wrestlers in Japan and was called Forever-Mountain. His legs had been like logs; now they were like pillars. His big hands were hard as stones, and when he cracked his knuckles the sound was like trees splitting on a cold night.

Sometimes he did an exercise that wrestlers do in Japan—raising one foot high above the ground and bringing it down with a crash. Then people in nearby villages looked up at the winter sky and said that it was very late in the year for thunder.

Soon he could pull up a tree as well as the grandmother. He could even throw one—but only a small distance. One evening, near the end of his third month, he wrestled with Grandmother and held her down for half a minute.

"Heh-heh!" She chortled and got up, smiling with every wrinkle. "I'd never have believed it!"

Maru-me squealed with joy and threw her arms around him—gently, for she was afraid of cracking his ribs.

"Very good, very good! What a strong man," said her mother, who had just come home from the fields, carrying, as usual, the cow. She put the cow down and patted the wrestler on the back.

They agreed that he was now ready to show some *real* strength before the Emperor.

"Take the cow along with you tomorrow when you go," said the mother. "Sell her and buy yourself a belt—a silken belt. But the fattest and heaviest one you can find. Wear it when you appear before the Emperor, as a souvenir from us."

"I wouldn't think of taking your only cow. You've already done too much for me. And you'll need her to plow the fields, won't you?"

They burst out laughing. Maru-me squealed, her mother roared. The grandmother cackled so hard and long that she choked and had to be pounded on the back.

"Oh, dear," said the mother, still laughing. "You don't think we used our cow for *work*! Why, Grandmother here is stronger than five cows!"

"The cow is our pet," Maru-me giggled. "She has lovely brown eyes."

"But it really gets tiresome having to carry her back and forth each day so that she has enough grass to eat," said her mother.

"Then you must let me give you all the prize money that I win," said Forever-Mountain.

"Oh, no! We wouldn't think of it!" said Maru-me. "Because we all like you too much to sell you anything. And it is not proper to accept gifts of money from strangers."

"True," said Forever-Mountain. "I will now ask your mother's and grandmother's permission to marry you. I want to be one of the family."

70

"Oh! I'll make a wedding dress!" said Maru-me.

The mother and grandmother pretended to consider very seriously, but they quickly agreed.

Next morning Forever-Mountain tied his hair up in the topknot that all Japanese wrestlers wear, and got ready to leave. He thanked Maru-me and her mother and bowed very low to the grandmother, since she was the oldest and had been a fine wrestling partner. Then he picked up the cow and trudged up the mountain. When he reached the top, he slung the cow over one shoulder and waved good-bye to Maru-me.

At the first town he came to, Forever-Mountain sold the cow. She brought a good price because she was unusually fat from never having worked in her life. With the money, he bought the heaviest silken belt he could find.

When he reached the palace grounds, many of the other wrestlers were already there, sitting about, eating enormous bowls of rice, comparing one another's weight, and telling stories. They paid little attention to Forever-Mountain, except to wonder why he had arrived so late this year. Some of them noticed that he had grown very quiet and took no part at all in their boasting.

All the ladies and gentlemen of the court were waiting in a special courtyard for the wrestling to begin. They wore many robes, one on top of another, heavy with embroidery and gold cloth, and sweat ran down their faces and froze in the winter afternoon. The gentlemen had long swords so weighted with gold and precious stones that they could never have used them, even if they had known how. The court ladies, with their long black hair hanging down behind, had their faces painted dead white, which made them look frightened. They had pulled out their real eyebrows and painted new ones high above the place where eyebrows are supposed to be, and this made them all look as though they were very surprised at something.

Behind a screen sat the Emperor—by himself, because he was too noble for ordinary people to look at. He was a lonely old man with a kind, tired face. He hoped the wrestling would end quickly so that he could go to his room and write poems.

The first two wrestlers chosen to fight were Forever-Mountain and a wrestler who was said to have the biggest stomach in the country. He and Forever-Mountain both threw some salt into the ring. It was said that this drove away evil spirits.

Then the other wrestler, moving his stomach somewhat out of the way, raised his foot and brought it down with a fearful stamp. He glared fiercely at Forever-Mountain as if to say, "Now *you* stamp, you poor frightened man!"

Forever-Mountain raised his foot. He brought it down.

There was a sound like thunder, the earth shook, and the other wrestler bounced into the air and out of the ring, as gracefully as any soap bubble.

He picked himself up and bowed to the Emperor's screen.

"The earth-god is angry. Possibly there is something the matter with the salt," he said. "I do not think I shall wrestle this season." And he walked out, looking very suspiciously over one shoulder at Forever-Mountain.

Five other wrestlers then and there decided that they were not wrestling this season, either.

From then on, Forever-Mountain brought his foot down lightly. As each wrestler came into the ring, he picked him up very gently, carried him out, and placed him before the Emperor's screen, bowing most courteously every time.

The court ladies' eyebrows went up even higher. The gentlemen looked disturbed and a little afraid. They loved to see fierce, strong men tugging and grunting at each other, but Forever-Mountain was a little too much for them. Only the Emperor was happy. With the wrestling over so quickly, he would have that much more time to write his poems. He ordered all the prize money handed over to Forever-Mountain.

"But," he said, "you had better not wrestle any more." He stuck a finger through his screen and waggled it at the other wrestlers, who were sitting on the ground weeping with disappointment like great fat babies.

Forever-Mountain promised not to wrestle any more. Everybody looked relieved. The wrestlers sitting on the ground almost smiled.

"I think I shall become a farmer," Forever-Mountain said.

Maru-me was waiting for him. When she saw him coming, she ran down the mountain, picked him up, together with the heavy bags of prize money, and carried him halfway up the mountainside. Then she giggled and put him down. The rest of the day she let him carry her.

Forever-Mountain kept his promise to the Emperor and never fought in public again. His name was forgotten in the capital. But up in the mountains, sometimes the earth shakes and rumbles, and they say that it is Forever-Mountain and Maru-me's grandmother practicing wrestling.

Up the Slide

a story by Jack London

When Clay Dilham left the tent to get a sled load of firewood, he expected to be back in half an hour. So he told Swanson, who was cooking the dinner. Swanson and he belonged to different outfits, located about twenty miles apart on the Stuart River; but they had become traveling partners on a trip down the Yukon to Dawson to get the mail.

Swanson had laughed when Clay said he would be back in half an hour. It stood to reason, Swanson said, that good, dry firewood could not be found so close to Dawson; that whatever firewood there was originally had long since been gathered in; that firewood would not be selling at forty dollars a cord if any man could go out and get a sled load and be back in the time Clay expected to make it.

Then it was Clay's turn to laugh, as he sprang on the sled and *mushed* the dogs on the river trail. For, coming up from the Siwash village the previous day, he had noticed a small dead pine in an out-of-the-way place, which had defied discovery by eyes less sharp than his. And his eyes were both young and sharp, for his seventeenth birthday was just cleared.

A swift ten minutes over the ice brought him to the place, and figuring ten minutes to get the tree and ten minutes to return made him certain that Swanson's dinner would not wait.

Just below Dawson, and rising out of the Yukon itself, towered the great Moosehide Mountain, so named by Lieutenant Schwatka long ere the Klondike became famous. On the river side the mountain was scarred and gullied and gored; and it was up one of these gores or gullies that Clay had seen the tree.

Halting his dogs beneath, on the river ice, he looked up, and after some searching, rediscovered it. Being dead, its weather-beaten gray so blended with the gray wall of rock that a thousand men could pass by and never notice it. Taking root in a cranny, it had grown up, exhausted its bit of soil, and perished. Beneath it the wall fell sheer for a hundred feet to the river. All one had to do was to sink an ax into the dry trunk a dozen times and it would fall to the ice, and most probably smash conveniently to pieces. This Clay had figured on when confidently limiting the trip to half an hour.

He studied the cliff thoroughly before attempting it. So far as he was concerned, the longest way round was the shortest way to the tree. By making a long zigzag across the face of this slide and back again, he would arrive at the pine.

Fastening his ax across his shoulders so that it would not interfere with his movements, he clawed up the broken rock, hand and foot, like a cat, till the twenty feet were cleared and he could draw breath on the edge of the slide.

The slide was steep and its snow-covered surface slippery. Further, the heelless, walrus-hide soles of his *muclucs* were polished by much ice travel, and by his second step he realized how little he could depend upon them for clinging purposes. A slip at that point meant a plunge over the edge and a twenty-foot fall to the ice. A hundred feet farther along, and a slip would mean a fifty-foot fall.

He thrust his mittened hand through the snow to the earth to steady himself, and went on. But he was forced to exercise such care that the first zigzag consumed five minutes. Then, returning across the face of the slide toward the pine, he met with a new difficulty. The slope steepened considerably, so that little snow collected, while bent flat beneath this thin covering were long, dry last-year's grasses.

The surface they presented was as glassy as that of his muclucs, and when both surfaces came together his feet shot out, and he fell on his face, sliding downward, and convulsively clutching for something to stay himself.

This he succeeded in doing, although he lay quiet for a couple of minutes to get back his nerve. He would have taken off his muclucs and gone at it in his socks, only the cold was thirty below zero, and at such temperature his feet would quickly freeze. So he went on, and after ten minutes of risky work made the safe and solid rock where stood the pine.

A few strokes of the ax fell it into the chasm, and peeping over the edge, he indulged a laugh at the startled dogs. They were on the verge of bolting when he called aloud to them, soothingly, and they were reassured.

Then he turned about for the back trip. Going down, he knew, was even more dangerous than coming up, but how dangerous he did not realize till he had slipped half a dozen times, and each time saved himself by what appeared to him a miracle.

He sat down and looked at the treacherous snow-covered slope. It was manifestly impossible for him to make it with a whole body, and he did not wish to arrive at the bottom shattered like the pine tree.

But while he sat inactive the frost was stealing in on him, and the quick chilling of his body warned him that he could not delay. He must be doing something to keep his blood circulating. If he could not get down by going down, there only remained to him to get down by going up. It was a herculean task, but it was the only way out of the predicament.

From where he was he could not see the top of the cliff, but he reasoned that the gully in which lay the slide must give inward more and more as it approached the top. From what little he could see, the gully displayed this tendency; and he noticed, also, that the slide extended for many hundreds of feet upward, and that where it ended the rock was well broken up and favorable for climbing.

 So instead of taking the zigzag which led downward, he made a new one leading upward and crossing the slide at an angle of thirty degrees. The grasses gave him much trouble, and made him long for soft-tanned moosehide moccasins, which could make his feet cling like a second pair of hands.

He soon found that thrusting his mittened hands through the snow and clutching the grass roots was uncertain and unsafe. His mittens were too thick for him to be sure of his grip, so he took them off. But this brought with it new trouble. When he held on to a bunch of roots the snow, coming in contact with his bare warm hand, was melted, so that his hands and the wristbands of his woolen shirt were dripping with water. This the frost was quick to attack, and his fingers were numbed and made worthless.

Then he was forced to seek good footing where he could stand erect unsupported, to put on his mittens, and to thrash his hands against his sides until the heat came back into them.

While beating his hands against his sides he turned and looked down the long slippery slope, and figured, in case he slipped, that he would be flying with the speed of an express train ere he took the final plunge into the icy bed of the Yukon.

He passed the first outcropping rock, and the second, and at the end of an hour found himself above the third, and fully five hundred feet above the river. And here, with the end nearly two hundred feet above him, the pitch of the slide was increasing.

Each step became more difficult and perilous, and he was faint from exertion and from lack of Swanson's dinner. Three or four times he slipped slightly and recovered himself; but, growing careless from exhaustion and the long tension on his nerves, he tried to continue with too great haste, and was rewarded by a double slip of each foot, which tore him loose and started him down the slope.

On account of the steepness there was little snow; but what little there was was displaced by his body, so that he became the nucleus of a young avalanche. He clawed desperately with his hands, but there was little to cling to, and he sped downward faster and faster.

The first and second outcroppings were below him, but he knew that the first was almost out of line, and pinned his hope on the second. Yet the first was just enough in line to catch one of his feet and to whirl him over and head downward on his back.

The shock of this was severe in itself, and the fine snow enveloped him in a blinding, maddening cloud; but he was thinking quickly and clearly of what would happen if he brought up head first against the second outcropping. He twisted himself over on his stomach, thrust both hands out to one side, and pressed them heavily against the flying surface.

This had the effect of a brake, drawing his head and shoulders to the side. In this position he rolled over and over a couple of times, and then, with a quick jerk at the right moment, he got his body the rest of the way round.

And none too soon, for the next moment his feet drove into the outcropping, his legs doubled up, and the wind was driven from his stomach with the abruptness of the stop.

There was much snow down his neck and up his sleeves. At once and with unconcern he shook this out, only to discover, when he looked up to where he must climb again, that he had lost his nerve. He was shaking as if with a palsy, and sick and faint from a frightful nausea.

77

Fully ten minutes passed ere he could master these sensations and summon sufficient strength for the weary climb. His legs hurt him and he was limping, and he was conscious of a sore place in his back, where he had fallen on the ax.

In an hour he had regained the point of his tumble, and was contemplating the slide, which so suddenly steepened. It was plain to him that he could not go up with hands and feet alone, and he was beginning to lose his nerve again when he remembered the ax.

Reaching upward the distance of a step, he brushed away the snow, and in the frozen gravel and crumbled rock of the slide chopped a shallow resting place for his foot. Then he came up a step, reached forward, and repeated the maneuver. And so, step by step, foothole by foothole, a tiny speck of toiling life poised like a fly on the face of Moosehide Mountain, he fought his upward way.

Twilight was beginning to fall when he gained the head of the slide and drew himself into the rocky bottom of the gully. At this point the shoulder of the mountain began to bend back toward the crest, and in addition to its being less steep, the rocks afforded better handhold and foothold. The worst was over, and the best yet to come!

The gully opened out into a miniature basin, in which a floor of soil had been deposited, out of which, in turn, a tiny grove of pines had sprung. The trees were all dead, dry and seasoned, having long since exhausted the thin skin of earth.

Clay ran his experienced eye over the timber, and estimated that it would chop up into fifty cords at least. Beyond, the gully closed in and became barren rock again. On every hand was barren rock, so the wonder was small that the trees had escaped the eyes of men. They were only to be discovered as he had discovered them—by climbing after them.

He continued the ascent, and the white moon greeted him when he came out upon the crest of Moosehide Mountain. At his feet, a thousand feet below, sparkled the lights of Dawson.

But the descent on that side was precipitate and dangerous in the uncertain moonshine, and he elected to go down the mountain by its gentler northern flank. In a couple of hours he reached the Yukon at the Siwash village, and took the river trail back to where he had left the dogs. There he found Swanson, with a fire going, waiting for him to come down.

And although Swanson had a hearty laugh at his expense, nevertheless, a week or so later, in Dawson, there were fifty cords of wood sold at forty dollars a cord, and it was he and Swanson who sold them.

Delgadina

a fairy tale from Chile retold by Laura Simms

There was once a girl named Delgadina who lived with her mother in the mountains of Chile. She was beautiful, and she was kind.

One day Delgadina found a tiny red snake, no bigger than her finger, in the forest. She took him home and made a box for him. Then she fed him and slipped the box beneath her bed. In the morning when Delgadina looked at the snake she saw that he had grown three times his size. "My little red snake, how quickly you grow!" she said.

Every day the snake grew bigger and bigger until he filled the whole room where Delgadina slept. So Delgadina had to sleep in her mother's room.

The snake continued to grow. Delgadina's mother said to her, "My daughter, this snake is too big to stay in the house. You must tell him to go and live in the forest."

The girl led the snake through the trees and watched him crawl into the mouth of a cave. Every day Delgadina visited the snake and fed him. Still the snake continued to grow. "My little

79

red snake, how quickly you grow." She was astonished by his size.

One day, Delgadina's mother said, "My daughter, we are too poor to continue feeding the snake. Tell him to go and live in the ocean."

Sadly Delgadina went to the mouth of the cave and called out: "My little red snake!"

The large red snake slithered and lumbered to the mouth of the cave. "Delgadina, what do you want?" he asked.

"My little friend," replied Delgadina, "my mother says that we are too poor to continue to feed you. She says that you must go and live in the ocean. I will miss you."

"I will miss you, too, for I have grown to love you," said the snake. "But your mother is right. It is time for me to go. But before I go let me give you a gift. Take your hands and rub them on my eyes three times." Delgadina did as the snake bid her do. "Now, Delgadina, whenever you wash your hands and shake your fingers dry, golden coins will fall from your hands and you will want for nothing again." Delgadina thanked the snake. She kissed him goodbye and watched him as he turned and moved toward the ocean.

Delgadina grew up. She grew more beautiful and more kind. Because of the snake's gift she and her mother grew rich. But they were generous and whenever anyone asked them for something, they gave it gladly.

There was a king living not far from Delgadina's house, and he was looking for a wife. He heard about the beautiful girl who could shake gold from her fingers and whose heart was kind. He thought, "This young woman would make a good queen." But he didn't know Delgadina's family, so he wondered how he could meet her.

In the kingdom there lived an old woman who was wicked and jealous. When she heard that the king wanted to meet Delgadina, she went before him and announced, "I know Delgadina's mother very well, and I could bring the girl to you. If you give me a golden coach with four white horses and a dress of diamonds and pearls, then I will bring Delgadina to you tomorrow."

The king didn't know that she was wicked. He gladly gave her the golden coach with four white horses and the dress of diamonds and pearls.

The old woman was pleased. She had a bony, ugly girl and she had no intention of marrying Delgadina to the king. She wanted her own daughter to be the queen. So she dressed the bony, ugly girl in the beautiful dress of diamonds and pearls. She sat her in the golden carriage, shut the door, and drove off to Delgadina's house.

Delgadina's mother saw the beautiful shining carriage with the four white horses approach, and she knew it must come from the king's palace. The old woman stopped the carriage in front of Delgadina's mother and said, "The king would like to marry your daughter."

Delgadina's mother was delighted. She spoke to her daughter, and Delgadina agreed to the wedding because she had heard that the king excelled in goodness and generosity. When the girl's good mother prepared to go along with her, the old woman stated, "We'll come back for you in a few days."

So lovely Delgadina dressed in her best gown, climbed alone into the carriage, and bid her mother goodbye. Barely able to hide her delight, the old woman locked the door, whipped the horses, and rode off as fast as she could.

In a little while Delgadina realized they were not riding in the direction of the king's palace. Instead they were riding up the winding road to the edge of the cliffs that overlooked the ocean. Then she noticed the bony, ugly girl in the dress of diamonds and pearls seated beside her. "I want to go home," she cried.

Delgadina knocked at the window for the old woman to stop. But the old woman did not heed her and urged the horses faster and faster until they climbed to the highest cliffs. There she stopped the carriage and unlocked the gilded door. She grabbed Delgadina and tore out her eyes. Then she threw the girl into the ocean and drove her own daughter to the royal palace instead.

Everyone in the kingdom was ready for a wedding. There were banners and music. A great feast had been prepared, and a

81

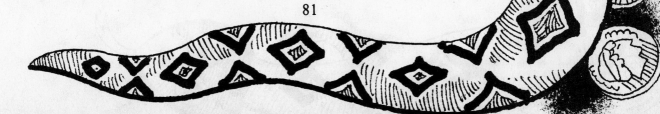

red rug was laid down from the palace to the road where the carriage would arrive. But who stepped out of the carriage but the old woman's bony, ugly daughter.

When the king saw her he thought, "Is that Delgadina?" On second thought he said to himself, "Well, if her heart is kind I will marry her. Yet I must know the truth. I will know she is Delgadina if she can shake gold from her fingers."

He said to the bony, ugly girl, "Why don't you wash your hands before we get married?"

But the girl was clever. She answered, "I never wash before morning." So the king had to marry her.

By morning he couldn't stand the sight of her. He watched her wash her hands in hopes that if she couldn't shake gold from her fingers he could prove she was a phony and be rid of her. The girl went to the well, washed her hands, and shook her fingers dry. No gold fell from her hands. The king sat back and silently rejoiced, "Good, now I can be rid of her."

But the clever girl raged, "I spent one night with you, and look what happened. I lost all my magic, and now I'm stuck!" The king was speechless.

I know you must be wondering what happened to Delgadina. She was washed ashore on an island. An old shepherd found her and took her home. Delgadina was blind. She lay ill for many, many days.

When she finally awoke, she was so heartbroken she wouldn't tell the shepherd her name or from where she had come. The shepherd continued to care for her, and, as best she could, she cared for him. But each morning, and each evening, she went down to the shore, looked out in the direction she imagined her mother lived, and sang,

"I wish I could go home again,

My mother I would see.

For she is very far away,

Somewhere across the sea."

One day, as Delgadina sat singing, she heard a tumult in the waves and a familiar voice sorrowfully said, "Delgadina, I heard your sad song across the sea. Whatever has happened to you?"

Delgadina reached out and touched the face of her friend. "My little red snake, how glad I am to hear your voice." She told him the story of all that had passed.

The red snake exclaimed, "Delgadina, I can make you better. Take your hands, and rub them on my eyes three times. Now press your hands on your own eyes." Delgadina did just as the snake bid her do. "Now, Delgadina, lift your hands from your eyes."

When Delgadina lifted her hands, she was healed. She could see again. The snake said, "Now, Delgadina, go to the shepherd, wash your hands, and shake him a pile of gold to last him all his life." Delgadina did as the snake bid her do. She told the shepherd the whole story of her life and bid him goodby. The shepherd thanked her for the gold and said farewell.

Bright-eyed Delgadina ran down to the shore and climbed on the back of the snake. He carried her across the ocean to her mother's home. When she and her mother saw one another, they laughed and they cried. They were so happy to be together again. She told her mother all that had occurred.

Several weeks passed, and the king heard that the real Delgadina had returned. He would have preferred to marry her and be rid of the girl he had mistakenly married. He knew it would be difficult to outwit the clever girl and prove she really wasn't Delgadina.

One day he thought of a plan. He decided to hold a feast in honor of his bony, ugly wife and invite every single person in all of Chile. He ordered the royal cooks to fry the greasiest chicken in the world. There would be no towels by the well, so everyone who washed their hands would have to shake their fingers dry. She who shook her fingers and had gold fall from her hands would be the true Delgadina, and he would marry her.

Everybody came to the feast, including Delgadina and her mother. The bony, ugly wife was pleased to have a party in her honor. All the people, including the soldiers and the guards, ate greasy chicken, and they all washed their hands and shook their fingers dry. But when Delgadina shook her fingers, gold fell from her hands. The only ones who saw it were the king, the wicked old woman, and her scheming daughter.

83

Now the king was glad, for indeed, the minute he had set eyes on Delgadina, he had fallen in love with her. But the ugly wife was angry. The old woman said to her daughter, "We'd better get out of here as fast as we can, but let's not go empty-handed. Let's get that golden carriage and fill it with treasures, and let's take that dress of diamonds and pearls as well."

They filled the carriage from top to bottom. The king saw them do it. He didn't care about his riches, for he loved Delgadina. The guards didn't see, because they were busy eating chicken. So the old woman and her daughter got into the carriage filled with treasure and rode away as fast as they could.

The king was so pleased to be rid of them that he stamped his foot on the ground three times. The earth shook.

The sound of the earth shaking woke up the snake who was sleeping in the ocean not far from the palace. The snake looked up and saw the wicked old woman and her daughter riding down the road. So he burrowed a hole underneath the earth and made a tunnel. He slithered along below the ground until he came directly under their carriage. Then he wiggled and turned and stood up on his tail, blowing the carriage to bits. The conniving mother and her dishonest daughter were never seen or heard of again.

So it was that the king married the real Delgadina. And they ruled together with love, with kindness, and with wealth. But when they had a problem that they couldn't solve, the king and Delgadina would stamp on the ground three times. Then the snake would slither out of the ocean and Delgadina would place a small red crown on his head. The king and Delgadina would ask him the question and the snake would answer. So Delgadina and the king and the snake ruled with wisdom, with wealth, and with kindness, and they all lived happily ever after, and may you live as well.

84

Why Is the NBA Shot Clock 24 Seconds?

from Imponderables: The Solution to the Mysteries of
Everyday Life *by David Feldman*

During the 1953–1954 season, the National Basketball League was beset by difficulties. Attendance was low; many franchises were in financial trouble.

Professional basketball's problem was not a trivial one: Fans found the game boring. Hoop fans like to see plenty of shooting and scoring, but the rules did absolutely nothing to encourage teams with a lead to shoot the ball. If a team led in the late stages of the game, the custom was to have its best ball handler dribble in the backcourt, forcing opponents to foul intentionally, resulting in tedious but profitable free throws for the stalling team. There was also no incentive for teams in the lead to run cross court and set up their offense quickly, further dragging the pace of the game.

The owners knew they had a problem, but the solution was the brainchild of an unlikely savior named Danny Biasone. Biasone, a bowling alley proprietor, bought the Syracuse Nationals franchise for the princely sum of $1000. Biasone might not have had the clout within the league to compete with the Knicks or Celtics owners, but he concluded that a clock was necessary to force players to shoot at regular intervals and speed up the game.

How did Biasone arrive at 24 seconds? He figured that the average game contains about 120 shots between the two teams. Since there are 48 minutes, or 2880 seconds, in an NBA game, teams averaged exactly one shot every 24 seconds. Figuring that players would be forced to shoot before the 24 seconds expired, a shot clock would compel teams to shoot more often and, presumably, score more often.

85

Biasone invited club owners to watch a demonstration of how a game would be played with a clock. All could see that the shot clock would add excitement to the game, and it was instituted in regular play at the beginning of the 1954–1955 season.

The shot clock changed basketball immediately. Scoring did increase, an average of 14 points per game in one season. Most importantly, attendance rose quickly. NBA historian Charles Paikert quoted former league president Maurice Podoloff as saying that the adoption of the clock "was the most important event in the NBA and Danny Biasone is the most important man in the NBA."

Biasone's shot clock had another effect that perhaps he did not foresee—it changed the type of player needed to build a championship team. The Minneapolis Lakers dominated the NBA before the shot clock, led by the physically bruising but slow and lumbering George Mikan. The Lakers, with the shot clock, could no longer afford to loiter downcourt while Mikan hauled down a rebound and casually jogged across the half-court line. Mikan retired the year the shot clock was instituted. He returned for the 1955–1956 season, but he averaged only 10 points versus a career average of 22 points, and he quit after half a season.

The shot clock was tailor-made for the team Red Auerbach was fashioning in Boston. In Bill Russell, the Celtics found a tall center who was also exceptionally quick and could spark a fast break offense.

Although Paikert notes that Biasone has so far been denied a place in the basketball Hall of Fame, he was justly rewarded in one respect. In the premier season of the 24-second clock, his Nationals won their first and only championship. Biasone sold the Nationals in 1963. They became the Philadelphia 76ers and went on to win many more championships.

How many more shots are taken today than in Biasone's era? In the regulation 1984–1985 season, NBA players took 168,048 shots in 943 games, an average of 178 shots per game—58 more shots per game, an almost 50 percent increase.

Dividing the number of shots per game (178) into the number of seconds per regulation game (2880), we find that a shot is taken on an average of every 16.17 seconds. Considering how many quick shots and tips are attempted on the offensive boards, which would bring down this average, it is surprising how much time most offenses take in getting off shots, and perhaps a tribute to the defensive skills in the NBA.

How Mink Stole Time

*a Salish story from the Pacific Northwest
retold by Joseph Bruchac*

Long ago, the People had no light. It was hard for them to move around in the darkness and they were always cold. Mink took pity on them. He heard that on the other side of the world there was something called the Sun. It was being kept there by those on the other side of the world. So Mink decided to steal the Sun for the People. It was not an easy job, but Mink was a great thief. He stole the Sun and placed it in the sky so that it would share its light equally with the people on both sides of the world. Now it was no longer dark and cold all the time. Now there was day and night because of the Sun. The People were very happy and they praised Mink. He grew proud of himself because of that praise.

"Perhaps," he said, "there is something else I can steal for the People."

A long time passed and Mink saw nothing that was worth stealing. Then the Europeans came. They were new people with a lot of power.

"What is it that these new people have that we do not have?" Mink said. Then he saw what it was. The Europeans had something they called Time. They used it to give them their power. So Mink decided he would steal Time. He waited until it was dark and sneaked into their house. There, in the biggest room, they kept Time up on a shelf. They kept it in a shiny box which made noises. As it made noises, two small arrows on the front of that box moved in circles. Mink could see it was a powerful thing. So he carried it off.

Now Mink and the People had Time. But Mink soon found that it was not easy to have Time. He had to watch the hands of that shiny box all of the time to see what the time was. He had to keep three keys tied around his neck so that he could use them to wind up that box full of time so it would keep on ticking. Now that Mink had Time, he no longer had the time to do the things he used to do. There was no time for him to fish and hunt as he had done before. He had to get up at a certain time and go to bed at a certain time. He had to go to meetings and work when that box full of time told him it was time. He and the People were no longer free.

Because Mink stole Time, it now owned him and the People. It has been that way ever since then. Time owns us the way we used to own the Sun.

The Twelve Months

a Czechoslovakian folk tale retold
by Virginia Haviland

There was once a widow who had a daughter named
Holena. In the cottage with them lived Holena's stepsister,
Marushka. Now Marushka was so pretty and good that the other
two disliked her and made her do all the hard work. She had to
sweep the rooms, cook, wash, sew, spin and weave, and she had
to bring in the hay from the meadow and milk the cow. Holena,
who was not pretty, did nothing but dress up in her best clothes
and amuse herself with one thing after another.

But Marushka never complained. Patiently she bore the
scoldings and bad tempers of the mother and daughter. Holena's
ugliness increased, while Marushka became even lovelier to look
at. This made the other two more tyrannical and grumpy than
ever. At length they determined to get rid of her, for they knew
that Holena would have no suitors while Marushka was there to
be seen.

One day in the middle of winter Holena said she wanted
some violets. "Listen!" she cried to Marushka. "You must go up
on the mountain and find me some violets. And they must be
fresh and sweet-scented. Do you hear?"

"But whoever heard of violets blooming in the snow!" cried
Marushka.

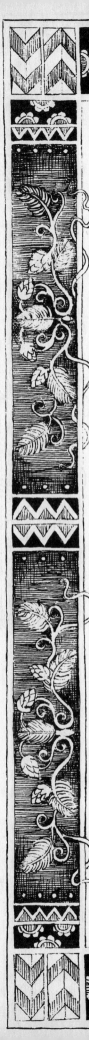

"You wretched creature! Do you dare to disobey me? Not another word! Off with you, and don't come back without the violets!"

The stepmother added her threats, and the two pushed Marushka out of the cottage and shut the door behind her.

Marushka, weeping, made her way to the mountain. The snow lay deep and there was no trace of any other human being. For a long time she wandered hither and thither, and lost herself in the woods. She became hungry and she shivered with cold and was almost ready to give up when she saw a light in the distance. She climbed toward it, until she had reacned the very top of the mountain.

Upon the highest peak she found a large fire burning and twelve men in long white robes sitting around it. Three had white hair, three were not quite so old, three were young and handsome, and the rest still younger. These were the twelve months of the year, and they sat silently looking at the fire, each one on a block of stone. The great January was placed higher than the others. He was older than they, and his hair and beard were white as snow. In his hand he held a wand.

At first Marushka was afraid, but after a while her courage returned. Drawing near, she said, "Good men, may I warm myself at your fire? I am chilled by the winter cold."

The great January raised his head and asked, "What brings you here, my child? What do you seek?"

"I am looking for violets," replied Marushka.

"This is not the season for violets. Do you not see the snow everywhere?"

"Yes," was Marushka's reply, "but my stepmother and my stepsister have ordered me to bring them violets from your mountain. If I return without them, they will kill me. I pray you, good sirs, to tell me where to find them."

The great January arose and went over to one of the youngest of the months. Placing his wand in that month's hand, he said, "Brother March, do you take the highest place."

March obeyed, at the same time waving his wand over the fire. Immediately the flames rose toward the sky. The snow began to melt, the trees and shrubs to bud. The grass became green and between the blades peeped the pale primrose. It was spring, and the meadows turned blue with violets.

"Gather them quickly, Marushka," said March.

Joyfully, Marushka hastened to pick the flowers and soon had a large bouquet. She thanked the months and hastened home. Holena and her mother were amazed at the sight of the flowers and at their fragrance, which filled the house.

"Where did you pick them?" asked Holena.

"Under the trees on the mountain," replied Marushka.

Holena took the flowers, but without thanking Marushka for the trouble she had taken to get them.

The next day Holena called to Marushka again and said, "I long to taste strawberries. Run and fetch me some from the mountain, and see to it that they are sweet and ripe."

"But whoever heard of strawberries ripening in the snow?" said Marushka.

"Hold your tongue! Go after the strawberries and don't come back without them."

Holena's mother also ordered Marushka to gather the berries. They pushed her out of the house and bolted the door behind her.

Unhappily, Marushka made her way to the mountain again and climbed until she came to the fire around which sat the twelve months.

"Good men, may I warm myself at your fire? The winter wind chills me."

The great January raised his head and asked, "Why do you come here? What do you seek?"

"I am looking for strawberries," she replied.

"But we are in the midst of winter. Strawberries do not grow in the snow."

"I know," said Marushka sadly, "but my stepmother and stepsister have ordered me to bring them strawberries. I dare not return without them. Pray, good sirs, tell me where to find them."

The great January arose and went over to the month opposite him and, putting his wand into that month's hand, said, "Brother June, do you take the highest place."

June obeyed, and as he waved his wand over the fire, the flames leaped toward the sky. Instantly the snow melted, the earth became green with grass and the trees with leaves. Birds began to sing and flowers blossomed in the forest. It was summer, and in the sunny glades, star-shaped blooms changed into ripe, red strawberries.

"Gather them quickly," said June.

Joyfully, Marushka thanked the months and, when she had filled her apron, ran happily home. The strawberries greatly surprised Holena and her mother. "Wherever did you find them?" asked Holena crossly.

"Up on the mountain," replied Marushka.

Holena gave a few to her mother and ate the rest herself. Not even one did she offer to Marushka. But on the third day she had tired of strawberries and fancied having some fresh, red apples.

"Run, Marushka," she demanded, "and fetch me fresh, red apples from the mountain."

"Apples in winter!" exclaimed Marushka. "Why, the trees have neither leaves nor fruit on them now."

"You idle girl! Go this minute, and don't come back unless you bring the apples."

As before, the widow added her commands and threats. The two seized Marushka roughly and turned her out of the house.

Poor Marushka went weeping through deep snow up the mountain till she came again to the fire around which sat the twelve months.

"Good men, may I warm myself at your fire?"

The great January raised his head and asked, "Why come you here? What do you seek?"

"I come to look for red apples," replied Marushka.

"But this is winter and not the season for apples," answered January.

"I know. But my stepmother and her daughter have ordered me to fetch them red apples from the mountain, and I dare not return without them. Pray, good sirs, tell me where to find them."

The great January arose and went to one of the elderly months, to whom he handed his wand. "Brother September, do you take the highest place."

September moved to the highest seat, which January had occupied. He waved the wand over the fire and a flare of red flames made the snow disappear. The trees leafed out, then brightened with autumn colors. A frosty wind began to scatter the leaves through the forest.

Marushka looked about and spied an apple tree on which hung ripe, red fruit. She ran and shook the tree. One apple fell and then another. "That is enough," said September. "Now hurry home."

Marushka thanked the months and went down the mountain joyfully.

At home Holena and her mother marveled at the fruit. "Where did you gather these apples?" Holena asked.

"On the mountaintop," answered Marushka.

"Why did you not bring more?" said Holena fretfully. "You must have eaten them on your way back, you wicked girl."

"No, I have not even tasted them," declared Marushka. "I shook the tree twice. One apple fell each time. I was not allowed to shake it again, but was told to return home."

Holena would not believe her, and spoke so harshly that Marushka wept bitterly and took refuge in the kitchen.

Holena and her mother ate the apples. Never before had they tasted such delicious fruit. When they had finished the two apples, they both longed for more.

"Mother," said Holena, "give me my cloak and I will go fetch more apples. I will not send Marushka because the good-for-nothing wretch would eat them on her way. I will find the

93

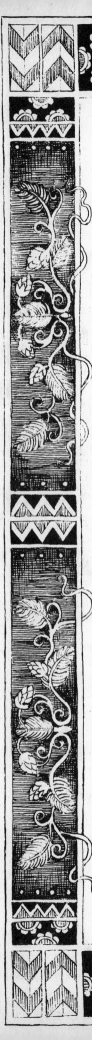

tree, and no matter who cries 'Stop!' I shall not leave until I
have shaken all the apples from the tree."

Holena's mother brought a warm cloak and hood and helped
her daughter put them on. Then Holena took the road to the
mountain while her mother stood at the window and watched
her disappear in the distance.

Snow covered everything and not a footprint was to be seen
anywhere, but Holena pushed on until she reached the
mountaintop. There were the flaming fire and the twelve months
seated about it. At first Holena was frightened and she hesitated
to go nearer. But then she went close and warmed her hands,
without asking permission. The great January inquired severely,
"What has brought you here? What do you seek?"

"I need not tell you," replied Holena. "What business is it
of yours?"

January frowned and waved his wand over his head. Instantly
the sky filled with clouds, snow began to fall, and the fire and
the twelve months disappeared. Holena found herself alone in a
wild storm. Although she tried to make her way home, she only
wandered vainly hither and thither through the white forest.

Meanwhile, Holena's mother looked from the cottage
window for her return. The hours passed slowly and she became
alarmed. "Can it be that the apples have charmed her away from
home?" she wondered. Finally, she put on her own hood and
cloak and set out to search for her daughter. But the snow
continued to blow in great drifts, covering everything. The icy
north wind whistled through the mountain forests. No voice
answered her cry. Neither mother nor daughter ever returned
home.

Marushka lived on in the little cottage, and it and the field
and cow became hers. In time an honest young farmer came to
share them with her, and they were contented and happy as long
as they lived.

TIME

*a folk tale from Liberia by Harold Courlander
and George Herzog*

Once there was a rich man in Africa whose
name was Time. He owned more goats, chickens,
and cattle than he could count. He possessed
more land than he had ever seen, and on his
farms were grown vast quantities of rice, manioc,
and all kinds of foods. He had immense stores of cloth, and his many
granaries were always overflowing with grain. His reputation had
spread far beyond his own tribe. Traders came from distant towns to
do business with Time. Dancers, acrobats, and wrestlers came to
perform for him. Tribes far and wide sent messengers just to see
Time face to face and to return and tell the people what he looked
like, and how he lived. To the strangers who visited him Time gave
rich presents of cows, goats, and fine cloth. People said that a man
who had not seen Time hadn't really lived.

But Time grew old, and his fortunes changed. His wealth
disappeared. His cattle grew fewer and fewer, his lands grew small,
and his stores of grain shrank to nothing. His well-fed body became
lean and starved. His house became dilapidated and uncared for, and
Time came to look like the poorest of beggars. Yet in distant
countries they didn't know about Time's change of fortune.

One day the people of a tribe far from Time's town appointed a
number of messengers to visit him.

"Go to Time's country and see him," the messengers were told. "After you have looked at him come back and tell us if he is as rich and generous as people say."

The messengers set out on their long trip, and walked for many days. When at last they came to the edge of the town where Time lived they met a poor old man, thin and wrinkled, and dressed in rags.

"Man, tell us," they asked him, "does Time live here? And if so, where is his house?"

"Yes, Time lives here," the old man said. "Enter the town and people will show you where to find him."

They went into the town and greeted the townspeople.

"We have come to see Time, whose reputation has spread so far," the messengers said. "We want to meet this wonderful man, so that we can go back to our country and describe him to our people."

While they talked there, the old beggar whom the messengers had seen at the edge of the town came walking toward them.

"Time, the man for whom you have been looking, is coming now," someone said.

The visitors looked, and when they saw Time they were very dejected.

"Can this be the man whose name is known even in our country?" they asked. They couldn't believe it, for this beggar was the poorest of all poor people. Never had they seen a man looking so miserable.

When Time came to where they were sitting they shook hands with him and asked:

"Man, are you really Time, of whom everyone has heard?"

"Yes," he said, "I am Time."

"But how can that be? We listened and listened to stories about Time in our country. Travelers came with great tales about his fabulous wealth and influence. Our people sent us here to see him, so that we could return and tell them about Time."

"Well, I am Time. My fortunes have changed," Time said. "I was once the richest man in the world, and now I am the poorest."

"Well, then, that's the way it is," they said sadly. "But whatever shall we tell our people now?"

Time thought for a while, and then he said to them:

"When you get to your country once more and see your people, tell them this: 'Behold, Time isn't what it used to be!'"

Damon and Pythias

a Greek myth retold by William F. Russell

Damon [DAY-mun] and Pythias [PITH-ee-us] were two noble young men who lived on the island of Sicily [SIS-uh-lee] in a city called Syracuse. They were such close companions and were so devoted to each other that all the people of the city admired them as the highest examples of true friendship. Each trusted the other so completely that nobody could ever have persuaded one that the other had been unfaithful or dishonest, even if that had been the case.

Now it happened that Syracuse was, at that time, ruled by a famous tyrant named Dionysius [die-oh-NISH-us], who had gained the throne for himself through treachery, and who from then on flaunted his power by behaving cruelly to his own subjects and to all strangers and enemies who were so unfortunate as to fall into his clutches. This tyrant, Dionysius, was so unjustly cruel that once, when he awoke from a restless sleep during which he dreamt that a certain man in the town had attempted to kill him, he immediately had that man put to death.

It happened that Pythias had, quite unjustly, been accused by Dionysius of trying to overthrow him, and for this supposed crime of treason Pythias was sentenced by the king to die. Try as he might, Pythias could not prove his innocence to the king's satisfaction, and so, all hope now lost, the noble youth asked only for a few days' freedom so that he could settle his business affairs and see to it that his relatives would be cared for after he was executed. Dionysius, the hardhearted tyrant, however, would not believe Pythias's promise to return and would not allow him to leave unless he left behind him a hostage, someone who would be put to death in his place if he should fail to return within the stated time.

Pythias immediately thought of his friend Damon, and he unhesitatingly sent for him in this hour of dire necessity, never thinking for a moment that his trusty companion would refuse his request. Nor did he, for Damon hastened straightaway to the palace—much to the amazement of King Dionysius—and gladly offered to be held hostage for his friend, in spite of the dangerous condition that had been attached to this favor. Therefore, Pythias was permitted to settle his earthly affairs before departing to the Land of the Shades, while Damon remained behind in the dungeon, the captive of the tyrant Dionysius.

After Pythias had been released, Dionysius asked Damon if he did not feel afraid, for Pythias might very well take advantage of the opportunity he had been given and simply not return at all, and then he, Damon, would be executed in his place. But Damon replied at once with a willing smile: "There is no need for me to feel afraid, O King, since I have perfect faith in the word of my true friend, and I know that he will certainly return before the appointed time—unless, of course, he dies or is held captive by some evil force. Even so, even should the noble Pythias be captured and held against his will, it would be an honor for me to die in his place."

Such devotion and perfect faith as this was unheard of to the friendless tyrant; still, though he could not help admiring the true nobility of his captive, he nevertheless determined that Damon should certainly be put to death should Pythias not return by the appointed time.

And, as the Fates would have it, by a strange turn of events, Pythias *was* detained far longer in his task than he had imagined. Though he never for a single minute intended to evade the sentence of death to which he had been so unjustly committed, Pythias met with several accidents and unavoidable delays. Now his time was running out and he had yet to overcome the many impediments that had been placed in his path. At last he succeeded in clearing away all the hindrances, and he sped back the many miles to the palace of the king, his heart almost bursting with grief and fear that he might arrive too late.

Meanwhile, when the last day of the allotted time arrived, Dionysius commanded that the place of execution should be

readied at once, since he was still ruthlessly determined that if one of his victims escaped him, the other should not. And so, entering the chamber in which Damon was confined, he began to utter words of sarcastic pity for the "foolish faith," as he termed it, that the young man of Syracuse had in his friend.

In reply, however, Damon merely smiled, since, in spite of the fact that the eleventh hour had already arrived, he still believed that his lifelong companion would not fail him. Even when, a short time later, he was actually led out to the site of his execution, his serenity remained the same.

Great excitement stirred the crowd that had gathered to witness the execution, for all the people had heard of the bargain that had been struck between the two friends. There was much sobbing and cries of sympathy were heard all around as the captive was brought out, though he himself somehow retained complete composure even at this moment of darkest danger.

Presently the excitement grew more intense still as a swift runner could be seen approaching the palace courtyard at an astonishing speed, and wild shrieks of relief and joy went up as Pythias, breathless and exhausted, rushed headlong through the crowd and flung himself into the arms of his beloved friend, sobbing with relief that he had, by the grace of the gods, arrived in time to save Damon's life.

This final exhibition of devoted love and faithfulness was more than even the stony heart of Dionysius, the tyrant, could resist. As the throng of spectators melted into tears at the companions' embrace, the king approached the pair and declared that Pythias was hereby pardoned and his death sentence canceled. In addition, he begged the pair to allow him to become their friend, to try to be as much a friend to them both as they had shown each other to be.

Thus did the two friends of Syracuse, by the faithful love they bore to each other, conquer the hard heart of a tyrant king, and in the annals of true friendship there are no more honored names than those of Damon and Pythias—for no person can do more than be willing to lay down his life for the sake of his friend.

Papa's Parrot

a story by Cynthia Rylant

Though his father was fat and merely owned a candy and nut shop, Harry Tillian liked his papa. Harry stopped liking candy and nuts when he was around seven, but, in spite of this, he and Mr. Tillian had remained friends and were still friends the year Harry turned twelve.

For years, after school, Harry had always stopped in to see his father at work. Many of Harry's friends stopped there, too, to spend a few cents choosing penny candy from the giant bins or to sample Mr. Tillian's latest batch of roasted peanuts. Mr. Tillian looked forward to seeing his son and his son's friends every day. He liked the company.

When Harry entered junior high school, though, he didn't come by the candy and nut shop as often. Nor did his friends. They were older and they had more spending money. They went to a burger place. They played video games. They shopped for records. None of them were much interested in candy and nuts anymore.

A new group of children came to Mr. Tillian's shop now. But not Harry Tillian and his friends.

The year Harry turned twelve was also the year Mr. Tillian got a parrot. He went to a pet store one day and bought one for more money than he could really afford. He brought the parrot to his shop, set its cage near the sign for maple clusters and named it Rocky.

Harry thought this was the strangest thing his father had ever done, and he told him so, but Mr. Tillian just ignored him.

Rocky was good company for Mr. Tillian. When business was slow, Mr. Tillian would turn on a small color television he had sitting in a corner, and he and Rocky would watch the soap operas. Rocky liked to scream when the romantic music came on, and Mr. Tillian would yell at him to shut up, but they seemed to enjoy themselves.

The more Mr. Tillian grew to like his parrot, and the more he talked to it instead of to people, the more embarrassed Harry became. Harry would stroll past the shop, on his way somewhere else, and he'd take a quick look inside to see what his dad was doing. Mr. Tillian was always talking to the bird. So Harry kept walking.

At home things were different. Harry and his father joked with each other at the dinner table as they always had—Mr. Tillian teasing Harry about his smelly socks; Harry teasing Mr. Tillian about his blubbery stomach. At home things seemed all right.

But one day, Mr. Tillian became ill. He had been at work, unpacking boxes of caramels, when he had grabbed his chest and fallen over on top of the candy. A customer had found him, and he was taken to the hospital in an ambulance.

Mr. Tillian couldn't leave the hospital. He lay in bed, tubes in his arms, and he worried about his shop. New shipments of candy and nuts would be arriving. Rocky would be hungry. Who would take care of things?

Harry said he would. Harry told his father that he would go to the store every day after school and unpack boxes. He would sort out all the candy and nuts. He would even feed Rocky.

So, the next morning, while Mr. Tillian lay in his hospital bed, Harry took the shop key to school with him. After school he left his friends and walked to the empty shop alone. In all the days of his life, Harry had never seen the shop closed after school. Harry didn't even remember what the CLOSED sign looked like. The key stuck in the lock three times, and inside he had to search all the walls for the light switch.

The shop was as his father had left it. Even the caramels were still spilled on the floor. Harry bent down and picked them up one by one, dropping them back in the boxes. The bird in its cage watched him silently.

Harry opened the new boxes his father hadn't gotten to. Peppermints. Jawbreakers. Toffee creams. Strawberry kisses. Harry traveled from bin to bin, putting the candies where they belonged.

"Hello!"

Harry jumped, spilling a box of jawbreakers.

"Hello, Rocky!"

Harry stared at the parrot. He had forgotten it was there. The bird had been so quiet, and Harry had been thinking only of the candy.

"Hello," Harry said.

"Hello, Rocky!" answered the parrot.

Harry walked slowly over to the cage. The parrot's food cup was empty. Its water was dirty. The bottom of the cage was a mess.

Harry carried the cage into the back room.

"Hello, Rocky!"

"Is that all you can say, you dumb bird?" Harry mumbled. The bird said nothing else.

 Harry cleaned the bottom of the cage, refilled the food and water cups, then put the cage back in its place and resumed sorting the candy.

"Where's Harry?"

Harry looked up.

"Where's Harry?"

Harry stared at the parrot.

"Where's Harry?"

Chills ran down Harry's back. What could the bird mean? It was like something from "The Twilight Zone."

"Where's Harry?"

Harry swallowed and said, "I'm here. I'm here, you stupid bird."

"You stupid bird!" said the parrot.

Well, at least he's got one thing straight, thought Harry.

"Miss him! Miss him! Where's Harry? You stupid bird!"

Harry stood with a handful of peppermints.

"What?" he asked.

"Where's Harry?" said the parrot.

"I'm *here*, you stupid bird! I'm here!" Harry yelled. He threw the peppermints at the cage, and the bird screamed and clung to its perch.

Harry sobbed, "I'm here." The tears were coming.

Harry leaned over the glass counter.

"Papa." Harry buried his face in his arms.

"Where's Harry?" repeated the bird.

Harry sighed and wiped his face on his sleeve. He watched the parrot. He understood now: someone had been saying, for a long time, "Where's Harry? Miss him."

Harry finished his unpacking, then swept the floor of the shop. He checked the furnace so the bird wouldn't get cold. Then he left to go visit his papa.

The Lion's Whisker

a folk tale from Ethiopia retold by Len Cabral

Once there was a boy whose mother had died. He was very sad that his mother had died, he was angry that she had died, and he was confused about her death.

After about a year's time his father remarried a woman named Sonia who came from the highlands. She loved the boy very much. But the boy was so sad, so angry, and so confused about his mother's death that now he felt threatened by Sonia's presence. Even though both his father and Sonia loved the boy very much, he felt his father would not love him as much because of Sonia's presence.

Sonia would make beautiful clothing for the boy, but the boy would wear the clothes and run through the briars and rip them.

She'd make delicious meals for the boy, but the boy wouldn't touch the food. Try as she would, she could not win this boy's love.

One morning, the father got up and went hunting. Sonia said to herself, "Today, I'm going to talk to my stepson about our feelings toward one another. For I love him dearly, and I need for him to return that love to me."

Sonia went into the boy's room. The boy was sitting on his bed. He had a feeling that Sonia was going to come in and talk to him about the way he felt. He didn't want to talk about his feelings. He was sad, he was angry, he was confused, and he felt threatened.

When Sonia came into the room and said, "Son, I want to talk about our feelings toward one another," he didn't even let her finish.

He jumped off the bed and said, "I hate you. You're not my real mother. I'll never love you. I'm running away." And he ran away.

This crushed Sonia. She cried and cried. Finally her husband came home and she said, "Our son ran away."

The father went down to the riverbank where many of the boys and girls would go and spend time. The boy was there, throwing rocks into the water. He wasn't trying to make them skip or anything. He wasn't even throwing flat rocks, he was throwing round rocks.

The father walked over to the boy and placed his arm on his son's shoulder. They sat down on a log and talked for a long, long time. Then they walked home, arm in arm.

When they returned home, Sonia had prepared a special meal for them. They sat down and ate.

After the meal the father and the boy went to their rooms. But Sonia left the house. She walked out of the village, down a dirt road into the wilderness. Sonia went to the home of a wise old man, a man so wise he knew the ways of the mind and the ways of the heart.

Sonia said, "You must give me a love potion, so that I may give it to my stepson, so that he will learn to love me. For I love him dearly and I need him to return that love to me."

The old man said, "First you must bring me a whisker from a ferocious mountain lion."

Sonia could not believe what she had heard. "But how can I do that?" she asked.

"Use your wits," he replied.

Sonia returned home. All night long she thought about what the old man had told her to do.

Early the next morning she left the house. The only thing she took with her was a sack with a piece of meat in it. She walked away from the lowlands to the highlands. She walked to the cliffs at the edge of the mountains, and there she found a cave. She said to herself, "Surely there must be a ferocious mountain lion living in that cave."

Sonia reached into the sack and took out the piece of meat. She walked up to the cave and placed the piece of meat in front of the cave. Then she went back one hundred yards and she hid in the bushes. As she expected, a ferocious mountain lion came out of the cave, smelled the meat, ate it, and went back into the cave. She did this every day for a month.

On the first morning of the second month, Sonia placed the piece of meat in front of the lion's cave and went back fifty yards. She did not hide in the bushes. She stood in the open. The mountain lion came out of the cave, looked at Sonia, smelled the meat, ate the meat, and went back into the cave. She continued to do this every day for a month.

On the first morning of the third month, Sonia placed the meat in front of the lion's cave, and went back twenty yards. The mountain lion came out of the cave and looked right at Sonia. Sonia was frightened. She was shaking like a leaf. But she was a brave woman. The mountain lion smelled the meat, ate the meat, and went back into the cave. As before, she continued to do this every day for a month.

On the first day of the fourth month, Sonia placed the meat in front of the lion's cave and took three short steps back. The mountain lion came out of the cave, looked right at Sonia, smelled the meat, and started to eat the meat. Sonia inched forward. She leaned over, reached out, grabbed one of the lion's whiskers, and PULLED!

The mountain lion was still eating the meat. Sonia inched away until she got around a clump of bushes. Then she ran all the way back to the wise old man's house. She knocked at the door. When he came to greet her she said, "Here is a whisker from a ferocious mountain lion. Now give me my love potion, so that I may give it to my stepson, so he will learn to love me. For I love him dearly, and I need him to return that love to me."

The wise old man took the whisker from Sonia. He said, "Indeed, this is a whisker from a ferocious mountain lion."

"Yes, it is!" Sonia exclaimed. "Now give me my love potion!"

"I'll not give you a love potion," the wise man said.

Sonia gasped, "But you said, you said . . ."

He silenced her and said, "You must approach your stepson the same way you approached the lion."

Sonia thought about what he had said. "You mean slowly, and patiently?" The wise man nodded.

Sonia returned home. She approached her stepson slowly, and patiently.

After a month the boy started to smile at her. In two months' time he helped her around the house. In three months' time they'd go for long walks together. The boy showed her how to skip rocks across the water—the nice flat rocks. By the end of four months' time they had become friends.

The boy never forgot his real mother. But now, he found room in his heart to love his stepmother, also. And that's the story of the lion's whisker.

The Snow Maiden

a Russian folk tale selected by
Sidonie Matsner Gruenberg

A long time ago, in the land of Russia, there lived near the forest a peasant named Ivan with his wife Marie. These two good people, though they loved each other dearly and had many friendly neighbors, were unhappy, for they had no children. They used to look out of the window and watch the children of their neighbors playing and laughing together and they wished with all their hearts that they, too, had a little child of their own.

One winter day, as they stood at the window of their little hut, they saw the neighbors' children playing in the snow. The children were having a good time romping, throwing snowballs at each other, and making a big snow man.

Ivan turned to his wife and said: "Look, Wife, the children are having a good time making a man out of snow. Let us go into the garden and make a snow man."

"That is a fine idea," said the wife, and the two good people went out into the garden.

Then Marie turned to her husband. "I've been thinking, Husband," she said. "Since we have no children of our own, let us make a little snow girl instead of a snow man."

"That is a fine idea," said Ivan, and they started to make a little girl out of snow. For so many years they had dreamed of having a little girl of their own that now they fashioned one with love and care—the prettiest maiden ever seen.

They rolled the snow together, and Ivan made a little body with dainty little hands and feet. Marie fashioned a beautiful head with eyes and nose and mouth and hair—all of snow. Then, very carefully, they placed the head on the shoulders of the little statue and looked at their little snow girl. Never had they seen anything so lovely and never had they wished more fervently for a real little girl of their own.

"Little snow maiden," Ivan said, "speak to me!"

"Yes, my darling," said Marie. "Come to life so you can play and romp and laugh like other children!"

Just then they noticed that the snow maiden's eyes began to quiver. A faint rosy color was creeping into her cheeks. At first they thought they were dreaming, but then they saw a real little girl with blue eyes and golden hair and rosy cheeks standing before them, where a moment before the snow figure had stood.

At first they were too astonished to speak and just gazed at the little girl. Then Ivan said: "Where did you come from? And who are you?"

"I came from the land of cold and snow," the child replied. "And I am your daughter, your own little girl."

She ran to Marie and Ivan and kissed them, and all three of them wept for joy. But soon they were talking and smiling again, for this was the happiest moment of their lives. They called to their neighbors in the huts near by, who came over to see what was going on. Word soon got around of the couple's good fortune, and all the little girls of the village came to see the lovely little girl, the daughter of Ivan and Marie. Everybody stayed in the hut till late that night, laughing and singing and dancing to celebrate the glad occasion.

All that winter she played with the other boys and girls while Ivan and Marie would stand in the window of their little hut watching her. Now they were happy, for one of the children playing in the snow was their own child and, it seemed to them, she was the loveliest child of all.

"No child could be prettier than our little girl," Ivan would say.

"Nowhere in the world is there a better child than she is," Marie would add.

And Ivan would agree with her. "She is the best child of all," he would say; "always good, always happy, always sweet."

And indeed it was true. Everyone loved the little snow maiden.
Everyone loved to hear her laughing and singing all day long, and
they loved to watch her running and dancing with the other children.
But when the first signs of spring appeared, when the air became
warmer and the snows started to melt, the little girl didn't seem as
gay as before. She always seemed tired now and unhappy.

One day she came to Ivan and Marie and sang a sad little song:

"The time has come for me to go
Away up North to the land of snow."

These were the words she sang and, as she sang them, her eyes
filled with tears. Her mother and father began to weep when they
heard this song and Marie cried out, "Stay with us, my darling! Do
not go away!"

Ivan jumped up and barred the door so she could not get out, and
Marie put her arms around the little girl and held her tight. But even
as she held her, the snow maiden started to melt away, and soon
there was nothing left but her white fur cap and her white fur coat
and her high white boots in a puddle on the floor.

Ivan and Marie wept bitter tears, and Marie folded away the little
clothes, saying, "Maybe she will come back to us some day."

All that summer they were sad and lonely, thinking of the dear
little girl who had gone away. And then one night, when winter
came, they heard a merry laugh outside their hut and they heard a
happy voice singing,

"Mother! Father! Open the door!
The snow has brought me back once more!"

Ivan threw open the door and the snow maiden ran to the arms
of her father and mother. All that winter she stayed with them and
played with the other children of the village. But in the spring she
had to go back North to the land of cold and snow. Ivan and Marie
did not mind her going this time, however, for they knew that every
winter, when it got cold and the snow began to fall, the little snow
maiden would come back to Russia again and live with them until
spring.

THE POWER OF LIGHT

a true story by Isaac Bashevis Singer

During World War II, after the Nazis had bombed and burned the Warsaw ghetto, a boy and a girl were hiding in one of the ruins—David, fourteen years old, and Rebecca, thirteen.

It was winter and bitter cold outside. For weeks Rebecca had not left the dark, partially collapsed cellar that was their hiding place, but every few days David would go out to search for food. All the stores had been destroyed in the bombing, and David sometimes found stale bread, cans of food, or whatever else had been buried. Making his way through the ruins was dangerous. Sometimes bricks and mortar would fall down, and he could easily lose his way. But if he and Rebecca did not want to die from hunger, he had to take the risk.

That day was one of the coldest. Rebecca sat on the ground wrapped in all the garments she possessed; still, she could not get warm. David had left many hours before, and Rebecca listened in the darkness for the sound of his return, knowing that if he did not come back nothing remained to her but death.

Suddenly she heard heavy breathing and the sound of a bundle being dropped. David had made his way home. Rebecca could not help but cry "David!"

"Rebecca!"

In the darkness they embraced and kissed. Then David said, "Rebecca, I found a treasure."

"What kind of treasure?"

"Cheese, potatoes, dried mushrooms, and a package of candy—and I have another surprise for you."

"What surprise?"

"Later."

Both were too hungry for a long talk. Ravenously they ate the frozen potatoes, the mushrooms, and part of the cheese. They each had one piece of candy. Then Rebecca asked, "What is it now, day or night?"

"I think night has fallen," David replied. He had a wristwatch and kept track of day and night and also of the days of the week and the month. After a while Rebecca asked again, "What is the surprise?"

"Rebecca, today is the first day of Hanukkah, and I found a candle and some matches."

"Hanukkah tonight?"

"Yes."

"Oh, my God!"

"I am going to bless the Hanukkah candle," David said.

He lit a match and there was light. Rebecca and David stared at their hiding place—bricks, pipes, and the uneven ground. He lighted the candle. Rebecca blinked her eyes. For the first time in weeks she really saw David. His hair was matted and his face streaked with dirt, but his eyes shone with joy. In spite of the starvation and persecution David had grown taller, and he seemed older than his age and manly. Young as they both were, they had decided to marry if they could manage to escape from war-ridden Warsaw. As a token of their engagement, David had given Rebecca a shiny groschen he found in his pocket on the day when the building where both of them lived was bombed.

Now David pronounced the benediction over the Hanukkah candle, and Rebecca said, "Amen." They had both lost their families, and they had good reason to be angry with God for sending them so many afflictions, but the light of the candle brought peace into their souls. That glimmer of light, surrounded by so many shadows, seemed to say without words: Evil has not yet taken complete dominion. A spark of hope is still left.

For some time David and Rebecca had thought about escaping from Warsaw. But how? The ghetto was watched by the Nazis day and night. Each step was dangerous. Rebecca kept delaying their departure. It would be easier in the summer, she often said, but David knew that in their predicament they had little chance of lasting until then. Somewhere in the forest there were young men and women called partisans who fought the Nazi invaders. David wanted to reach them. Now, by the light of the Hanukkah candle, Rebecca suddenly felt renewed courage. She said, "David, let's leave."

"When?"

"When you think it's the right time," she answered.

"The right time is now," David said. "I have a plan."

For a long time David explained the details of his plan to Rebecca. It was more than risky. The Nazis had enclosed the ghetto with barbed wire and posted guards armed with machine guns on the surrounding roofs. At night searchlights lit up all possible exits from the destroyed ghetto. But in his wanderings through the ruins, David had found an opening to a sewer which he thought might lead to the other side. David told Rebecca that their chances of remaining alive were slim. They could drown in the dirty water or freeze to death. Also, the sewers were full of hungry rats. But Rebecca agreed to take the risk; to remain in the cellar for the winter would mean certain death.

When the Hanukkah light began to sputter and flicker before going out, David and Rebecca gathered their few belongings. She packed the remaining food in a kerchief, and David took his matches and a piece of lead pipe for a weapon.

In moments of great danger people become unusually courageous. David and Rebecca were soon on their way through the ruins. They came to passages so narrow they had to crawl on hands and knees. But the food they had eaten, and the joy the Hanukkah candle had awakened in them, gave them the courage to continue. After some time David found the entrance to the sewer. Luckily the sewage had frozen, and it seemed that the rats had left because of the extreme cold. From time to time David and Rebecca stopped to rest and to listen. After a while they crawled on, slowly and carefully. Suddenly they stopped in their tracks. From above they could hear the clanging of a trolley car. They had reached the other side of the ghetto. All they needed now was to find a way to get out of the sewer and to leave the city as quickly as possible.

Many miracles seemed to happen that Hanukkah night. Because the Nazis were afraid of enemy planes, they had ordered a complete blackout. Because of the bitter cold, there were fewer Gestapo guards. David and Rebecca managed to leave the sewer and steal out of the city without being caught. At dawn they reached a forest where they were able to rest and have a bite to eat.

Even though the partisans were not very far from Warsaw, it took David and Rebecca a week to reach them. They walked at night and hid during the days—sometimes in granaries and sometimes in barns. Some peasants stealthily helped the partisans and those who were running away from the Nazis. From time to time David and Rebecca got a piece of bread, a few potatoes, a radish, or whatever the peasants could spare. In one village they encountered a Jewish partisan who had come to get food for his group. He belonged to the Haganah, an organization that sent men from Israel to rescue Jewish refugees from the Nazis in occupied Poland. This young man brought David and Rebecca to the other partisans who roamed the forest. It was the last day of Hanukkah, and that evening the partisans lit eight candles. Some of them played dreidel on the stump of an oak tree while others kept watch.

From the day David and Rebecca met the partisans, their life became like a tale in a storybook. They joined more and more refugees who all had but one desire—to settle in the land of Israel. They did not always travel by train or bus. They walked. They slept in stables, in burned-out houses, and wherever they could hide from the enemy. To reach their destination, they had to cross Czechoslovakia, Hungary, and Yugoslavia. Somewhere at the seashore in Yugoslavia, in the middle of the night, a small boat manned by a Haganah crew waited for them, and all the refugees with their meager belongings were packed into it. This all happened silently and in great secrecy, because the Nazis occupied Yugoslavia.

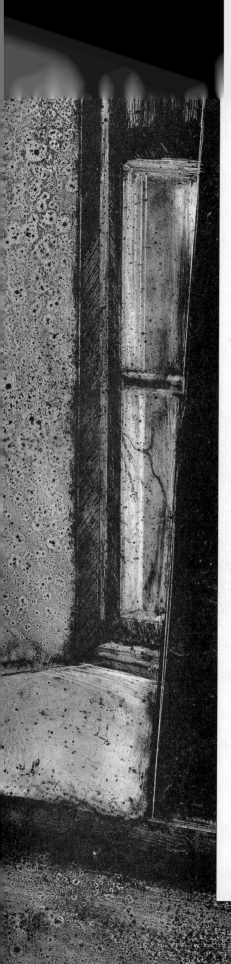

But their dangers were far from over. Even though it was spring, the sea was stormy and the boat was too small for such a long trip. Nazi planes spied the boat and tried without success to sink it with bombs. They also feared the Nazi submarines which were lurking in the depths. There was nothing the refugees could do besides pray to God, and this time God seemed to hear their prayers, because they managed to land safely.

The Jews of Israel greeted them with a love that made them forget their suffering. They were the first refugees who had reached the Holy Land, and they were offered all the help and comfort that could be given. Rebecca and David found relatives in Israel who accepted them with open arms, and although they had become quite emaciated, they were basically healthy and recovered quickly. After some rest they were sent to a special school where foreigners were taught modern Hebrew. Both David and Rebecca were diligent students. After finishing high school, David was able to enter the academy of engineering in Haifa, and Rebecca, who excelled in languages and literature, studied in Tel Aviv—but they always met on weekends. When Rebecca was eighteen, she and David were married. They found a small house with a garden in Ramat Gan, a suburb of Tel Aviv.

I know all this because David and Rebecca told me their story on a Hanukkah evening in their house in Ramat Gan about eight years later. The Hanukkah candles were burning, and Rebecca was frying potato pancakes served with applesauce for all of us. David and I were playing dreidel with their little son, Menahem Eliezer, named after both of his grandfathers. David told me that this large wooden dreidel was the same one the partisans had played with on that Hanukkah evening in the forest in Poland. Rebecca said to me, "If it had not been for that little candle David brought to our hiding place, we wouldn't be sitting here today. That glimmer of light awakened in us a hope and strength we didn't know we possessed. We'll give the dreidel to Menahem Eliezer when he is old enough to understand what we went through and how miraculously we were saved."

SMALL STAR AND THE MUD PONY

a Pawnee story from Nebraska retold by Dorothy de Wit

On the banks of a wide river that runs through the prairies of western Nebraska there was at one time a village called Fish-Hawk. None of the people in it was wealthy or famous; but their earth lodges were comfortable, corn grew in their fields, buffalo supplied meat, skin hides, cooking utensils, and household articles, and most of the families owned at least one horse.

During the long winters, stories were told around the fires; the women made moccasins, pouches, and shirts fringed, beaded, or decorated with porcupine quills dyed red, blue, yellow, and green. Often the people played with plum stones and baskets or darts. However, when spring and fall came, the women worked planting corn or harvesting it, drying meat and other foods.

The men and boys enjoyed ring-and-stick contests or readied their weapons for the summer buffalo hunts. And there were many ceremonials to the great Tirawa, with dancing and feasting.

In one small lodge, however, where Small Star lived with his father and mother, there was little corn and little meat. Worst of all, there were no horses! This made Small Star very unhappy, for he loved horses more than anything. When the other boys took their horses to the river to water them, he sat apart and watched with envy.

One day Small Star decided to build a corral in a hollow across the river. He picked willow boughs and found some rocks, and he made a small gate. Then, when it was finished, he dug a great quantity of mud from the riverbank and brought it to the corral. He filled a buffalo bladder with water from the river and poured it over the mud, making it very sticky. Then, carefully, he began to mold two small ponies from the soft mud, taking great pains with the tails, the hooves and the ears. One little horse he left dun-colored; the other he made sorrel, by mixing in some red clay. He also smoothed some white clay across its face to make a blaze. It was dark when he had finished, and he was too tired to be hungry. When he arrived home, he immediately fell on his sleeping pad and went to sleep without telling his parents anything about his day's work.

Early the next morning he crept from the lodge, crossed the river, and unlatched the corral gate. There stood his two little ponies, their tails out and their heads lifted, almost as though they were breathing after a run. Small Star patted them with delight; then he gathered fresh grass and cottonwood shoots to feed them and spent the rest of the day talking to them as though they could understand his joy in their company. At night he closed the corral carefully, went home, and again told no one about his new ponies.

Every day after that he visited them, fed them, and brought them water to drink. But one morning he saw that the dun pony had dried out and lay crumbled to dust. The bald-faced sorrel still stood. Small Star cried and determined to take special care of the one that remained. After that he spent even more time in the corral, sleeping there at times.

One day a runner came into the village. "The buffalo are returning," he said. "They have been seen in great herds on the plains to the west. It is time to go out for the summer hunting." At once, the tipis were brought out and packed, and food and equipment assembled for the hunt. Excitement was everywhere, with children running here and there, dogs barking, and horses trampling and neighing. Small Star's parents looked for him, as they packed their meager belongings, but they could not find him, for he was across the river in the corral with his mud pony. At last they left with the rest of the villagers, thinking he must be with the other children.

When Small Star returned to Fish-Hawk village, he saw only scattered possessions and empty earth lodges—no animals, no people, and no food remained. He felt very lonely and hungry, and he wondered what he should do. He had no idea where the villagers were going, and he knew they moved fast when they went on the summer buffalo hunt. He searched till he found some parched corn and jerky that had been left behind; then he lay down in his empty lodge, feeling lost and frightened. He slept fitfully and in his dreams seemed to be chasing his mud pony around. Then, in his dream, a star rose in the western sky, brilliant and low-hanging, and he heard the voice of Great Tirawa speaking to him: "Small Star, I have seen your grief, and I know how you love your mud pony. I will help you. Go out to him tomorrow, and take care of him." The dream faded, and Small Star awoke; but only the night wind sighed around the lodge. A large star shone in the west, as in his dream, and Small Star slept again, with tears on his cheeks.

The following day he hunted through the village for more forgotten food, then ran to give his mud pony fresh grass. As he watered him, he kept thinking of the words of Tirawa and the dream, and he wondered what they meant. That night he slept beside his horse, and in his dreams the mud pony spoke to him: "Small Star, little master, do not be afraid, for I am of the earth, and you have fashioned me of the mud from the riverbank. Now

Mother Earth has taken pity on you. If you will do as I say, all will go well for you, and someday you will become a great chief."

When morning came, Small Star looked for his mud pony. It was gone! But standing outside the corral and neighing softly was a sorrel horse with a white blaze across its face. The pony was pawing the ground and shaking its mane! Small Star leaped to his feet and ran to it. He felt its shining coat, nuzzled its velvety cheek. "Are you real, beautiful one? Are you indeed my mud pony come alive? Ah, Tirawa, how great, how kind you are! Hear my thanks. I will remember your words and do as you wish!"

Small Star found a rope, put it around his pony's neck, and led him to the river to drink. The pony spoke to him: "I am truly your mud pony! Mother Earth has listened to your heart; you and I will travel to your people now. They are far away, but I know where to go. Lead me to the top of the bank; then mount, and do not direct me, for I know my way."

Small Star could hardly believe his ears, but he did as the pony told him. They traveled on and on, and when night fell, they came to the first site the villagers had used, and again the pony spoke: "Go forage for your food in the camp, for I shall find my own food." So Small Star picked up whatever he could find left behind. He slept the night with his head against the pony's warm flank. The next day, and the next, they did the same thing, each time moving farther out on the great plains, till at noon of the fourth day they found a campsite with coals still warm in the fire pit. Then Small Star knew they would soon catch up with the villagers. And indeed, at sunset they saw their tipis ahead.

Then the mud pony said, "Leave me here and go find your tipi. Waken your mother, for she has grieved for you. When the people break camp tomorrow, stay behind, and I shall be waiting for you to ride."

So Small Star went gladly and, after hunting for the smallest tipi, went in and threw some dried grass on the coals, which spurted up. He wakened his mother gently. "See, I am here! I have come back to you." At first his mother could not believe that he was real, but at last she hugged him and cried over him.

Then she prepared food for him, and his parents rejoiced to find him alive and well. In the morning all the relatives and friends came to the tipi to share his parents' happiness. The next day Small Star rose early and went back to where the pony waited. Small Star mounted, and they followed the villagers at a distance.

For several days they continued on in this way. Then the pony spoke again: "My son, it is time for the people to see that you have a horse. The chief will send for it, and he will offer you four horses for me. Take them. I shall return to you!"

The boy rode his pony proudly into the camp, and everybody pressed around him. "What a fine little horse! How lively, how sturdy! He is just the color of Mother Earth!" They were happy and pleased for Small Star, for they knew how much he loved horses and how poor his parents were. Word reached the village chief, who came himself to see the pony. He examined it carefully and invited the boy to eat with him in his tipi that night—a great honor for anyone!

Small Star thought to himself, "It is just as the pony told me!" He went and ate in the great chief's tipi, and when the chief told him how pleased he was with the sorrel horse and offered four of his best mounts in exchange, Small Star accepted the offer.

The chief took the pony and set him out to graze, but the pony would not eat. Nevertheless, the chief was satisfied with his new horse and waited eagerly for the coming hunt to try him out. That night the boy was lonely and dreamed of his pony. In his dream the pony said, "Do not mourn, for I shall be back. But take a buffalo hide, and tan it carefully, my son. Be sure that you place it around me each night, to protect me." And so each night Small Star carefully covered the pony with the buffalo hide he had tanned.

Scouts appeared in the camp—a great herd of buffalo was approaching, and many hunters would be needed. At the head, and first into the herd, rode the chief on the sorrel pony. He was proud of the horse's speed and quick response to his leading and his skill in the hunt. When the chief was the first to bring down a buffalo, he was elated! It spurred him to try again and again, and he rode on and on—indeed, he would have taken many more, but suddenly the horse stumbled. Its hind foot was injured and hung disjointedly! The pony was ruined, and the chief was very angry! He returned to the encampment and demanded that Small Star return his four horses. Then, in disgust, he pushed the mud pony toward the boy. Small Star appeared to be very upset, but secretly he was delighted! The chief exclaimed loudly, for all to hear, "Hah! A fine horse! Even though he could run well, he looks just like a mud pony!" From that time on, Small Star's name was changed, and he was called Mud-Pony-Boy.

He took his horse to the outskirts of the camp, and there he worked over him, using herbs and compresses. And before long the foot had healed. The chief wanted to have the pony back; but Mud-Pony-Boy would not agree, and no more was said.

The villagers of Fish-Hawk had moved on to try for more buffalo when suddenly an enemy force appeared on the horizon. The women and children ran to their tipis as the men rode out to war. The pony spoke to Mud-Pony-Boy: "My son, heed my words. Go and coat yourself with mud, the same color as mine. When the warriors shoot at you, their arrows will not pierce the earth covering. Therefore, do not be afraid. Be daring!" Mud-Pony-Boy covered himself with mud and rode out at full speed into the midst of the enemy braves. He unseated an enemy warrior, who turned and fled in fear!

Mud-Pony-Boy rode back to camp in triumph with the other men. They hailed him and said, "Mud-Pony-Boy has become a brave!"

Shortly thereafter the people of Fish-Hawk struck their summer camp and returned to their earth-lodge village on the bank of the great river, far to the east. They had plenty of food and other provisions for winter, and their corn stood waiting to be harvested.

But soon after they had returned, another enemy tribe invaded the village. There were many warriors, and among them was one whose spirit powers were those of Turtle. He was a very great warrior, and Mud-Pony-Boy watched him carefully and soon discovered that the warrior could not be hurt except in one place. Only under his arm could he be fatally wounded. Mud-Pony-Boy wheeled his pony around, and just as the warrior raised his arm to pull his bowstring, Mud-Pony-Boy thrust his sharp, long lance into Turtle Man's armpit and killed him. After that Mud-Pony-Boy took many horses and did many brave deeds. The enemy was routed, and peace returned to Fish-Hawk village. Each night, however, Mud-Pony-Boy was very careful to place the buffalo hide over his beloved pony.

Years passed, and the men met in council. "Mud-Pony-Boy has many times shown himself to be a brave and skillful leader. Our chief is old now. Let him choose Mud-Pony-Boy as his successor, to become chief when the time comes."

The months went by, and one day Mud-Pony-Boy found among his herd of horses a new colt, sorrel-colored with a white blaze on its face. It was the image of his mud pony! That night in his dream his beloved pony spoke to him again: "My son, you have done well. You have proved yourself a true brave and a wise man. You will become a great chief, and people will love you and trust your judgment. My task is finished. I must go back to Mother Earth. Raise the colt, and love it as you have loved me."

That night a storm arose, and when Mud-Pony-Boy took the buffalo hide to cover his horse, he could not find it. He grieved and could not sleep, and early the following morning he crossed the river and went to the corral he had built in his childhood. The sorrel pony lay on the ground, a mound of river mud, with only a dab of white clay where the blaze had once been.

He again heard the voice of his pony: "Do not weep. We were together over many years and have done all that was needed. I have gone back to Mother Earth. You will become a great chief, and your colt will become a great horse, as dear to you as I have been."

Mud-Pony-Boy returned to his village, and he did, indeed, become a great chief, and his colt, a great horse.

The Magic Pomegranate

a Jewish folk tale retold by Peninnah Schram

Once there were three brothers who loved adventure. One day they decided to go on a journey, each one to a different country, and to meet again on a certain day ten years later. Each brother was to bring back with him an unusual gift.

The oldest brother decided to go to the East. When he arrived in a certain Eastern town, he was fascinated by what he saw there: Magicians, dancing girls, jugglers, and acrobats were everywhere. As the brother was watching the entertainments, he saw one magician hold up a magic glass through which he could see to the distant corners of the kingdom.

"Ah!" thought the oldest brother, "I would like to have that glass, for that would certainly be an unusual object to share with my brothers." He asked the magician, "Tell me, how much is that glass? I should like to buy it from you." At first, the magician would not part with his magic glass, but after much pleading by the older brother, and some bargaining, they agreed upon a price and the magician sold the glass to the oldest brother.

The second brother traveled to a country in the West. Wherever he went, he kept his eyes open, and his mind as well. He was always on the lookout for the most unusual gift he could bring back to his brothers.

One day, he was attracted by the cries of an old carpet seller, who called out, "Carpets for sale! Beautiful! Wonderful! Carpets here!" The brother approached the carpet seller and began to examine his carpets, when suddenly he saw the carpet at the bottom of the pile begin to move. It seemed to be moving by itself! "What kind of carpet is this one?" he asked, pointing to the bottom one, which was quite visible by then.

The old merchant motioned for him to bend down and whispered in his ear, "This is a magic carpet. Buy it, and it will take you anywhere you want to go—and quickly too!" The second brother and the carpet seller finally settled upon a price, and the brother took the magic carpet with him, satisfied that he had a most unusual gift.

The youngest brother went South, and when he arrived in a certain country, he traveled far and wide to see what he could find to bring back to his brothers.

Now, this was a country noted for its many forests. One day, the youngest brother was walking in a grove of trees, when he noticed something strange—a tree that was of a different shape from the hundreds of other trees around it. It was covered with orange-red blossoms, and it was so beautiful!

As the younger brother came closer, he saw that there was only one red pomegranate on the tree.

"This is strange indeed," thought the young man. "A pomegranate tree with only one pomegranate." He approached the tree slowly, laughing to himself and thinking of the story he would tell his brothers about the pomegranate tree full of blossoms with only one fruit on it. As he reached for the pomegranate, it fell into his hand even before he could pluck it from the branch. As soon as that happened, another pomegranate burst from one of the blossoms. When the brother saw this, he looked at the pomegranate in his hand and said to himself, "This must be a magic pomegranate. It was the only one on the tree, and yet as soon as it fell into my hands when I was about to reach for it, a new pomegranate appeared suddenly. But what kind of magic does it perform, I wonder?"

The youngest brother examined the pomegranate, marveling at its beauty. "The shape is so perfect," he thought, "crowned with the crown of King Solomon." He walked away from the tree looking at his mysterious new treasure. When he looked back to see the pomegranate tree once more, it was no longer there. It had disappeared. "Now I know this is a magic pomegranate, and so this is what I will bring to my brothers."

Ten years passed, and when the three brothers met as they had planned, they embraced with delight. They eagerly showed each other the unusual objects they had brought back from their journeys.

The oldest brother said, "Let me look through my glass and see what I can see." When he held up the glass, he saw, in a far-off kingdom, a young princess lying ill in bed, near death.

"Quickly, dear brothers, get on my magic carpet and we'll fly there!" said the second brother. In what seemed like seconds, the three brothers arrived at the far-off kingdom.

In the royal palace of this kingdom, the King, whose daughter lay ill, was grief-stricken. He had sent for every doctor in the country to cure the princess; but they had all failed and there was no hope left for the princess. Finally, the King had sent a messenger throughout the country saying, "Whoever can save my daughter, the princess, will have her hand in marriage, and half the kingdom!"

As if in a dream, the youngest brother heard a voice whisper inside him. "The pomegranate!" The youngest brother approached the King and asked, "May I try to cure the princess?" The King agreed and led the young man to the princess' chambers.

When the young man saw the princess, he approached quietly and sat by her side. Then he took the pomegranate from his pocket, cut it open with gentle care, carefully cut each kernel from its place, and then fed the juicy red kernels to the princess. In a few moments, the princess felt stronger, and the color returned to her cheeks. Soon, she sat up in her bed, fully restored to health.

The King was overjoyed. He hugged his daughter and, turning to the three young men, he announced, "The man who saved my daughter will marry her."

The three brothers began to quarrel, each one claiming to be the one who should marry the princess.

The oldest brother said, "If it were not for my magic glass, we would never have known the princess was ill in the first place. So, since I discovered this first, I deserve to marry the princess."

"But, brothers, it was because of my magic carpet that we could arrive so quickly," argued the second brother. "Otherwise, the princess would have died. I deserve to marry the princess."

Then the youngest brother said, "It was my magic pomegranate that actually healed the princess. I deserve to marry her."

Since the three brothers could not decide which one should marry the princess, the King tried to decide. He looked at the three clever young men, but he could not decide who deserved to marry his daughter.

The King finally turned to the princess and asked, "Who do you think deserves to marry you, my daughter?"

The princess answered simply, "I will ask each of them a question." She turned to the oldest brother and asked, "Has your magic glass changed in any way since you arrived in this Kingdom?"

"No," replied the oldest brother. "My glass is the same as always, and I can look through it and see to every corner of this Kingdom."

The princess then asked the second brother, "Has your magic carpet changed in any way since you arrived in this Kingdom?" And the second brother answered, "No, my carpet is the same, and I can fly anywhere on it, as always."

Turning to the youngest brother, the princess asked, "Has your magic pomegranate changed in any way since you arrived in this Kingdom?" And the youngest brother answered, "Yes, princess, my pomegranate is no longer whole, for I gave you a portion of it."

The princess turned to the three young men and said, "I will marry the youngest brother because he performed the greatest good deed—because he gave up something of his own."

The brothers and the King all understood the wisdom of the princess. A lavish wedding was arranged for the princess and the youngest brother.

And the King appointed the princess and all three brothers to become his royal advisers.

Island of the Blue Dolphins

from the book by Scott O'Dell

In the Pacific, off the coast of California, is an island shaped like the dolphins that live in the sea around it. Karana's people had lived on this island for centuries. Then one day Aleutian sea-otter hunters came and tried to cheat the Indians. A battle was fought and many of the Indians were killed. The survivors feared the hunters would return and kill the rest of them. When a group of sailors offered to take the Indians to the mainland, Karana's people decided to leave. But Karana and her brother were left on the island. When her brother was killed by wild dogs, Karana realized she needed to build a shelter with a fence around it to protect her from the wild animals.

Chapter 12

Many years before, two whales had washed up on the sandspit. Most of the bones had been taken away to make ornaments, but ribs were still there, half-buried in the sand.

These I used in making the fence. One by one I dug them up and carried them to the headland. They were long and curved, and when I had scooped out holes and set them in the earth they stood taller than I did.

126

I put the ribs together with their edges almost touching, and standing so that they curved outward, which made them impossible to climb. Between them I wove many strands of bull kelp, which shrinks as it dries and pulls very tight. I would have used seal sinew to bind the ribs together, for this is stronger than kelp, but wild animals like it and soon would have gnawed the fence down. Much time went into its building. It would have taken me longer except that the rock made one end of the fence and part of a side.

For a place to go in and out, I dug a hole under the fence just wide and deep enough to crawl through. The bottom and sides I lined with stones. On the outside I covered the hole with a mat woven of brush to shed the rain, and on the inside with a flat rock which I was strong enough to move.

I was able to take eight steps between the sides of the fence, which gave me all the room I would need to store the things I gathered and wished to protect.

I built the fence first because it was too cold to sleep on the rock and I did not like to sleep in the shelter I had made until I was safe from the wild dogs.

The house took longer to build than the fence because it rained many days and because the wood which I needed was scarce.

There was a legend among our people that the island had once been covered with tall trees. This was a long time ago, at the beginning of the world when Tumaiyowit and Mukat ruled. The two gods quarreled about many things. Tumaiyowit wished people to die. Mukat did not. Tumaiyowit angrily went down, down to another world under this world, taking his belongings with him, so people die because he did.

In that time there were tall trees, but now there were only a few in the ravines and these were small and crooked. It was very hard to find one that would make a good pole. I searched many days, going out early in the morning and coming back at night, before I found enough for the house.

I used the rock for the back of the house and the front I left open since the wind did not blow from this direction. The poles

127

I made of equal length, using fire to cut them as well as a stone knife which caused me much difficulty because I had never made such a tool before. There were four poles on each side, set in the earth, and twice that many for the roof. These I bound together with sinew and covered with female kelp, which has broad leaves.

The winter was half over before I finished the house, but I slept there every night and felt secure because of the strong fence. The foxes came when I was cooking my food and stood outside gazing through the cracks, and the wild dogs also came, gnawing at the whale ribs, growling because they could not get in.

I shot two of them, but not the leader.

While I was building the fence and the house, I ate shellfish and perch which I cooked on a flat rock. Afterwards I made two utensils. Along the shore there were stones that the sea had worn smooth. Most of them were round, but I found two with hollow places in the center which I deepened and broadened by rubbing them with sand. Using these to cook in, I saved the juices of the fish which are good and were wasted before.

For cooking seeds and roots I wove a tight basket of fine reeds, which was easy because I had learned how to do it from my sister Ulape. After the basket had dried in the sun, I gathered lumps of pitch on the shore, softened them over the fire, and rubbed them on the inside of the basket so that it would hold water. By heating small stones and dropping them into a mixture of water and seeds in the basket I could make gruel.

I made a place for fire in the floor of my house, hollowing it out and lining it with rocks. In the village of Ghalas-at we made new fires every night, but now I made one fire which I covered with ashes when I went to bed. The next night I would remove the ashes and blow on the embers. In this way I saved myself much work.

There were many gray mice on the island and now that I had food to keep from one meal to the other, I needed a safe place to put it. On the face of the rock, which was the back wall of my house, were several cracks as high as my shoulder. These I cut out and smoothed to make shelves where I could store my food and the mice could not reach it.

By the time winter was over and grass began to show green on the hills my house was comfortable. I was sheltered from the wind and rain and prowling animals. I could cook anything I wished to eat. Everything I wanted was there at hand.

It was now time to make plans for getting rid of the wild dogs which had killed my brother and would kill me should they ever come upon me unarmed. I needed another and heavier spear, also a larger bow and sharper arrows. To collect the material for these weapons, I searched the whole island, taking many suns to do it. This left only the nights to work on them. Since I could not see well by the dim fire I used for cooking, I made lamps of the dried bodies of little fish which we call *sai-sai*.

The *sai-sai* is the color of silver and not much bigger than a finger. On nights when the moon shines full, these little fish come swimming out of the sea in schools so thick that you can almost walk on them. They come with the waves and twist and turn on the sand as if they were dancing.

I caught many basketfuls of *sai-sai* and put them out in the sun. Hung up by their tails from the poles of the roof, they made much odor, but burned with a very clear light.

I made the bow and arrows first and was pleased when I tried them that I could shoot farther and much straighter than I had before.

The spear I left to the last. I wondered, as I smoothed and shaped the long handle and fitted a stone collar around the end both to give the spear weight and to hold the spear point, if I could make this point the way the men of our tribe did, from the tooth of a sea elephant.

Many nights I thought about it, wondering how I could possibly kill one of these great beasts. I could not use a net of kelp, because that needed the strength of several men. Nor could I remember that a bull elephant had ever been killed with an arrow or with a spear. Only after they had been caught in a net were they killed and then with a club. We killed many cows for their oil, using spears, but the teeth were not large.

129

How I would do this, I did not know. Yet the more I thought about it, the greater was my determination to try, for there was nothing to be found on the island that made such good spear points as the tusklike teeth of the bull sea elephant.

Chapter 13

I did not sleep much the night before I went to the place of the sea elephants. I thought again about the law that forbade women to make weapons. I wondered if my arrows would go straight and, if they did, would they pierce the animal's tough hide. What if one of the bulls turned on me? What if I were injured and then had to fight the wild dogs as I dragged myself homeward?

I thought about these things most of the night, but with the sun I was up and on my way to the place where the sea elephants lived.

When I reached the cliff, the animals had left the reef and gathered along the shore. Like gray boulders the bulls sat on the pebbly slope. Below them the cows and their babies played in the waves.

Perhaps it is not right to speak of young sea elephants as babies, for they are as large as a man. But they are still babies in many ways. They follow their mothers around, waddling along on their flippers like children learning to walk, making crying sounds and sounds of pleasure that only the young make. And before they will leave the shore and learn to swim their mothers have to push them into the sea, which is often difficult to do because of their size.

Some distance separated the bulls from each other, for they are bad-tempered, very jealous by nature and quick to fight over anything that displeases them. There were six of them below me on the slope, each sitting alone like a great chief, watching his herd of cows and babies.

The cow has a smooth body and a face that looks much like that of a mouse, with a sharp-pointed nose and whiskers, but the bull is different. His nose has a large hump on it which hangs down over his mouth. His skin is rough and looks like wet earth that has dried in the sun and cracked. He is an ugly animal.

From the top of the cliff I looked down at each of the sea elephants and tried to choose the smallest of the six.

They were all the same size save one, which was the farthest from me and partly hidden by a rock. He was about half as large as the others, a young bull. Since no cows were playing among the waves in front of him, I knew that he did not have a herd of his own, and for that reason would not be so wary or quickly angered.

Quietly I let myself down over the edge of the cliff. To reach him I had to pass behind the others, being careful not to alarm them. They fear nothing and would not move if they saw me, but it was better, I thought, not to put them on their guard. I carried my new bow, which was almost as tall as I was, and five arrows.

The path was rough and covered with small stones. I took pains not to send them tumbling down the slope. I was also careful not to be seen by the cows, which get alarmed easily and would have warned the rest of the herd with their cries.

I crawled behind a big rock near the young bull. I then got to my feet and fitted an arrow to the bow, although I suddenly remembered my father's warning that, because I was a woman, the bow would break.

The sun was far in the west, but luckily my shadow fell away from the young bull. The distance between us was short and his back was turned squarely toward me. Still I did not know where to place the first arrow, whether in his shoulders or in his head. The skin of the sea elephant is rough, yet very thin, but beneath it are thick layers of fat, and though his body is large, his head is small and makes a poor target.

While I stood there behind the rock, not knowing what to do, again aware of my father's warning that a bow in the hands of a woman would always break in a time of danger, the animal began to move toward the shore. At first I thought that by some chance he had heard me. I soon saw that he was on his way toward the cows that belonged to the old bull sitting nearby.

131

The sea elephant moves fast in spite of his size, waddling along on his great flippers which he uses like hands. The bull was nearing the water. I let the arrow go and it went straight. At the last instant he changed direction and, though the bow did not break, the arrow passed harmlessly to one side.

I had failed to notice that the old bull was moving down the slope until I heard stones grating against each other. Quickly he overtook his rival and with a single thrust of his shoulders overturned him. The young bull stood as high as a tall man and was twice that length, yet from the force of the blow he rolled into the water and lay there stunned.

The old bull bore down upon him, swinging his head and bellowing so loud it echoed against the cliffs. The herd of cows and calves, who were lying in the waves and scratching their backs with their flippers, stopped to watch the battle.

Two of the cows were in the bull's path as he waddled toward his rival, but he went over them as if they were small stones. Using his tusklike teeth, he ripped a long gash in the young bull's side.

The young bull raised himself and as he turned his small eyes shone fiercely red. When the old bull slashed at him again, he struck first and sunk his teeth into the other's neck. He did not let go and the two rolled over in the waves, splashing water high into the air.

The cows had scattered by now, but the other bulls still sat quietly on the slope.

The two fighters paused, getting ready for a new attack. It was a good chance to send an arrow into the young bull, who lay on his back with his teeth still grasping the other's neck. But I hoped that he would win the battle, and I stood there and did not move.

The old bull had many deep scars on his head and shoulders from battles he had fought before. Suddenly he lashed out with his tail, trying to loose the hold on his neck, and struck the side of a rock. With his tail against the rock, he flung his body out of the water and thus broke away.

He came quickly up the slope, his great mouth open, the young bull close behind him. He came toward me and, in haste to get out of his way, not knowing whether he was bent on attacking me, I stepped back. In doing so, I tripped over a stone and fell to my knees.

I felt a sharp pain in my leg, but was quickly up. By this time the old bull had whirled around and turned upon his pursuer so fast that the young bull was taken by surprise. Again the young bull's flank was ripped deep, and again the force of the blow threw him backward into the water.

The waves grew redder from his blood, but this time he rolled over and was waiting for the charge. He met the old bull with his shoulder. The sound was like rocks crashing together. Once more the young bull caught the other's throat, and together they disappeared beneath a wave. When they came up they were still locked together.

The sun had gone down and it was so dark I could no longer see clearly. My leg had now begun to hurt. Since I had a long way to go, I left them. I could hear their bellowing as I went up the cliff and for a long time afterward.

Chapter 14

My leg hurt so much by the time I had reached the house that it was hard for me to crawl under the fence and move aside the heavy rock.

For five suns I could not go out because my leg had swollen so badly and I had no herbs with which to treat it. I had enough food to eat, but on the third day the water in the basket ran low. Two days later the basket was empty. It was necessary then for me to go to the spring in the ravine.

I started out when the sun rose. I took with me shellfish to eat, also my spear and my bow and arrows. I went very slowly, for I had to crawl on my hands and knees, carrying the food tied to my back, and dragging the weapons.

There was a short way to the spring, but it was over many rocks which I could not climb, so I had to take a longer way through the brush. I reached the ravine when the sun was

133

overhead. The spring was not far off and I rested there, though I was very thirsty, cutting a lobe from a cactus bush to chew on.

While I was resting there, sucking the juice from the cactus, I saw the big gray dog, the leader of the wild pack, in the brush above me. His head was down and he was moving slowly, sniffing the tracks I had made. He saw me soon after I saw him and stopped. Behind him was the rest of the pack, trotting along one after the other. The pack stopped too.

I took up my bow and fitted an arrow, but as I did this the big dog faded away into the brush and was quickly followed by the others. In the time of one breath they were gone. There was nothing to aim my arrow at. It was as if they had not been there at all.

I listened. They were moving so silently I could not hear their steps, but I was sure that they would try to surround me. Slowly I crawled on, stopping to listen, to glance back, to measure the distance between me and the spring. My leg hurt. I left my bow and arrows behind as I went on, for the brush had grown heavy and I could not use them. In one hand I dragged my spear.

I came to the spring. It flowed out of a crack in a rock and the rock rose high on three sides of it. The wild dogs could not attack me from any of these directions, so I lay on the earth and drank, watching the ravine below me. I drank for a long time and filled my basket and then, feeling better, crawled toward the mouth of the cave.

A ledge of black rock ran out above it. Some low bushes grew there and among them, with just his head showing, stood the big gray dog. He did not move, but his yellow eyes followed me, turning slowly as I drew near the cave. Another head showed behind him and another. They were too far away for me to reach with my spear.

Suddenly I saw brush moving on the opposite bank of the ravine. The pack had split up and were waiting on both sides of the ravine for me to pass them.

The cave was now in front of me. I crawled to the mouth and into it. Above me I could hear feet running and the cracking of brush, which was followed by silence.

134

I was safe. I knew the wild dogs would come back and they did as night fell, stalking around in the brush until morning, but not venturing close.

Although the mouth of the cave was small, once you were inside, it spread out and you could stand up. Water dropped from the roof and the cave was cold without a fire, but here I stayed for six suns, until my leg was well, crawling out only once to fetch water from the spring.

While I was living there I decided that I would make the cave into another house, where I could stay should I again get hurt or sick. And this I did as soon as I was strong and could walk.

The cave went far back into the hill, around many turns, but I needed only that part which lay near the opening and which the sun could reach during some of the day.

A long time before this my ancestors had used the cave, why I do not know, and along the walls on each side they had cut figures in the stone. There were figures of pelicans floating on the water and flying, of dolphins, whales, sea elephants, gulls, ravens, dogs, and foxes. Near the opening of the cave they had also cut two deep basins in the stone, which I decided to use for storing water since they held much more than the baskets.

I made shelves in the side of the rock as I had done in the other house, and gathered shellfish and seeds to store there. I also gathered herbs from the hill above the spring in case I should need them. The bow and arrows I had first made I likewise took to the cave. At the last, after I had made a good bed of seaweed and collected dry wood for my fires, I closed the opening with stones, except for a small hole at the top which I could crawl through.

All this I did, thinking of the days I had been sick and without water. It was hard work, much of it a man's work, but not until I was finished did I go back to the place where the sea elephants lived.

The tide was low when I reached it. Far up on the slope lay the body of the old bull. Gulls had picked his bones clean, but I found what I had come for.

Some of the teeth were as long as my hand and half its width. They were curved at the tops and some were broken, but when I had ground the best of them down with sand, I had for my work four good spear points, broad at the bottom and very sharp at the ends.

I made two more spears from these points and at last was ready to go to the cave of the wild dogs.

Chapter 15

There had been wild dogs on the Island of the Blue Dolphins as long as I remember, but after the Aleuts had slain most of the men of our tribe and their dogs had left to join the others, the pack became much bolder. It spent the nights running through the village and during the day was never far off. It was then that we made plans to get rid of them, but the ship came and everyone left Ghalas-at.

I am sure that the pack grew bolder because of their leader, the big one with the thick fur around his neck and the yellow eyes.

I had never seen this dog before the Aleuts came and no one else had, so he must have come with them and been left behind when they sailed away. He was a much larger dog than any of ours, which besides have short hair and brown eyes. I was sure that he was an Aleut dog.

Already I had killed four of the pack, but there were many left, more than in the beginning, for some had been born in the meantime. The young dogs were even wilder than the old ones.

I first went to the hill near the cave when the pack was away and collected armloads of brush which I placed near the mouth of their lair. Then I waited until the pack was in the cave. It went there early in the morning to sleep after it had spent the night prowling. I took with me the big bow and five arrows and two of the spears. I went quietly, circling around the mouth of the cave and came up to it from the side. There I left all of my weapons except one spear.

I set fire to the brush and pushed it into the cave. If the wild dogs heard me, there was no sound from them. Nearby was a ledge of rock which I climbed, taking my weapons with me.

The fire burned high. Some of the smoke trailed out over the hill, but much of it stayed in the cave. Soon the pack would have to leave. I did not hope to kill more than five of them because I had only that many arrows, but if the leader was one of the five I would be satisfied. It might be wiser if I waited and saved all my arrows for him, and this I decided to do.

None of the dogs appeared before the fire died. Then three ran out and away. Seven more followed and a long time afterwards a like number. There were many more still left in the cave.

The leader came next. Unlike the others, he did not run away. He jumped over the ashes and stood at the mouth of the cave, sniffing the air. I was so close to him that I could see his nose quivering, but he did not see me until I raised my bow. Fortunately I did not frighten him.

He stood facing me, his front legs spread as if he were ready to spring, his yellow eyes narrowed to slits. The arrow struck him in the chest. He turned away from me, took one step and fell. I sent another arrow toward him which went wide.

At this time three more dogs trotted out of the cave. I used the last of my arrows and killed two of them.

Carrying both of the spears, I climbed down from the ledge and went through the brush to the place where the leader had fallen. He was not there. While I had been shooting at the other dogs, he had gone. He could not have gone far because of his wound, but though I looked everywhere, around the ledge where I had been standing and in front of the cave, I did not find him.

I waited for a long time and then went inside the cave. It was deep, but I could see clearly.

Far back in a corner was the half-eaten carcass of a fox. Beside it was a black dog with four gray pups. One of the pups came slowly toward me, a round ball of fur that I could have held in my hand. I wanted to hold it, but the mother leaped to her feet and bared her teeth. I raised my spear as I backed out of the cave, yet I did not use it. The wounded leader was not there.

Night was coming and I left the cave, going along the foot of the hill that led to the cliff. I had not gone far on this trail that the wild dogs used when I saw the broken shaft of an arrow. It had been gnawed off near the tip and I knew it was from the arrow which had wounded the leader.

Farther on I saw his tracks in the dust. They were uneven as if he were traveling slowly. I followed them toward the cliff, but finally lost them in the darkness.

The next day and the next it rained and I did not go to look for him. I spent those days making more arrows, and on the third day, with these arrows and my spear, I went out along the trail the wild dogs had made to and from my house.

There were no tracks after the rain, but I followed the trail to the pile of rocks where I had seen them before. On the far side of the rocks I found the big gray dog. He had the broken arrow in his chest and he was lying with one of his legs under him.

He was about ten paces from me so I could see him clearly. I was sure that he was dead, but I lifted the spear and took good aim at him. Just as I was about to throw the spear, he raised his head a little from the earth and then let it drop.

This surprised me greatly and I stood there for a while not knowing what to do, whether to use the spear or my bow. I was used to animals playing dead until they suddenly turned on you or ran away.

The spear was the better of the two weapons at this distance, but I could not use it as well as the other, so I climbed onto the rocks where I could see him if he ran. I placed my feet carefully. I had a second arrow ready should I need it. I fitted an arrow and pulled back the string, aiming at his head.

Why I did not send the arrow I cannot say. I stood on the rock with the bow pulled back and my hand would not let it go. The big dog lay there and did not move and this may be the reason. If he had gotten up I would have killed him. I stood there for a long time looking down at him and then I climbed off the rocks.

He did not move when I went up to him, nor could I see him breathing until I was very close. The head of the arrow was in his chest and the broken shaft was covered with blood. The thick fur around his neck was matted from the rain.

I do not think that he knew I was picking him up, for his body was limp, as if he were dead. He was very heavy and the only way I could lift him was by kneeling and putting his legs around my shoulders.

In this manner, stopping to rest when I was tired, I carried him to the headland.

I could not get through the opening under the fence, so I cut the bindings and lifted out two of the whale ribs and thus took him into the house. He did not look at me or raise his head when I laid him on the floor, but his mouth was open and he was breathing.

The arrow had a small point, which was fortunate, and came out easily though it had gone deep. He did not move while I did this, nor afterwards as I cleaned the wound with a peeled stick from a coral bush. This bush has poisonous berries, yet its wood often heals wounds that nothing else will.

I had not gathered food for many days and the baskets were empty, so I left water for the dog and, after mending the fence, went down to the sea. I had no thought that he would live and I did not care.

All day I was among the rocks gathering shellfish and only once did I think of the wounded dog, my enemy, lying there in the house, and then to wonder why I had not killed him.

He was still alive when I got back, though he had not moved from the place where I had left him. Again I cleaned the wound with a coral twig. I then lifted his head and put water in his mouth, which he swallowed. This was the first time that he had looked at me since the time I had found him on the trail. His eyes were sunken and they looked out at me from far back in his head.

Before I went to sleep I gave him more water. In the morning I left food for him when I went down to the sea,

139

and when I came home he had eaten it. He was lying in the corner, watching me. While I made a fire and cooked my supper, he watched me. His yellow eyes followed me wherever I moved.

That night I slept on the rock, for I was afraid of him, and at dawn as I went out I left the hole under the fence open so he could go. But he was there when I got back, lying in the sun with his head on his paws. I had speared two fish, which I cooked for my supper. Since he was very thin, I gave him one of them, and after he had eaten it he came over and lay down by the fire, watching me with his yellow eyes that were very narrow and slanted up at the corners.

Four nights I slept on the rock, and every morning I left the hole under the fence open so he could leave. Each day I speared a fish for him and when I got home he was always at the fence waiting for it. He would not take the fish from me so I had to put it on the ground. Once I held out my hand to him, but at this he backed away and showed his teeth.

On the fourth day when I came back from the rocks early he was not there at the fence waiting. A strange feeling came over me. Always before when I returned, I had hoped that he would be gone. But now as I crawled under the fence I did not feel the same.

I called out, "Dog, Dog," for I had no other name for him.

I ran toward the house, calling it. He was inside. He was just getting to his feet, stretching himself and yawning. He looked first at the fish I carried and then at me and moved his tail.

That night I stayed in the house. Before I fell asleep I thought of a name for him, for I could not call him Dog. The name I thought of was Rontu, which means in our language Fox Eyes.

MARGARET H. LIPPERT is a professional storyteller who comes from a family of Irish storytellers. A classroom teacher for many years, she taught children's literature and storytelling at Bank Street College of Education and at Teachers College, Columbia University, where she earned her doctorate. She has lived and taught in Tanzania, East Africa, and in Guatemala, Central America. She now lives in the Cascade Mountains in Washington State with her husband and two daughters.

Authors and Storytellers

Baylor, Byrd, collected "The Boy Who Became a Deer" from a Hopi student, Roy Masayesva, in Arizona. Baylor grew up in the deserts of America's Southwest and spent many childhood summers in Mexico. This experience resulted in a variety of books for children including *Before You Came this Way*. Baylor received the Caldecott Medal from the American Library Association in 1973 for *When Clay Sings*, and again in 1976 for *The Desert Is Theirs*. She resides in Arizona and New Mexico.

Brooke, William J., author of "The Fitting of the Slipper," from his collection of five stories, *A Telling of the Tales*, lives in New York City. An actor and singer, he is especially active in the Gilbert and Sullivan repertory. Brooke has also co-authored musical revues that have been performed throughout the United States and in Canada.

Bruchac, Joseph, reteller of "How Mink Stole Time," is a poet, novelist, and storyteller. Born in the Adirondacks, his stories draw on the legends and myths of those mountains, as well as on his own Native American (Abenaki) ancestry. Bruchac and Michael J. Caduto are co-authors of the books *Keepers of the Earth* and *Keepers of the Animals*.

Cabral, Len, reteller of "The Lion's Whisker," is a storyteller from Cape Verde who gives storytelling workshops throughout the United States and Canada. Cabral lives in Rhode Island, where he co-founded the Sidewalk Storytellers in 1976. He has produced two audiocassettes of traditional stories, *Ananzi* and *Nho Lobo*.

Cisneros, Sandra, author of "Papa Who Wakes Up Tired in the Dark," has been a poet-in-the-schools, an arts administrator, a college recruiter and has taught high school dropouts. Most recently, she was a visiting writer at a number of universities around the country. Cisneros received the American Book Award from the Before Columbus Foundation, 1985, for *The House on Mango Street*.

Cornplanter, Jesse J., teller of the Seneca story "The Power of the Little People," is a soldier, craftsman, musician, actor and tale-teller. A member of the Clan of the Snipe, Cornplanter lives on the Tonawanda Seneca Reservation.

Courlander, Harold, teller of "Time," is a well-known folklorist and author of many books of folk tales including *The Fire on the Mountain* and *Uncle Bouqui of Haiti*. He worked for the United States Information Agency and the United States Mission to the United Nations. Courlander and George Herzog are coauthors of *The Cow-Tail Switch and Other West African Stories*.

de Wit, Dorothy, reteller of "Small Star and the Mud Pony," is a reviewer for *School Library Journal*, *Top of the News*, and *Previews*. She is also a former member of a marionette troupe who still uses her puppeteering skill in her library work. Since 1961, she has been on the staff of the Cuyahoga County Public Library in Ohio, and since 1966 she has been Regional Children's Librarian at the Maple Heights Regional Branch. Her books include *The Talking Stone: An Anthology of Native American Tales and Legends* and *Children's Faces Looking Up: Programming for Story-tellers*.

Feldman, David, author of "Why Is the NBA Shot Clock 24 Seconds?" has a master's degree in popular culture from Bowling Green State University in Ohio. While at Bowling Green, he taught the first college course ever offered on soap operas. Formerly in the programming department of NBC-TV, Feldman consults and lectures on the media. He lives in New York City.

Green, Roger Lancelyn, reteller of "The Story of the Shipwrecked Sailor," is the author of *Tales of Ancient Egypt*. His other collections of legends and myths include *Tales of the Greek Heroes*, *A Book of Dragons*, *Myths of the Norsemen*, and *The Tale of Troy*.

Gruenberg, Sidonie Matsner (1881–1974), collector of "The Snow Maiden," made children her career for a great many years. She joined the staff of the Child Study Association of America in 1906 and became its executive director in 1923. Until her retirement in 1950, Gruenberg lectured at a number of colleges and universities, including Columbia University and the University of Colorado. She wrote twelve books devoted to child rearing and health, including the popular *Encyclopedia of Child Care and Guidance*.

Haviland, Virginia, reteller of "The Twelve Months," is a well-known and highly acclaimed expert in the field of children's literature. She served as the Reading Advisor for Children at the Boston Public Library and, for nearly twenty years, was the Head of the Children's Book Section of the Library of Congress. She was also a chairperson of the Newbery-Caldecott Awards Committee, a judge for the National Book Award in children's literature, and a jury member for the Hans Christian Andersen Medal. In 1976, Haviland received the Regina Medal for distinguished service in the field of children's literature. Her books include *Children and Literature: Views and Reviews* and *The Best of Children's Books*.

Herzog, George, teller of "Time," wrote *The Cow-Tail Switch and Other West African Stories* with Harold Courlander.

Leach, Maria, teller of "The Great Bear," is one of America's best-known folklorists. She is the compiler-editor of the *Standard Dictionary of Folklore, Mythology, and Legend* and other folklore collections for children and adults. A member of the American Folklore Society, of which she has been a Councilor, Leach lives in Nova Scotia.

London, Jack (1876–1916), author of "Up the Slide," is best remembered for his short stories and novels of adventure. He published his first book, *The Son of the Wolf*, in 1900, when he was 24. By that time, he had worked a variety of jobs, including newsboy and fruit picker. He had raided oyster beds with his own sloop, and had joined the Alaskan gold rush. Disciplined to write a thousand words a day, he wrote popular adventure fiction such as the famous story "To Build A Fire" and the bestselling novel *The Call of the Wild*.

Lord, Walter, author of *A Night to Remember*, is best known for his account of the sinking of the *Titanic*. An adaptation of the work appeared on Kraft Television Theatre in 1956 and was made into a feature film by J. Arthur Rank in 1959. As an historian, Lord is basically ". . . interested in the people who are caught in great events more than the events themselves . . . people stay the same—history is a wonderful guide to human behavior and that is why people fascinate me so much."

Masayesva, Roy, teller of "The Boy Who Became a Deer," was a student at the Hoteville-Bacabi Community School in Arizona when he told the story to Byrd Baylor. Baylor published the story in her collection *And It Is Still That Way: Legends told by Arizona Indian Children*. In retelling this story, Roy drew on his Hopi heritage.

O'Dell, Scott (1898–1989), author of *Island of the Blue Dolphins*, is, through his great-grandfather, related to the Scottish romantic writer, Sir Walter Scott. As prolific as his famous cousin, O'Dell wrote twenty-five children's books, most of which dealt with the history of his native Southern California. Before becoming a full-time writer, a career which spanned nearly fifty years, he worked as a farmer, as a cameraman and technical director for Paramount Studios, and as a journalist. O'Dell received the Newbery Honor awards in 1967 for *The King's Fifth*; in 1968 for *The Black Pearl*; and in 1971 for *Sing Down the Moon*. *Island of the Blue Dolphins* received seven awards, including the Newbery Medal and the Hans Christian Andersen award of merit.

Russell, William F., reteller of "Damon and Pythias," is the author of *Classics to Read Aloud to Your Children* and *More Classics to Read Aloud to Your Children*. "Damon and Pythias" is from his book *Classic Myths to Read Aloud*. Dr. Russell lives in Geneva, Illinois.

Rylant, Cynthia, author of "Papa's Parrot," grew up in two small West Virginia towns—Cool Ridge and Beaver—which gave her "a lifetime's worth of material for my writing." She has written over seventeen books, including *A Fine White Dust*, which received a Newbery Honor award, and *A Kindness*, which was named an American Library Association Best Book for Young Adults. When she is not writing, Rylant, who lives with her family in Akron, Ohio, loves to see films and to watch whales, sea otters, and dolphins.

Schram, Peninnah, reteller of "The Magic Pomegranate," is a professional storyteller, recording artist, and author. Currently an Associate Professor of Speech and Drama at Stern College of Yeshiva University, Schram is also Founder and Director of The Jewish Storytelling Center in New York and the National Jewish Storytelling Network. A native of New London, Connecticut, she lives with her family in New York.

Simms, Laura, reteller of "Delgadina," is a professional storyteller for the American Museum of Natural History, the Hans Christian Andersen Society, and the New York Foundation for the Arts. She has recorded five audiocassettes of stories including *The Incredible Journey* and *Stories: As Old As the World, As Fresh As the Rain*. Her books include *The Squeaky Door* and *The Snake Princess*.

144

Singer, Isaac Bashevis (1904–1991), author of "The Power of Light," was a short story writer and novelist who received the Nobel Prize for literature in 1978. After working twelve years in his native Poland for the Yiddish and Hebrew press, Singer emigrated to New York in 1935, where he joined the staff of the *Jewish Daily Forward*. His first important novel, *The Family Moskat*, appeared in 1950. Although he wrote in Yiddish, he supervised translations of his novels and short stories into English. Singer usually wrote about the people and places of his childhood. Many of the stories he wrote are based on folk tales his mother told him, which she, in turn, heard from her mother and grandmother. His collection of stories *Zlateh the Goat and Other Stories* won the Newbery Honor award in 1967.

Soto, Gary, author of "La Bamba," began writing when he was in college. "My intention," he says, "was to major in geography, but then I gravitated toward literature." His childhood experiences as a migrant worker and of growing up in California's Central Valley are woven into the stories of his contemporary young characters. *Living up the Street*, Soto's collection of autobiographical essays, won the Before Columbus Foundation's American Book Award in 1985. An associate professor at the University of California, Berkeley, he lives with his wife and daughter in Albany, California.

Stamm, Claus, teller of "Three Strong Women," is the author of *Three Strong Women: A Tall Tale from Japan*, a collection of tales and legends about women from Japan. His other books include *The Dumplings and the Demons* and *The Very Special Badgers: A Tale of Magic from Japan*.

INDEX

INDEX OF LITERATURE BY ORIGIN

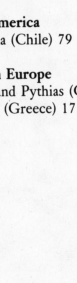

AUTHOR AND STORYTELLER INDEX

ℐNDEX OF TITLES

Acknowledgments

The publisher gratefully acknowledges permission to reprint the following copyrighted material:

Jason Aronson, Inc.
"The Magic Pomegranate" by Peninnah Schram from JEWISH STORIES ONE GENER-ATION TELLS ANOTHER retold by Peninnah Schram. Copyright © 1987 by Peninnah Schram. Reprinted by permission of Jason Aronson, Inc.

Byrd Baylor
"The Boy Who Became a Deer" from AND IT IS STILL THAT WAY: Legends told by Arizona Indian Children with notes by Byrd Baylor. Copyright © 1976 by Byrd Baylor. Published by Trails West Press, Santa Fe, New Mexico. Reprinted by permission of Byrd Baylor.

Susan Bergholz Literary Services
"Papa Who Wakes Up Tired in the Dark" from THE HOUSE ON MANGO STREET by Sandra Cisneros. Copyright © by Sandra Cisneros 1984. Published by Vintage Books, a Division of Random House, Inc., New York, and by Alfred A. Knopf in hardcover in 1994. Reprinted by permission of Susan Bergholz Literary Services, New York.

The Bodley Head Ltd.
"The Story of the Shipwrecked Sailor" from TALES OF ANCIENT EGYPT selected and retold by Roger Lancelyn Green. Copyright © 1967 by Roger Lancelyn Green. Reprinted by permission of The Bodley Head Ltd.

Len Cabral
"The Lion's Whisker." Copyright © 1991 by Len Cabral. Used with permission of the author.

Dorothy de Wit
"Small Star and the Mud Pony" from THE TALKING STONE by Dorothy de Wit. Copyright © 1979 by Dorothy M. de Wit. Reprinted by permission of Adriaan de Wit for the Estate of Dorothy de Wit.

Farrar, Straus & Giroux, Inc.
"The Power of Light" from THE POWER OF LIGHT: Eight Stories for Hanukkah by Isaac Bashevis Singer. Text copyright © 1980 by Isaac Bashevis Singer. Reprinted by permission of Farrar, Straus & Giroux, Inc.

Harcourt Brace Jovanovich, Publishers
"La Bamba" from BASEBALL IN APRIL AND OTHER STORIES by Gary Soto. Copyright © 1990 by Gary Soto. Reprinted by permission of Harcourt Brace & Company.

"La Bamba" (Adaptation and arrangement by Ritchie Valens) © 1958 PICTURE OUR MUSIC (Renewed). All Rights for the USA administered by WINDSWEPT PACIFIC ENTERTAINMENT Co. d/b/a LONGITUDE MUSIC Co. All Rights for the World (excluding USA) administered by WARNER-TAMERLANE PUBLISHING Corp. All Rights Reserved. Used by permission.

"Up the Slide" by Jack London from ADVENTURES IN READING Grade 8 Harcourt Brace Jovanovich Anthology. Copyright © 1989 by Harcourt Brace Jovanovich. Reprinted by permission of Harcourt Brace Jovanovich, Publishers.

HarperCollins Publishers
"The Fitting of the Slipper" from A TELLING OF THE TALES: Five Stories by William J. Brooke. Text copyright © 1990 by William J. Brooke. Reprinted by permission of HarperCollins Publishers, Inc.

"The Power of the Little People" from LEGENDS OF THE LONGHOUSE by Jesse J. Cornplanter. Copyright 1938 by Jesse J. Cornplanter and Namee Price Henricks. Copyright © renewed 1966 by Jesse Cornplanter. Reprinted by permission of HarperCollins Publishers, Inc.

PLAYS, POEMS, AND CHORAL READINGS

CORRELATIONS ▶▶▶▶▶▶▶

Each play, poem, and choral reading selection has been developed to reinforce the unit theme in the Student Anthology.

Level 12
Unit 1: Making the Grade

THEME: Learning experiences can lead to new understandings and insights. In school, students study math and social studies, but they also learn about who they are and how they fit in.

PLAY: *The Pirates' Funeral*—a dramatic adaptation of several chapters from *The Adventures of Tom Sawyer*, in which Tom and several pals devise an elaborate hoax to teach a schoolmate a lesson

CHORAL READING: "Spelling Bee"—a poem describing the unanticipated outcome of a school spelling bee

POEMS: "Young Soul"
"About the Teeth of Sharks"
"He ate and drank the precious Words"
"Manners"
"From Whitman"

Unit 2: Dare to Discover

THEME: Finders and seekers experience a sense of awe at the wonders of our world. Any valuable discovery is worth the effort to find it.

PLAY: *The Treasure Seekers*—a play about a relentless search for sunken treasure where the clues rely upon historical research

CHORAL READING: "Thumbprint" and "Books Fall Open"—poems that focus on the acquisition of different types of knowledge

POEMS: "Ithaca"
"Mummy"
"My Horse, Fly like a Bird"
"Pegasus in Pound"
"The Song of Wandering Aengus"

UNIT THEMES, PLAYS, POEMS, AND CHORAL READINGS

Unit 3: Unlikely Heroes

THEME: Self-assurance and determination will help you achieve the seemingly impossible. An unflagging belief in yourself and your own abilities can make even the most difficult goal achievable.

PLAY: *The Tennessee Tornado*—a dramatization focusing on Wilma Rudolph's incredible determination to overcome paralysis to become the fastest woman in the world

CHORAL READING: "It Couldn't Be Done" and "Get a Transfer"—poems that speak to the power of positive thinking

POEMS: "At the Top of My Voice"
"Instead of Gentle Human Beings/En vez de Humanos Dulces"
"Another Mountain"
"The Wall of China"
"Hatshepsut's Obelisk"

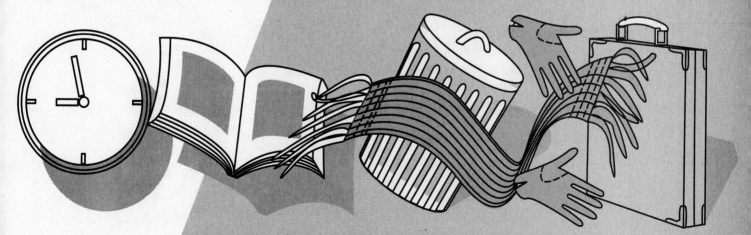

Unit 4: Time and Time Again

THEME: Time is both the outline that frames our lives and the yardstick with which we measure them. Time is something that we can neither see nor feel, but it has a profound effect on our lives.

PLAY: *Countdown to Zero*—a fictionalized drama that explores some unexpected consequences resulting from a change in the earth's orbit

CHORAL READING: "No Present Like the Time"—a poem that looks at time from a new perspective

POEMS: "From the Most Distant Time"
"The Clock Ticks"
"A Time to Talk"
"To Miss Rápida/A Miss Rápida"
"The Echoing Green"

Unit 5: Coming Home

THEME: To be a part of a community is one of the most basic human needs. Everyone needs a place to fit in.

PLAY:: *The Secret Garden*—a dramatic adaptation of the classic novel in which two unhappy children eventually bloom like the garden they discover

CHORAL READING: "Something for Everyone"—a poem that celebrates the diversity of families and lifestyles

POEMS: "My José"
"The Delight Song of Tsoai-Talee"
"I Ask My Mother to Sing"
"Enchantment"
3 haiku on horses

Unit 6: Call It Courage

THEME: A moment of decision may lead to an act of personal courage. Individuals facing challenges can achieve great acts of heroism.

PLAY: *A Thousand Miles to Freedom*—a play set in 1848 based on the true account of two slaves who devise an ingenious plan to escape from bondage

CHORAL READING: Excerpts from *The Call to Arms* and *The Declaration of Independence*—two documents that mark dramatic turning points in our nation's history

POEMS: "Gold Medalist"
"Sea Calm"
"The Courage that My Mother Had"
"The Rescue"
"Señora X No More"

INTRODUCTION ▶▶▶▶▶▶

We read for many different reasons, but chief among them should be the discovery that reading can be both fun and purposeful. And what could be more entertaining than working together to make words come alive in a Readers Theater or choral reading presentation? This book of plays and choral readings has been developed to give you and your students an opportunity to enjoy reading aloud together. At the same time, your students will be developing their reading fluency skills through these enjoyable and motivating oral-reading experiences.

The following pages provide a compilation of hints and tips gathered from teachers who have made oral-reading techniques work in their classrooms. Unlike dramatic productions requiring memorization, elaborate sets, costumes, and stage directions, Readers Theater and choral reading only require a set of scripts and a group of enthusiastic readers—the former you are holding, while the latter wait in the wings of your classroom!

READERS THEATER—A DESCRIPTION

Readers Theater has been used by teachers for many years. Also known as Dramatic Reading, Chamber Theater, or Story Theater, the name Readers Theater seems most appropriate because it puts the emphasis where it belongs—on the *reading* rather than the memorization of a script. Unlike traditional drama in which performers memorize lines and move about a stage, Readers Theater is simply the rehearsed oral reading of a script by a group of performers. It requires no training in drama or the performing arts on the part of students or teachers; there are no complicated guidelines to follow. While simple costumes or backdrops can be used to help establish characterization and setting, they are optional. The fact that Readers Theater involves such simple techniques makes it a viable option for every classroom.

READERS THEATER AND CHORAL READING—THE BENEFITS

Among the chief benefits of Readers Theater and choral reading is the development of oral-reading fluency. Identified by some reading authorities as a frequently "neglected goal" of reading instruction, fluency training has been recognized as an important aspect of proficient reading.

Two essential components for successful fluency training are repeated reading and active listening. Most students can sharpen their active listening skills by attending while the teacher reads aloud for a brief period every day. However, convincing students to repeatedly read the same selection orally until fluency is achieved is quite a different matter. Usually the response is less than enthusiastic.

Enter Readers Theater and choral reading!—both natural partners for fluency training. The oral reading of plays and poetry generates a natural excitement and a willingness to rehearse that enables teachers to integrate repeated reading practice into their instructional program. The goal of a polished performance is a genuinely motivating force that provides a rationale for the fluency training that all students need. Readers Theater and choral reading offer students a *meaningful* context in which to practice expression, shading, phrasing, diction, pitch, and rate, as well as word recognition skills. (For additional information on fluency training and its benefits, see the articles listed in the Bibliography.)

Readers Theater and choral reading also develop active listening skills on the part of both participants and audience. Readers must listen attentively to pick up on cues or to chime in as a member of a group. Audience members also are encouraged to sharpen listening skills as they interpret the dialog and narration to visualize settings and characters that are described rather than visibly presented on stage.

In addition to developing fluency skills, Readers Theater and choral reading can also help students internalize literature, thereby improving their comprehension. Dramatizations enable readers to "become" the characters they play. What better way to reinforce character and plot development than through plays? Dramatizations also expose students to the rich heritage of oral language and storytelling. Through the oral reading of scripts and poetry, students internalize the rhythm of repeated refrains, certain language conventions, and traditional story structure.

A final benefit of Readers Theater and choral reading is derived from the high levels of student interaction and involvement within cooperative learning groups. Through these shared oral-reading experiences, students learn to work together, take turns, listen to each other, and employ group decision-making and problem-solving strategies in casting and production decisions.

Unlike many group activities in which all participants must function on or about the same level to effectively complete the task, a Readers Theater group using the scripts in this book can be composed of students with widely differing reading abilities. The scripts have been written to include roles of varying length and difficulty, enabling students of all ability levels to fully participate and contribute to the achievement of the common goal: a shared oral-reading experience.

LAUNCHING READERS THEATER IN YOUR CLASSROOM

As the following steps indicate, introducing Readers Theater to your class is a straightforward procedure. The only rules are: Keep it simple! and Keep it fun!

1. SCRIPT PREPARATION

Decide when you want to introduce the Readers Theater play within a unit. Then duplicate a copy of the script for each cast member and the director. (Since scripts sometimes have a habit of disappearing, you might make a few extras, just in case.) Students can make construction-paper covers, using the full-page art that precedes each script for decoration, if they wish.

2. ROLE ASSIGNMENT

The plays in this collection were purposefully written with roles requiring varying levels of reading proficiency. Initially you may want to take into account individual reading ability when making role assignments, but once students have become familiar

with a play, roles can and should be switched. Because the characters are read rather than acted, the part of a boy can be read by a girl and vice versa. As students become familiar with Readers Theater, they should be encouraged to assume responsibility for casting decisions as they participate within the cooperative decision-making environment of a Readers Theater group.

3. REHEARSALS

In the first rehearsal, students in the cast should sit together in a Readers Theater group—perhaps gathered around a table—and read through the script to get a sense of the plot and characters. If the play is an adaptation, you may want to read aloud the original story. (Sources for stories that have been adapted appear in the Bibliography.) At this time, roles should be assigned or agreed upon, and students can be encouraged to identify their lines with a transparent highlighter.

Subsequent rehearsals should include paired repeated readings where two characters rehearse their lines together. Having a tape recorder available for these readings will enable students to evaluate their progress. In these early rehearsals, students should focus on word recognition and on listening

for cues. Once these goals have been achieved, attention can be turned to articulation, expression, rate, shading, and phrasing. Invite students to make "reader's notes" in pencil in their scripts. A slash, for example, can be used as a reminder of a pause not indicated by punctuation. An underline can indicate that a word needs special emphasis. These notations can be a valuable aid to oral reading.

During rehearsals, students may decide to add their own personal touches to a script. If the cast decides to add, delete, or alter a speech, this change should be made in all copies of the script.

4. BLOCKING AND FOCUS

In Readers Theater, the performers usually do not move about the stage. However, there are two bits of "stage business" that require rehearsal—where the performers will sit in relation to each other, and where they should look when they are speaking.

Each play is accompanied by a blocking diagram that suggests a seating arrangement. Before the performance, students will need to practice entering, assuming their places on stools or chairs, and exiting. If music stands are available, you may wish to have students use them to hold their scripts during a performance. In some cases, a music stand for the narrator has been suggested in the blocking diagram.

Focus should be an important part of the rehearsal process because, with the exception of a simple gesture or two, focus is the only direct action employed during a Readers Theater presentation. Basically, there are two kinds of focus that students can use: on-stage and off-stage focus. In on-stage focus, the characters look at each other when they speak. In off-stage focus, the characters direct their gaze to a spot on the wall behind the audience. In both types of focus, it is important that students be familiar enough with their lines so their eyes and heads are up rather than buried in a script.

5. PROPS AND COSTUMES

While elaborate costumes and props are not necessary for Readers Theater, even the simplest costumes, such as hats, scarves, or animal ears can help students assume their character. Costume suggestions can be found on the resource pages following several of the plays.

Making background murals or very simple props can help students deepen their understanding of a play. Involvement in discussions about what to emphasize in a drawing or in the scenery or about which free-standing props would suggest the setting (a tree) or occasion (a birthday cake) allows a further involvement and commitment on the part of participants. Either the performers or another group of students acting as stage crew can create the props and costumes.

Hand-held props are not suggested for Readers Theater because the hands should be free to hold the script. For a similar reason, masks should be avoided since they may impair the performers' ability to see the script or project the lines.

6. THE STAGE

Readers Theater does not require a proscenium stage with a curtain, just an open area with enough space for the cast and an audience. A corner of the classroom will work as well as the school auditorium. For plays that lend themselves to puppet dramatizations, simple directions for both the puppets and the stage are included in the resource pages. In staging a Readers Theater puppet show, it generally works best to have one cast read the script while another cast operates the puppets.

7. SHARING THE PERFORMANCE

Readers Theater presentations are meant to be shared, but the audience can range from one person to a packed auditorium. Before the performance begins, you or a student may wish to briefly introduce the conventions of Readers Theater so that the audience understands its role in interpreting dialog to visualize the characters and the action. Students may enjoy making programs, tickets, and posters for the production, especially if another class or parents are invited to attend. On the day of the performance, have the characters enter, take their places, and read!

8. PERFORMANCE FOLLOW-UP

After the performance, suggest that the cast gather to discuss their reading of the play. To guide their discussion, they may use the Self-Evaluation Form. By assessing their own performances as readers, as listeners, and as group members, students can set personal goals to work toward during their next oral-reading experience.

WRITE YOUR OWN READERS THEATER PLAY

After participating in a Readers Theater performance, some students will be eager to write their own plays. The Write Your Own Readers Theater Play resource pages have been designed to guide students through this process.

The teacher resource page presents an overview of the steps and highlights some of the major differences between narrative and drama. Once students understand those differences, they can work with partners or in small groups to complete the student resource pages.

- *Getting Started* guides students in answering the question, "How do I get an idea for a play?"

- *The Plot* defines plot structure and gives a model of a plot outline. Building on the previous worksheet, students develop their own plot outline based on one of the play ideas previously identified.

- *Creating Characters* discusses methods for developing realistic characters and models how to write character sketches.

- *A Readers Theater Script* illustrates the proper format for a script. Additionally, it focuses attention on key questions involving the role of the narrator and the importance of creating dialog consistent with a character sketch.

- *Ready, Set, Write!* is a writing-process checklist to help students keep track of the steps involved in prewriting, drafting, revising, proofreading, and publishing a Readers Theater play.

THE CHORAL READING EXPERIENCE

Choral reading, like Readers Theater, is an activity that promotes fluency through cooperative effort. In choral reading, speaking and listening are complementary processes—groups of students practice reading poetry for another group to listen to. During practice sessions, the group will need a director, usually the teacher in the early sessions. As students become more experienced with this technique, they can explore taking on the responsibilities of the director.

TYPES OF CHORAL READING

Choral reading promotes fluency by giving support to readers, by providing an opportunity for repeated reading with special attention to rhythm and meter, and by encouraging active listening. The four major types of choral reading are

- refrain
- line-by-line
- antiphonal
- unison

In a poem with a refrain, the verse can be read by a solo voice, by a group (the most common choice), or in combination. In line-by-line choral reading, each line or group of lines is read by a different group or solo voice. Antiphonal choral readings are somewhat like call and response, with one group answering another. Unison readings—perhaps the most difficult of all—are read by the entire group.

The choral readings for each unit have suggestions for groups and solo voices. Your students should first try reading the poems as arranged. After they are familiar with a particular reading, encourage them to try other arrangements or other poems.

SIZE AND ORGANIZATION OF THE CHORAL READING GROUP

You and your students may want to experiment with the size of the choral reading group, which will vary depending upon the number of students who want to participate and the particular piece being performed. Most often, members of a group should stand together. Sometimes, readers with solo parts are also part of a group. In these cases, the soloists should stand in the front row of the group. Resource pages suggest arrangements of speakers for choral reading.

THE RESOURCE PAGES

This book includes both teacher and student resource pages. Resource pages follow the plays and always include a blocking diagram for the play. Other resource pages may include costume suggestions and patterns, a pronunciation guide, prop suggestions, puppets, puppet-show directions, sound effects, and audiotaping instructions for radio plays. Resource pages for the choral readings include blocking diagrams. The final resource page is a self-evaluation form for readers and listeners.

BIBLIOGRAPHY

ARTICLES ON READING FLUENCY

ALLINGTON, R.L. 1983. Fluency: The neglected reading goal. *The Reading Teacher* 36:556-61.
BEAVER, J.M. 1982. Say it! Over and over. *Language Arts* 59:143-48.
DOWHOWER, S.L. 1987. Effects of repeated reading on second-grade transitional readers' fluency and comprehension. *Reading Research Quarterly* 22:389-406.
_____. 1989. Repeated reading: Research into practice. *The Reading Teacher* 42:502-7.
KOSKINEN, P.S., and I.H. BLUM. 1986. Paired repeated reading: A classroom strategy for developing fluent reading. *The Reading Teacher* 40:70-75.
MICCINATI, J.L. 1985. Using prosodic cues to teach oral reading fluency. *The Reading Teacher* 39:206-12.
RASINSKI, T. 1989. Fluency for everyone: Incorporating fluency instruction in the classroom. *The Reading Teacher* 42:690-93.

_____, and J.B. ZUTELL. 1990. Making a place for fluency instruction in the regular reading curriculum. *Reading Research and Instruction* 29:85-91.
SAMUELS, S.J. 1988. Decoding and automaticity: Helping poor readers become automatic at word recognition. *The Reading Teacher* 41:756-60.

ARTICLES ON READERS THEATER AND DRAMATIC READING

ANDERSEN, D.R. 1987. Around the world in eighty days. *Instructor* 97(October): 62-63.
_____. 1989. The shy exclamation point. *Instructor* 98(February): 54.
_____. 1988. The sound of great voices. *Instructor* 97(January): 46-47.
BENNETT, S., and K. BEATTY. 1988. Grades 1 and 2 love readers theatre. *The Reading Teacher* 41:485.
BIDWELL, S.M. 1990. Using drama to increase motivation, comprehension and fluency. *Journal of Reading* 34:38-41.
BURNS, G., and E. KIZER. 1987. Audio-visual effects in readers' theatre: A case study. *International Journal of Instructional Media* 14(3): 223-37.
DICKINSON, E. 1987. Readers Theatre: A creative method to increase reading fluency and comprehension skills. *The New England Reading Association Journal* 23(22): 7-11.
EPPERHEIMER, D. 1991. Readers' Theatre and technology: A perfect mix. *The California Reader* 24(Spring): 14-15.
FREEDMAN, M. 1990. Readers Theatre: An exciting way to motivate reluctant readers. *The New England Reading Association Journal* 26(Autumn): 9-12.
HOWARD, W.L., and others. 1989. Using choral responding to increase active student response. *Teaching Exceptional Children*. 21(Spring): 72-75.
NAVASCUES, M. 1988. Oral and dramatic interpretation of literature in the Spanish class. *Hispania* 71(March): 186-89.
STEWIG, J.W. 1990. Children's books for readers' theatre. *Perspectives* Spring:vii-x.

BOOKS ON READERS THEATER

BAUER, CAROLINE FELLER. *Celebrations: Read-Aloud Holiday and Theme Book Programs*. New York: H.W. Wilson, 1985.
_____. *Presenting Reader's Theatre: Plays and Poems to Read Aloud*. New York: H.W. Wilson, 1987.
COGER, LESLIE IRENE, and MELVIN R. WHITE. *Readers Theatre Handbook: A Dramatic Approach to Literature*. 3d ed. Glenview, Ill.: Scott, Foresman, 1982.

FORKERT, OTTO MAURICE. *Children's Theatre that Captures Its Audience*. Chicago: Coach House Press, 1962.

LAUGHLIN, MILDRED KNIGHT, and KATHY HOWARD LATROBE. *Readers Theatre for Children*. Englewood, Colo.: Teacher Ideas Press, 1990.

SIERRA, JUDY, and ROBERT KAMINSKI. *Twice Upon a Time: Stories to Tell, Retell, Act Out, and Write About*. New York: H.W. Wilson, 1989.

SLOYER, SHIRLEE. *Readers Theatre: Story Dramatization in the Classroom*. Urbana, Ill.: National Council of Teachers of English, 1982.

_____ . "Readers Theatre: A Reading Motivator." In *Selected Articles on the Teaching of Reading*. New York: Barnell Loft, 1977.

BOOKS ON CHORAL READING

AGGERTT, OTIS J., and ELBERT R. BOWEN. *Communicative Reading*. New York: Macmillan, 1972.

GOTTLIEB, MARVIN R. *Oral Interpretation*. New York: McGraw-Hill, 1980.

JOHNSON, ALBERT, and BERTHA JOHNSON. *Oral Reading: Creative and Interpretive*. South Brunswick: A. S. Barnes, 1971.

BOOKS ON COSTUMES, MAKE-UP, AND PROPS

ARNOLD, A. *Arts and Crafts for Children and Young People*. London: Macmillan, 1976.

BARWELL, EVE. *Disguises You Can Make*. New York: Lothrop, Lee & Shepard, 1977.

CHERNOFF, GOLDIE TAUB. *Easy Costumes You Don't Have to Sew*. New York: Four Winds Press, 1975.

HALEY, GAIL E. *Costumes for Plays and Playing*. New York: Metheun, 1982.

Make and Play Paperback Set (includes costumes, face painting, hats, masks, and T-shirt painting). New York: Franklin Watts, 1990.

McCASLIN, NELLIE. *Shows on a Shoestring: An Easy Guide to Amateur Productions*. New York: David McKay, 1979.

MORIN, ALICE. *Newspaper Theatre: Creative Play Production for Low Budgets and No Budgets*. Belmont, Calif.: Fearon Teacher Aids, 1989.

PARISH, PEGGY. *Costumes to Make*. New York: Macmillan, 1970.

PITCHER, CAROLINE, consultant. *Masks and Puppets*. New York: Franklin Watts, 1984.

PURDY, SUSAN. *Costumes for You to Make*. Philadelphia: J.B. Lippincott, 1971.

SOURCES FOR ADAPTATIONS

The Adventures of Tom Sawyer, by Mark Twain. New York: Signet Classic, 1980.

The Secret Garden, by Frances Hodgson Burnett. New York: Dell, 1987.

The Pirates' Funeral

By JOE CLARO

based on an incident in THE ADVENTURES OF TOM SAWYER by Mark Twain

CAST

Mark Twain
Tom Sawyer
Becky Thatcher
Joe Harper
Huckleberry Finn

Aunt Polly
Sid Sawyer
Mrs. Harper
Reverend Sprague

MARK TWAIN: My name is Samuel Clemens, but you probably know me by my pen name, Mark Twain. I've been a Mississippi riverboat pilot, a printer, a journalist, and a travel writer—so, as you can see, I've gotten around quite a bit. But most of the events I'm going to tell you about happened either to me or to friends of mine right in my own hometown of Hannibal, Missouri, where I grew up in the 1840s. It wouldn't surprise me one bit, however, if some of the people you're about to meet act just like people you know. Take Tom Sawyer, for instance. Tom lived with his Aunt Polly in St. Petersburg, Missouri. Now Aunt Polly loved Tom dearly, though bringing him up correctly was sometimes a trial, for Tom was full of fun and mischief. He was quick-witted, too, make no mistake about that. On the day I'm thinking of, Tom was at school putting all his wits to the task at hand. Oh no, it wasn't reading or writing he was working so hard at. He was trying to win the admiration of a certain new girl at school—Becky Thatcher—without seeming to be doing so, of course.

TOM: Say, Jeff, want me to learn you how to walk the fence? Come on now, don't be afeard. I can even walk it blindfolded. You stand right here and I'll show you. Now just you watch!

MARK TWAIN: Jeff was mesmerized. But from Becky, there was not so much as a glance. Why if truth be told, Tom had done everything he could think of to make Becky notice him. He'd tried yelling, laughing, throwing handsprings, standing on his head, jumping over the schoolyard fence at risk of life and limb—in short, he'd done just about all the heroic things he could conceive of. But despite his efforts, Becky seemed to be unconscious of it all. Finally, in desperation, he fell tumbling and sprawling under her nose.

TOM: Say, Becky! Becky Thatcher! Just watch me walk on my hands! See?

BECKY: Humph! Some people around here think they're mighty smart—always showing off. Go away and leave me alone, Tom Sawyer! Your childish behavior is just too tiresome.

MARK TWAIN: Poor Tom. His cheeks burned. His eyes filled with tears. Embarrassed by Becky Thatcher in front of all his classmates, he felt forsaken and friendless. As he wandered out of the schoolyard and down Meadow Lane, he could hear the school bell tinkling faintly in the background—it was too late now. He had been driven out into the cold world and had to submit to what cruel fate had in store for him.

TOM: I haven't a friend in the world. Nobody loves me. I reckon I'll just have to leave this place forever. I'll just pick up and go. Then I'll . . . I'll lead a life of crime, that's what I'll do! There's no other choice for a poor, friendless boy. Someday, they'll all be sorry for the way they treated me.

MARK TWAIN: Just at this moment, Tom met his sworn comrade, Joe Harper. Joe was as damp-eyed as Tom and also seemed to have some sad and dismal purpose in his heart.

JOE: Tom! Why aren't you in school? And what are you crying about?

TOM: I'm crying because I've tried to do right and get along, but they won't let me. I've decided to run away from home and never return. I hope at least that you won't forget me, Joe. By the way, why aren't *you* in school? And what are *you* crying about?

JOE: I was looking for you. I wanted to tell you that I'm leaving this place. I just got a whipping for drinking some cream. And I never even saw the stuff! It's plain as day that my ma is tired of me and wants me to go. I guess she'd be better off if I just disappeared. I just hope she'll be happy without me, and never regret forcing her poor boy to suffer and die out here in the unfeeling world.

TOM: Yes, they'll surely miss us, all right. But leaving is the only thing for us to do. Now I've been thinking, and I've got an idea about what we should do once we're free of this place.

JOE: I reckon you do, Tom. You always have ideas. But this time, I've got an idea of my own.

TOM: You do?

JOE: Yes! I'm going to become a hermit.

TOM: A hermit! That's no job for you!

JOE: All the same, it's what I've decided.

TOM: But what will you do?

JOE: I'll go live in a cave. I'll eat crusts of bread that I find on the road at night. Eventually, I'll die of cold and starvation.

TOM: Tarnation, that's a dumb idea if I ever heard one! Come along with me, Joe. I'm going to be a pirate!

JOE: A pirate?

TOM: Why, we'll go plowing over the seas in our black-hulled racer, the *Spirit of the Storm*, with a skull and crossbones flying from the top mast. We'll steal money and jewels from passing ships! And we'll ransom beautiful women, and eat like kings, and wear black velvet suits with crimson sashes and hats with waving plumes!

JOE: That does sound better than starving to death in a cold cave!

MARK TWAIN: Just then, Huckleberry Finn, known as Huck to his friends, appeared around the bend of Meadow Lane. Now Huck was a motherless boy whose father let him run wild. As a consequence, Huck was idle and lawless and vulgar and bad. This, of course, meant that he was envied by all the respectable boys who were under strict orders from their mothers not to play with him because he was such a "bad influence."

JOE: Look, here comes Huck Finn. Should we tell him our plans, Tom?

TOM: Sure, why not? Hello, Huckleberry!

HUCK: Hello, yourself, and see how you like it.

TOM: Huck, Joe and I have just decided to run away and become pirates.

HUCK: Well, that sounds like a good plan.

TOM: Huck, I have an idea. Why don't you come along with Joe and me? Why, you could be Huck Finn, the Red-Handed, and Joe could be Joe Harper, the Terror of the Seas.

JOE: And who will you be, Tom?

TOM: Why, I'll be Tom Sawyer, the Black Avenger of the Spanish Main!

Macmillan/McGraw-Hill

HUCK: When do we leave?

TOM: Right now! No, wait . . . pirates don't sneak off during the day. We'll meet at midnight, and then we'll take off.

JOE: Take off for where?

TOM: Well, let's see now. We want a place we can get to without too much trouble—just as a starting-off point, you understand.

HUCK: And it has to be a place where nobody can bother us.

TOM: I know! We'll head for Jackson's Island. It's only three miles downriver. We can swipe a raft and get there in no time.

JOE: Jackson's Island it is! We'll be the bulliest pirates that ever were!

TOM: We'll meet at the big tree on the riverbank, two miles north of town, at midnight, sharp. Bring your fishing lines and hooks and any provisions you can purloin in a dark and mysterious way.

MARK TWAIN: So Jackson's Island was their goal. All that day, Tom and Joe dropped vague hints to certain select friends that pretty soon the town would hear something, but they wouldn't tell what it was. At midnight, Tom showed up at the meeting place carrying a boiled ham. He let out a low whistle. He was answered by two other whistles coming from the dark.

JOE: Who goes there?

TOM: Tom Sawyer, the Black Avenger of the Spanish Main. Name your names.

HUCK: Huck Finn, the Red-Handed.

JOE: Joe Harper, the Terror of the Seas.

TOM: 'Tis well. Give the countersign.

HUCK/JOE: BLOOD!

TOM: Good. I brought a boiled ham. What have you got, Terror of the Seas?

JOE: A side of bacon and some corn pone.

TOM: And you, Red-Handed?

HUCK: I couldn't get any food. But I did bring a skillet.

TOM: Good. Now, let's get the raft.

MARK TWAIN: The raft was tied up not far from where the boys met. They knew all the raftsmen were in the village for the night. Still, they acted as though they might be discovered at any moment.

JOE: Shhh! Move quietly.

TOM: If the foe awakens, let him have it to the hilt!

HUCK: Right. Dead men tell no tales.

TOM: Joe, you take the forward oar. Huck, you're on the after oar.

Macmillan/McGraw-Hill

MARK TWAIN: The three would-be pirates shoved off quietly, with Tom standing in the middle of the raft giving orders. Soon they were drifting past the village they had agreed to leave forever. All three were silent, but their private thoughts were very similar.

TOM: My last look at St. Petersburg. If only Becky could see me now, facing peril and death on the wild sea with a grim smile on my lips. Then she'd be sorry for ignoring me.

JOE: I'll never come back here again. Won't my mother be broken-hearted to know that she drove her boy to a life of crime.

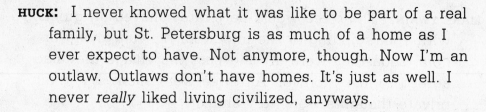

HUCK: I never knowed what it was like to be part of a real family, but St. Petersburg is as much of a home as I ever expect to have. Not anymore, though. Now I'm an outlaw. Outlaws don't have homes. It's just as well. I never *really* liked living civilized, anyways.

MARK TWAIN: It took the boys nearly two hours to reach the island. They waded ashore with their freight, including an old sail that they spread over some bushes for a tent to shelter their provisions. In the meantime, the empty raft began to drift downstream with the current.

HUCK: Grab holda that raft!

JOE: We'd best tie it to a rock.

TOM: Naw, let it go. We won't be needing the raft. This here's our new home.

MARK TWAIN: They all watched the raft slowly drift out of sight. It was as though they had broken the last link between themselves and civilization. As far as the boys were concerned, they were in heaven. They built a roaring fire and used the skillet to cook some bacon and corn pone. When they finished eating, they stretched out on the grass.

JOE: Ain't this terrific?

TOM: It's *great!* What would the other boys say if they could see us now?

JOE: What would they *say?* Well, they'd just die to be here. Don't you think so, Hucky?

HUCK: I reckon so. Anyways, *I'm* suited. I don't want nothing better'n this. I don't ever get as much to eat as we just had. And here they can't come bullying and picking at a feller.

TOM: It's just the life for me. You don't have to get up mornings, and you don't have to go to school, and wash, and all that blame foolishness. See, Joe, I was right. A pirate doesn't have to do *anything* when he's ashore. But a hermit—*he* has to be praying considerable. And then he doesn't have any fun anyway, all by himself that way.

Macmillan/McGraw-Hill

JOE: Yes, that's so. But I hadn't thought much about it, you know. I'd a good deal rather be a pirate, now that I've tried it.

TOM: Sure you would. People don't care much for hermits these days, like they used to in olden times, but a pirate's always respected. Besides, a hermit's got to sleep on the hardest place he can find and put sackcloth and ashes on his head, and stand out in the rain, and . . .

HUCK: What does he put sackcloth and ashes on his head for?

TOM: I dunno. But they've *got* to do it. That's what hermits always do. You'd have to do that if you was a hermit.

HUCK: Derned if I would.

TOM: Why, Huck, you'd *have* to. How would you get around it?

HUCK: Why, I just wouldn't stand it. I'd run away.

TOM: Run away! Well, you *would* be a nice old slouch of a hermit. You'd be a disgrace.

HUCK: What does *pirates* have to do, anyway?

TOM: Oh, they just have a bully time! They capture ships and burn 'em. They get the treasure off the ships and bury it in some awful place on their island, where there's ghosts and things to watch it. And they round up everybody in the ships and make 'em walk the plank.

JOE: Not the women, Tom. Why, pirates are noble! They don't harm the women.

TOM: That's right, they don't hurt the women. They're too noble for that. And the women are always beautiful, too.

JOE: And they wear the bulliest clothes! All gold and silver and covered with diamonds.

HUCK: Who?

JOE: Why, the pirates, of course.

HUCK: Look at what I have on. I reckon I ain't dressed fitten for a pirate. But I ain't got no other clothes but these.

TOM: Don't worry, Huck. We'll all have the finest clothes you can imagine.

HUCK: When?

TOM: Just as soon as we get started pirating.

MARK TWAIN: Gradually, the talk died down and drowsiness began to overtake them. The Red-Handed soon fell asleep. But the Terror of the Seas and the Black Avenger of the Spanish Main had more difficulty dropping off. Neither of them spoke. But their private thoughts showed that they felt a vague fear that they had done wrong to run away, and each had some doubts about pirating.

JOE: This surely is a swell place, but I can't help wondering if we're doing the wrong thing. I stole that side of bacon from Ma's kitchen. I wonder if she knows I'm the one who took it . . . I wonder what she's doing right now . . . I wonder if pirates ever think of the people they left behind. Oh, well, I guess I'd better stop wondering and try to get to sleep.

TOM: Well, we did it. We're pirates. But I wish I hadn't hooked that boiled ham from Aunt Polly. No, I didn't hook the ham. *Hooking* is what I do when I grab a piece of pie. This was *stealing*. And stealing's wrong. Well, it had to be done. From now on, though, we'll be pirates who don't steal anything.

MARK TWAIN: The next morning, the boys caught four fish with their hooks and lines. They feasted on fish and bacon. After breakfast, they chased one another around the island, then they went for a swim in the river. They played a game of marbles, took another swim, and then gradually wandered apart and stretched out on the sand to rest. All three fell to gazing longingly across the wide Mississippi River to where the village of St. Petersburg lay drowsing in the sun. Tom found himself writing "Becky" in the sand with his toe. Joe was getting more homesick by the minute. Even Huck was in a gloomy mood. Suddenly, they were shaken from their thoughts by a deep, booming sound that floated over the water from some distance away.

JOE: What was that?

TOM: I wonder!

HUCK: 'Taint thunder, becuz thunder . . .

JOE: Hark! Listen—don't talk!

TOM: I'll climb this tree and see if I spot anything.

HUCK: Sounded mighty like a cannon to me.

JOE: A cannon?

TOM: I can see it! You know, the little steam ferryboat? It's about a mile below the village, and her deck is crowded with people. And there's a great many skiffs following the ferry. Oh—there's a puff of smoke—they've just fired a cannon over the water!

HUCK: Why would they be doing that?

TOM: I know now! Somebody's drownded!

HUCK: That's it! Remember, they done that last summer when Bill Turner got drownded. They shoot a cannon over the water, and that makes the body float to the top.

JOE: By jings, I wish I was over there now.

HUCK: Me, too. I'd give heaps to know who it is.

TOM: Help me down from here, boys. I know who's drownded.

JOE/HUCK: Who?

TOM: Why, it's us, of course!

JOE: Us? You're right! They think we drowned!

HUCK: Ha, ha! They're looking for us!

TOM: They think we're dead!

JOE: Oh, this is too good! They miss us! The whole town is out looking for our dead bodies!

TOM: They must be heartbroken! Imagine how bad they must feel about the way they treated us!

HUCK: Tarnation, everybody's probably talking 'bout us. Oh, them other boys must surely be dying of envy!

MARK TWAIN: The boys felt like heroes. They returned to their pirate camp, slapping one another on the back and exchanging congratulations. They caught some fish, cooked it in the skillet, and never stopped talking about the news. But as darkness fell, the talk quieted and turned to other matters.

JOE: What do you two think about some day, maybe, going back to civilization?

TOM: What? Nothing could ever get me to go back there! We're pirates now!

JOE: Well, I didn't mean right away. I meant some day.

TOM: Absolutely not! We'll never go back.

HUCK: Never? Well, I don't know about that. I might go back when I got all them fancy clothes pirates wear.

TOM: Not me! I ain't never going back there!

MARK TWAIN: But Tom wasn't as committed as he made out to be. When Huck and Joe were sound asleep, he tiptoed away from the camp. He found a piece of white sycamore bark, and using a piece of red chalk that he had in his pocket, he wrote a note on it to his Aunt Polly. This was to let her know that he and his friends were safe. On another piece of bark, he wrote a note to Joe and Huck willing them all his earthly possessions if he wasn't back by breakfast. Then he ran to the beach,

Macmillan/McGraw-Hill

waded out as far as he could, and began swimming. Some time later, he reached the shore, three miles below the village.

TOM: Hark! There's the village clock striking ten. I'll rest a few minutes and then go to Aunt Polly's.

MARK TWAIN: Tom slipped through the deserted village streets and surreptitiously made his way to his aunt's house. He was surprised to see lights burning so late at night. He crept to the house and peeked in the window. There sat Aunt Polly, Tom's brother Sid, Joe Harper's mother, and the Reverend Mr. Sprague. Quiet as a cat, Tom slipped unnoticed into the house. Then he crawled under Aunt Polly's bed and listened.

AUNT POLLY: As I was saying, Tom warn't *bad*, so to say, only mischeevous. He warn't any more responsible than a colt. He never meant any harm, and he was the best-hearted boy that ever was. Ohhh, I miss him so!

SID: Don't cry, Aunt Polly.

MRS. HARPER: It was the same with my Joe. Always full of the dickens and up to every kind of mischief, but he was just as unselfish and kind as he could be. And to think I went and whipped him for taking that cream, never once recollecting that I throwed it out myself because it was sour. And I'll never see him again in this world—never, never, never! The poor abused boy!

SID: Well, I hope Tom's better off where he is. But if he'd been better in some ways . . .

AUNT POLLY: Sid! Not a word against my Tom, now that he's gone! God'll take care of him—don't you worry about that! Oh, Mrs. Harper, I don't know how to give him up! He was such a comfort to me, although he tormented my old heart right out of me, almost.

REV. SPRAGUE: The Lord giveth, and the Lord hath taken away.

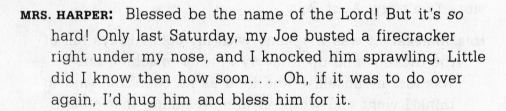

MRS. HARPER: Blessed be the name of the Lord! But it's *so* hard! Only last Saturday, my Joe busted a firecracker right under my nose, and I knocked him sprawling. Little did I know then how soon. . . . Oh, if it was to do over again, I'd hug him and bless him for it.

AUNT POLLY: Yes, yes, yes, I know just how you feel, Mrs. Harper. I know just *exactly* how you feel. No longer ago than yesterday noon, my Tom took and filled the cat full of patented painkiller medicine. I did think the creature would tear the house down. And, God forgive me, I cracked Tom's head with my thimble. Poor boy, poor, dead boy. But he's out of all his troubles now. And the last words I ever heard him say was to reproach me for being so strict with him.

MARK TWAIN: This memory was too much for Aunt Polly. She burst into tears, and Mrs. Harper did the same. Under the bed, Tom was having trouble holding back his own tears. He had to restrain himself from rushing out and overwhelming his Aunt Polly with hugs and kisses.

REV. SPRAGUE: Do not be ashamed of your tears, ladies. It's entirely appropriate to shed tears for the dear departed.

MRS. HARPER: Reverend Sprague, tell us again about the search party.

REV. SPRAGUE: Well, ladies, as you know, at first we thought the boys had merely run off. After all, they had told some of their friends that something surprising would happen soon.

SID: That's Tom, all right. Always a showoff!

REV. SPRAGUE: When we realized the raft was missing, we figured the boys had taken it, and we expected them to turn up just down the river a bit. Then, when we found the raft lodged against the shore some five or six miles downriver from the village, and the boys didn't come home for supper, hope for their safety began to diminish.

SID: Is everybody sure they've drowned?

REV. SPRAGUE: The men are going to continue searching until early Sunday. If the boys haven't been found by then, we'll have to give up, and I'll preach their funerals that morning.

MARK TWAIN: Tom shuddered to hear of plans for his own funeral. He remained motionless under the bed until everyone was gone and Aunt Polly was asleep. He waited until he heard her gentle snoring. Then he stole out from under the bed and stood looking down at his aunt in the dark. His heart was full of pity for her. He took the piece of sycamore bark out of his pocket and placed it by the candle. Suddenly, something occurred to him, and he stood in thought for several seconds. His face lighted with a happy solution, and he put the bark hastily back into his pocket. Then he leaned over, kissed Aunt Polly on the forehead, and made his stealthy exit, latching the door behind him. By dawn, Tom was back at the island. He hid behind a tree and listened as Huck and Joe talked about him.

JOE: No, Tom's true-blue, Huck. He's bound to come back. He won't desert. He knows that would be a disgrace to a pirate, and Tom's too proud for that sort of thing. He's up to something or other. I just wonder what.

HUCK: Well, the things he left behind is ours, ain't they, Joe?

JOE: Pretty near, but not yet, Huck. The note says the things are ours if he ain't back here by breakfast.

MARK TWAIN: With fine dramatic effect, Tom suddenly appeared from behind a tree.

Macmillan/McGraw-Hill

TOM: Which he is!

JOE: Tom! See, Huck? Didn't I tell you he'd be back?

HUCK: Tom, where you been?

TOM: I went back home.

JOE: Back home? And gave away our hiding place?

TOM: Course not! I sneaked in and listened to your mother and my aunt talking about how sad they are now that we're dead.

HUCK: And nobody saw you?

TOM: Nope. I heard the Reverend Sprague tell them how they knew we were dead because they found the raft we swiped. You should have heard the wailing in that room!

JOE: So they've given up looking for us! Hooray!

TOM: Not yet. They'll look until sunrise Sunday morning. Then we'll be officially dead. And you'll never guess what else.

HUCK: What? Tell us! Come on, tell us!

TOM: On Sunday morning, the Reverend Sprague will preach our funerals!

MARK TWAIN: This was better news than Huck and Joe could have imagined. The boys celebrated like heroes. They had a big breakfast and went for a refreshing swim. All the time, they congratulated one another on the success of their plan. Later, they lay stretched out in the woods.

TOM: I bet there's been pirates on this island before, boys. We'll explore the island again. They've hid treasures here somewhere. How'd you like to come upon a rotten chest full of gold and silver?

JOE: Maybe. I don't know. I've been thinking, Tom. Let's give it up. I want to go home. It's so lonesome.

TOM: Oh, no, Joe. You'll feel better by and by. Just think of all the fishing that's here.

JOE: I don't care for fishing. I want to go home.

TOM: But, Joe, there ain't such another swimming place anywhere.

JOE: Swimming's no good. I don't seem to care for it nearly as much as when there's someone like Ma to say I can't go in. I want to go home.

TOM: Oh, shucks! Baby! You want to see your mother, I reckon.

JOE: Yes, I *do* want to see my mother. And you would too, if you had one. I ain't any more baby than you are, so there!

TOM: Well, we'll let the crybaby go home to his mother, won't we, Huck? Poor thing! Does it want to see its mother? And so it shall. *You* like it here, don't you, Huck? We'll stay, won't we?

Macmillan/McGraw-Hill

HUCK: Well, y-e-s. . . .

JOE: I'll never speak to you as long as I live, Tom Sawyer! There now! I'm gonna get dressed.

TOM: Who cares! Nobody wants you to stay anyway. Go 'long home and get laughed at. Oh, you're a nice pirate, Joe Harper! Huck and me ain't crybabies. We'll stay, won't we, Huck? Let him go if he wants to. I reckon we can get along without him, all right.

HUCK: I want to go, too, Tom. It was beginning to get so lonesome. And now, with Joe gone, it'll be even worse. Let's all go.

TOM: I won't! You can both go, if you want to! I mean to stay.

HUCK: Tom, I wisht you'd come, too. Now, you think it over. We'll wait for you when we get to shore.

TOM: Well, you'll wait a blame long time, that's all!

MARK TWAIN: Tom watched Huck and Joe gather their things. And as they began to wade into the river, it suddenly dawned on Tom that Jackson's Island would be a lonely place without his two companions.

TOM: Wait! Wait! I want to tell you something!

JOE: What do you want to tell us, Tom?

TOM: I have a secret plan. I been thinking about it all day. When you hear it, you're not going to want to go anywhere.

HUCK: A secret plan? Well, tell us what it is.

MARK TWAIN: When Tom explained his secret, Huck and Joe cheered and laughed and danced around him.

HUCK: It's a great plan, Tom! I'll stay with you!

JOE: I can't wait! I'm staying, too!

MARK TWAIN: They made their plans, and the mutiny was laid to rest. Then after a hearty supper and some jolly conversation around the fire, the pirates finally fell asleep. Around midnight, the three awoke to a flashing light in the sky. A deep peal of thunder went rolling and tumbling down the heavens, and big raindrops fell pattering on the leaves.

TOM: Quick, boys! Go for the tent!

MARK TWAIN: They stumbled over roots and vines in the dark. One blinding flash after another came, and peal on peal of deafening thunder. A drenching rain poured down, and the rising hurricane drove it in sheets along the ground. One by one, the boys straggled in and took shelter under the makeshift tent they had rigged from the old piece of sail. They were cold, scared, and soaked to the skin. Next morning, they felt rusty and stiff-jointed.

JOE: Tom, this pirating business is beginning to look less and less cheerful every day.

MARK TWAIN: Saturday came and went, and the searchers found no sign of the missing boys. By Sunday morning, all of St. Petersburg was preparing for the solemn funeral. After Sunday school was over, Becky Thatcher stood outside the church talking to Tom's younger brother, Sid.

BECKY: Oh, if only I hadn't been so cruel to him. I wish I had something to remember him by.

SID: Come by the house after the funeral. You can take everything he ever owned—that should be enough to remember him by.

BECKY: Oh, Sid, I know you don't mean that! Just look around. Why, the whole village has turned out for the funeral.

SID: Yes, and they're all talking about what wonderful fellows the three of them were. Everybody's arguing about who saw the three of them last in life and saying that Tom did thus and so, or Joe said this or that!

BECKY: Why, you know that everyone's just looking for some way to remember the boys.

SID: Well, the last time I saw Tom, he was being cuffed by Aunt Polly for something or other. I guess I'll just have to remember him that way forever.

BECKY: Sid Sawyer! You'd better mind your tongue when you're talking about your dead brother.

MARK TWAIN: Inside the church, the Reverend Mr. Sprague waited until everyone was seated. Then he solemnly began the funeral service.

REV. SPRAGUE: We are gathered on this solemn occasion in memory of three of our brethren, who were cut down in the prime of their lives.

AUNT POLLY: Oh, it's so sad!

SID: There, there, Aunt Polly. Don't cry so.

REV. SPRAGUE: We are here to pay our last respects to Thomas Sawyer, Joseph Harper, and Huckleberry Finn.

MRS. HARPER: My boy! My poor, dead boy!

BECKY: Here, Mrs. Harper, take my handkerchief.

REV. SPRAGUE: These three lost lads were among the finest our community has ever known. St. Petersburg will be a poorer place without their sweet and noble presence.

MARK TWAIN: The minister's booming voice drowned out the sobs rising up from the entire congregation. Those members seated in the back of the church, however, were distracted by the creaking sound of the church door as it slowly opened.

REV. SPRAGUE: Let us remember them for all the fine things they did in life. Let us endeavor to be as good as each of these boys was.

MARK TWAIN: The rustling in the back of the church was turning into a small commotion.

REV. SPRAGUE: If only there were some way we could bring these boys back to life . . .

MARK TWAIN: The Reverend Mr. Sprague suddenly stopped speaking. His eyes were riveted on the doorway at the back of the church. Then all heads turned in that direction. Two people fainted. Many more gasped. Finally, the whole congregation rose and stared as Tom, Joe, and Huck came marching up the center aisle.

AUNT POLLY: Tom! It's my Tom! He's come back!

MARK TWAIN: There were shouts about miracles and more noise than anyone had ever heard in church before. The boys strutted proudly to the front of the congregation.

MRS. HARPER: Oh, Joe! Joe, let me hold you!

Macmillan/McGraw-Hill

MARK TWAIN: Aunt Polly smothered Tom in her arms. Mrs. Harper did the same to Joe. Finally, Tom pulled himself free.

TOM: Aunt Polly, it ain't fair. Somebody's got to be glad to see Huck.

AUNT POLLY: And so they shall! *I'm* glad to see him. Come here, Huck, and let me hug you!

MARK TWAIN: Well, Tom's secret plan to return home with his brother pirates and attend their own funerals was a rip-roaring success. But, as you can imagine, it didn't take long before someone asked where the boys had been all this time. Tom was only half through his explanation when Aunt Polly cuffed him on the ear for what he had done. Joe got a similar slap from his mother. Then both boys found themselves being hugged again. Then cuffed again. Then hugged, and cuffed, and hugged. Meanwhile, Huck slipped out of the church.

TOM: Hey, Huck, where you going?

HUCK: I don't care to be cuffed, but even less do I care to be hugged again!

MARK TWAIN: Finally, the whole congregation trooped out of the church and everyone went home.

AUNT POLLY: Tom, dear boy, I've a notion to skin you alive! I was that worried.

TOM: Auntie, I wish I hadn't done it—but I didn't think.

AUNT POLLY: Oh, child, you never think of anything but your own selfishness. You could come all the way over here from Jackson's Island in the night to laugh at our troubles, but you couldn't ever think to pity us and save us from sorrow.

TOM: Auntie, I know now it was mean, but I didn't mean to be mean. I didn't, honest. And besides, I didn't come over here to laugh at you that night.

AUNT POLLY: What did you come for, then?

TOM: It was to tell you not to be uneasy about us because we hadn't got drownded.

AUNT POLLY: I'd give the whole world to believe that, Tom. But it ain't reasonable because you didn't tell me, child.

TOM: Why, you see, when you got to talking about the funeral, I just got all full of the idea of our coming and surprising everyone, and I couldn't somehow bear to spoil it. So I just put the bark I had written on back in my pocket and kept mum.

AUNT POLLY: Bless your heart, child. Give me a kiss and then be off with you.

MARK TWAIN: Undoubtedly, there are those among you who think that Tom received his comeuppance, if not from Aunt Polly, then from his schoolmates. Yes, some might imagine that they would be indignant at the trick the boys had played. Or, perhaps, jealous of the adventure itself and the attention that was subsequently lavished on the boys. But the fact is that Tom had become a hero! Smaller boys than himself flocked at his heels. Boys of his own size pretended not to know he had been away at all, but they would have given anything to have his glittering notoriety. Tom basked in the admiration. It was food and drink to him. He decided that he could be independent of Becky Thatcher now. Glory was sufficient. Yes, indeed, he would live for glory!

BLOCKING DIAGRAM

Arrange eight chairs, as shown. The narrator, Mark Twain, can use a music stand to hold the script.

1. **MARK TWAIN**
2. **SID SAWYER**
3. **BECKY THATCHER**
4. **HUCKLEBERRY FINN**
5. **TOM SAWYER**
6. **JOE HARPER**
7. **AUNT POLLY**
8. **MRS. HARPER**
9. **REVEREND SPRAGUE**

Macmillan/McGraw-Hill

COSTUME SUGGESTIONS

Mark Twain This performer can wear a white shirt, light-colored pants, and a ribbon tie. A white jacket would be a nice addition.

Tom Sawyer and Joe Harper The boys can be dressed in overalls or cut-off jeans with suspenders. A straw hat would be a nice addition for Tom.

Huckleberry Finn Huck can wear frayed pants, a somewhat ragged shirt, and a bandana.

Aunt Polly This reader can be dressed in a long skirt and a blouse, with a shawl or apron added.

Becky Thatcher A frilly blouse and a full skirt with a sash would make an appropriate costume for Becky. She can also wear a large hair ribbon.

Mrs. Harper Joe's mother can wear a costume similar to Aunt Polly's with the addition of a hat.

Sid Sawyer Sid should be neatly dressed in knickers, a long-sleeved shirt, and a string tie. For knickers, tuck a pair of pants into knee socks and "blouse" each leg at the knee.

Reverend Sprague This performer can wear a white shirt, a dark jacket, and a black ribbon tie.

Making a Mural

A panoramic scene that includes St. Petersburg, the Mississippi River, and a view of Jackson's Island would make an effective backdrop for the Readers Theater performers.

Macmillan/McGraw-Hill

The Treasure Seekers

By
Robert Sim

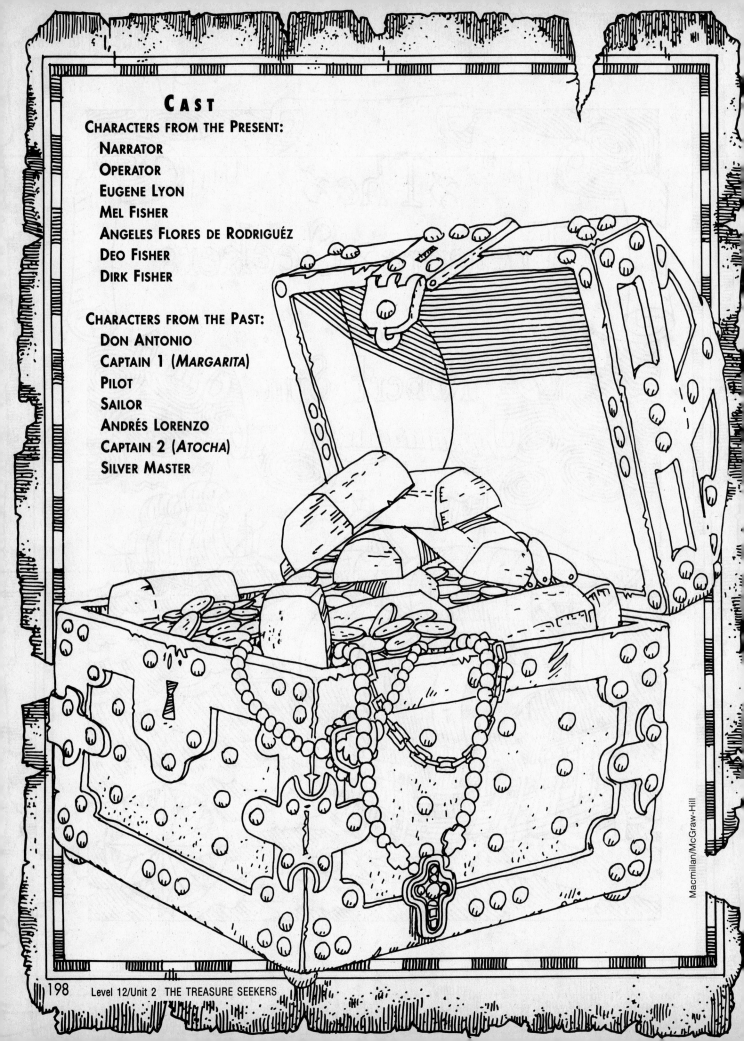

CAST

CHARACTERS FROM THE PRESENT:
NARRATOR
OPERATOR
EUGENE LYON
MEL FISHER
ANGELES FLORES DE RODRIGUÉZ
DEO FISHER
DIRK FISHER

CHARACTERS FROM THE PAST:
DON ANTONIO
CAPTAIN 1 (*MARGARITA*)
PILOT
SAILOR
ANDRÉS LORENZO
CAPTAIN 2 (*ATOCHA*)
SILVER MASTER

Macmillan/McGraw-Hill

NARRATOR: Our story begins in 1970 in Spain. Eugene Lyon was in the city of Seville doing research for a doctoral dissertation on Spanish history. Sitting at his desk, reading microfilm copies of old documents from the Archive of the Indies, he was interrupted by a telephone call that changed his life.

OPERATOR: This is the international operator. I have a call for a Mr. Eugene Lyon from a Mr. Mel Fisher in Key West, Florida, U.S.A.

EUGENE LYON: This is Eugene Lyon, operator.

OPERATOR: Hold please for your party, Mr. Lyon. Go ahead Mr. Fisher.

MEL FISHER: Gene? It's Mel Fisher.

EUGENE LYON: Mel! How's the treasure-hunting business?

MEL FISHER: To be honest, things aren't going all that well. That's why I'm calling you, Gene.

EUGENE LYON: I'm sorry to hear that. Is there anything I can do to help?

MEL FISHER: As a matter of fact, there may be. Do you remember that conversation we had about records of the Spanish galleon, the *Atocha?*

EUGENE LYON: Of course, I remember. The full name of the ship was the *Nuestra Señora de Atocha.* She was a 600-ton galleon, named for a famous shrine in Madrid. She sank, along with six other ships, during a violent hurricane that swept the Florida coast in September 1622. As I recall, all but five of the *Atocha's* 260 passengers were lost.

MEL FISHER: Gene, your memory never ceases to amaze me. The only thing you neglected to mention was the treasure that the *Atocha* carried. Along with tobacco, copper, and indigo, the ship was loaded with 901 silver bars, 161 gold bars or disks, and about 255,000 silver coins!

EUGENE LYON: I have a suspicion that's what *you're* interested in. Right?

MEL FISHER: Exactly right. I'm calling to ask you to spend some more time looking through the old records and ship manifests at the Archive of the Indies there in Seville. Somewhere there has to be a clue to the whereabouts of that galleon.

EUGENE LYON: I don't know, Mel. You have to understand that the records from the period are incomplete at best. And as I remember, to make things even worse, many of the documents are riddled with wormholes!

MEL FISHER: Gene, those old manifests and documents contain everything we know about the *Atocha*. There must be something in there—some small, unnoticed detail that will give us a clue as to where the ship went down.

EUGENE LYON: Well, I just don't want you to get your hopes up, Mel. The best information we have about the fleet location is secondhand, and it was written four years after the ships sank.

MEL FISHER: You mean the reports by that Cuban agent of the crown? What was his name . . . Melián?

EUGENE LYON: Exactly. Remember, Melián was in the salvage business himself. He had a lot to lose by accurately reporting the location of the ships that went down in that hurricane.

MEL FISHER: Okay, that's a good point. I guess if I were in his place, maybe I'd be a little vague about the whereabouts of those sunken galleons loaded with gold and jewels!

EUGENE LYON: Did you say *maybe?*

MEL FISHER: All right, you've got me there! Sure, I'd keep the information to myself! But Melián's reports to the Spanish court did say without question that the *Atocha* and her sister ship the *Santa Margarita* went down six to ten miles west of Florida.

EUGENE LYON: Correct. They supposedly sank near the atoll called *Cayos del Marquéz,* which today is called the Marquesas Keys.

MEL FISHER: Unfortunately, the ocean in that area is dotted with hundreds of little islands and reefs. I've spent years combing the Atlantic looking for the *Atocha* and the *Santa Margarita,* and I'm no closer today than when I started. Will you look at those records once more?

EUGENE LYON: All right, Mel. Lucky for you, I'm working with an excellent researcher—Angeles Flores de Rodriguéz. Her knowledge of the archives here in Seville and her ability to read and translate these old documents should help speed things up. She and I will review the documents once more, but I just want you to be

Macmillan/McGraw-Hill

prepared: I really don't expect to find anything more that will help you.

MEL FISHER: Gene, I'm convinced that the answer to this mystery is in those records somewhere. I just know it, and if we actually find the *Atocha* and the *Margarita,* it could be worth millions, maybe tens of millions.

EUGENE LYON: Okay, Mel. I'll look. But remember, from my point of view, there's much more than gold and silver at the end of this search. Finding those two shipwrecks would be like passing through a doorway into one of Spain's great moments in history.

MEL FISHER: Remind me of that line next time my partners ask me about the return on their investment.

EUGENE LYON: Okay, Mel. I'll look. I'll look.

NARRATOR: A week later, Eugene Lyon found himself in the Archive of the Indies blowing the dust off three-hundred-year-old documents. It was all at his fingertips: passenger lists, a detailed account of the cargo, even a schedule of where the fleet stopped and where it was headed. After all, the reign of King Philip IV was among the wealthiest in the history of Spain. Great fleets of mercantile ships sailed from Europe to South America, North America, and as far away as the Philippines. Careful records had to be kept.

SEÑORA FLORES: Buenos días, Señor Lyon.

EUGENE LYON: Buenos días, Señora. Are you ready to take another look at the documents dealing with the *Atocha* and the *Santa Margarita?*

SEÑORA FLORES: Your friend Mel Fisher certainly is persistent.

EUGENE LYON: That's why he's one of the best salvage operators in the business. He never gives up. Why don't we start with the eyewitness accounts of the sinking of the *Atocha?*

SEÑORA FLORES: Here you are.

EUGENE LYON: [*coughing*] I knew when I became a historian that I would search for meaning in the dust of history, but I never expected this much dust!

SEÑORA FLORES: These books are older than your country, Señor. You have to expect a little mold and mildew after three hundred and fifty years!

EUGENE LYON: A little I can live with. Now let's see: This account is from 1626; this one is from 1624. . . . Ah, here we are: 1622, the story of Don Antonio de Velasco, one of the survivors.

SEÑORA FLORES: As a soldier aboard the *Santa Margarita,* he knew much about the ship's cargo and destination; but when it comes to the actual shipwreck, he's not very helpful.

EUGENE LYON: Well, I'm not surprised when you consider that he was fighting for his life as the ship tore apart during a hurricane. But what he does tell us provides some clues. Let's look at his story again.

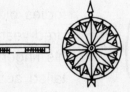

DON ANTONIO: My name is Don Antonio de Velasco. I serve His Majesty Philip, king of Spain, aboard the imperial galleon *Santa Margarita.* I am of noble birth, but I serve my king as a common soldier to gain military experience. I hope to return to the Indies one day, and a soldier's knowledge will serve me well.

CAPTAIN 1: At court there is time for idle chatter, but not on board my ship. If you have nothing to do, speak up. I am sure I can keep you busy.

DON ANTONIO: No, Captain. I am charged with guarding these silver ingots. They are very valuable and . . .

CAPTAIN 1: Then guard them. Don't talk to them. Have you seen the fleet pilot?

DON ANTONIO: Sí, Captain. He approaches now from the captain's walk.

PILOT: Good day, Captain.

CAPTAIN 1: Is it, Señor Pilot? There are great black clouds in the heavens. The seas rise and chop at our decks.

PILOT: It is to be expected, Captain. It is September, and we are well into hurricane season.

CAPTAIN 1: Havana is a comfortable place to wait out the winter, Señor Pilot.

PILOT: Captain, you know the value of your cargo. It would cost the king too much if we waited until spring to sail. King Philip is dependent upon the treasure stored in your holds to pay the war debts owed by the crown. Besides, I told you that if the new moon brought calm seas, our journey would be safe. The new moon was last night, and the waves rolled gently. We have nothing to fear.

CAPTAIN 1: I wish I could share your confidence in the moon. We are over-burdened with cargo and short on crew. Many of our men are sick with fever. Many others have deserted, wishing to spend the winter in these lush surroundings.

PILOT: When the governor finds and hangs them, Havana will look like any other grave. We must set sail, Captain, while our stores are full of food and drink.

CAPTAIN 1: Our stores are full of gold and silver, too. Let me remind you that, with all that extra weight, the *Santa Margarita* will not maneuver well in rough water.

PILOT: With you at the helm, what have we to fear?

CAPTAIN 1: You have the silvery tongue of a courtier, Señor Pilot!

PILOT: Then we sail?

CAPTAIN 1: We sail.

PILOT: Good, I will see that the other captains are informed of this decision.

CAPTAIN 1: Antonio, inform our distinguished passengers that we bid Havana goodbye at high tide.

DON ANTONIO: What of my post, Captain? The silver. . . ?

CAPTAIN 1: I'll watch the ingots while you do as I command.

DON ANTONIO: Sí, Captain.

CAPTAIN 1: Now that Antonio is gone, I can check my own horde of silver. Good. It is all there. We carry so much illegal cargo aboard the *Santa Margarita* and also aboard the *Atocha* that we could use another ship just for the contraband. It's a heavy load, but it will make me a wealthy man.

DON ANTONIO: I have informed the governor, the bishop, and our other passengers of your intention.

CAPTAIN 1: They were pleased?

DON ANTONIO: Yes, but worried about the weather. The bishop is concerned that the hurricane season has begun.

CAPTAIN 1: He is right, but the *Santa Margarita* is a fine oaken ship that has weathered many storms between Spain and the Indies. Our guests— and you for that matter—should worry more about the Dutch Armada. If we run into their warships, it will be life or death, of that you can be sure.

SAILOR: Captain, I bear a message from the *Atocha*.

CAPTAIN 1: Go on.

SAILOR: Our escort of eight armed ships is ready in the bay. The *Atocha* is fully laden with supplies and awaits your command.

CAPTAIN 1: Tell your captain that the *Santa Margarita,* the queen of the sea, will set her sails for Spain at the highest tide.

SAILOR: Sí, Captain. Praise Philip, King of Spain.

DON ANTONIO: The words of the *Atocha* sailor and the words of my own captain rang in my ears as we hoisted anchor and sailed away from Havana. The wind was full in our sails as we joined the great armed argosy beginning its perilous journey. The captain was right. The gold and silver— far more, it seemed, than the load recorded on our manifest—made our ship lie deep in the water. The bales of cotton, the chickens and turtles that would feed us, even the passengers in their gold chains and jewelry weighed less than the piles of gold and silver bars stacked below deck.

Macmillan/McGraw-Hill

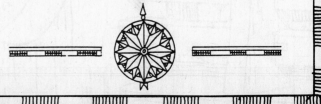

NARRATOR: The first-hand account of Don Antonio was not new to Gene Lyon or Señora Flores. Each time they read the story, they came to the same conclusion.

SEÑORA FLORES: There is the information showing that the passengers were nobility. They had jewels with them and lengths of gold chains.

EUGENE LYON: Gold was the currency of the day. If a nobleman or official needed to pay someone . . .

SEÑORA FLORES: . . . or bribe someone . . .

EUGENE LYON: . . . or bribe someone, he just took a link off a gold chain—instant money. But do you know what troubles me? I still cannot understand why they waited until the first week in September to begin their journey back to Spain. September is notorious for hurricanes and tropical storms. Why did they wait so long?

SEÑORA FLORES: Maybe the lack of a crew or the late arrival of an important passenger delayed them. After all, the governor of Venezuela was aboard. If he told them to wait, they would have to obey.

EUGENE LYON: It's another mystery that will never be solved.

SEÑORA FLORES: Maybe we should concentrate on what we do know.

EUGENE LYON: Agreed. Don Antonio's account has them heading north, presumably toward the Gulf Stream.

SEÑORA FLORES: You know, we have another eyewitness report from one of the five survivors of the *Atocha*—a seaman named Andrés Lorenzo.

EUGENE LYON: I've read it so many times I've almost memorized it; but let's have another look. Here it is, in this packet tied with a faded pink ribbon. Let's see . . .

ANDRÉS LORENZO: All was going well aboard the *Atocha*. The seas were rough, but all hands were seaworthy and true. We made good time out of Havana, and the first night passed without incident—and without sleep, at least for me. On the second day, the wind and rain increased steadily. The captain, while outwardly calm, showed signs of inner fear. He asked repeatedly for the men atop the mast to sight and report the whereabouts of the *Santa Margarita*.

CAPTAIN 2: Can you see her?

SAILOR: Sí, Captain, her mast is splintered. The topsail is spread across her deck, covering the wheel and blinding the crew, who are hacking at rope and sail and wood like wild men.

SILVER MASTER: You were wise, Captain, to order our sails lowered.

CAPTAIN 2: Wise in that, yes, but a fool to have left Havana. Silver Master, tend well to your treasure. Our brothers aboard the *Santa Margarita* will not survive this night.

SILVER MASTER: Captain, the anchors of the *Santa Margarita* have been thrown overboard.

CAPTAIN 2: It is the last desperate effort of a dying ship. The drag from the anchors will right her, but if the anchors catch on rocks, the *Santa Margarita* will be defenseless against the crushing storm.

SILVER MASTER: She has cleared the atoll; but, Captain, she's held fast. There must be a reef.

CAPTAIN 2: Adiós, *Santa Margarita*. Sailor, mark her!

SAILOR: One league west.

ANDRÉS LORENZO: No sooner had he spoken these words than the railing behind me broke free and so fiercely struck my back that I fell into the sea. Thank the patron saints that the decking fell with me, for I was able to cling to it and avoid the fate of my shipmates.

SAILOR: The cannon on deck are breaking free!

CAPTAIN 2: Secure those cannon before they smash our ship to pieces!

ANDRÉS LORENZO: The cannon rolled wildly along the planking, cutting ropes and bursting barricades. Many sailors fell before the bronze wheels as they scurried to escape. I could hear their anguished cries above the storm. With broken arms and injured legs, how could they swim? When the cannon at last crashed through the railings, my brothers on board had nowhere to lash themselves.

CAPTAIN 2: Tie yourselves to the mast!

SAILOR: With what, Captain, our tongues?

CAPTAIN 2: Your insolence condemns you!

SAILOR: Captain, you command dead men. Make your peace. We must all say our prayers.

ANDRÉS LORENZO: I watched the pounding storm take my shipmates to their graves. Listing badly to port, her oaken beams screaming in the wind, the *Atocha* made a small circle as though smoothing a place to sleep. All that gold and silver held her low in the water. And when the sea reached up finally, it was like a monster, and with a monster's fatal hand, it pulled her down.

NARRATOR: The deep silence in the library where Señora Flores sat with Gene Lyon went undisturbed for several moments. Only a clock striking the hour broke the quiet.

SEÑORA FLORES: May they rest in peace.

EUGENE LYON: Not if Mel Fisher has anything to say about it, Señora!

SEÑORA FLORES: You have trouble with this expedition, Señor Lyon?

EUGENE LYON: Let's just say that, as a historian, there are times when I am in conflict with some of the goals and methods of treasure hunters. There are some real differences of opinion about shipwreck salvage, you know.

SEÑORA FLORES: So, why do you help him?

EUGENE LYON: Sometimes, I wonder; but I really think that I want to locate the *Atocha* and the *Margarita* as much as Mel. If he does find them, these ships would present us with a unique time-capsule view into Spanish colonial trade and shipboard life.

SEÑORA FLORES: I wish you much success, Señor. Perhaps Lorenzo's account of where the shipwreck occurred will help you.

EUGENE LYON: Yes, with the most famous incomplete sentence in the history of treasure hunting.

SEÑORA FLORES: "One league west". . . but where was the *Atocha?*

EUGENE LYON: If we knew, we'd have the answer to our mystery. At least we know that the *Margarita* and the *Atocha* went down within sight of each other.

SEÑORA FLORES: The *Margarita* went down just east of the Cayos del Marquéz, the Marquesas Keys.

EUGENE LYON: Yes, and the *Atocha* went down somewhere nearby. So why, after fifteen years, has Mel Fisher discovered nothing in this area but a few silver coins and a lot of seashells?

SEÑORA FLORES: What did Lorenzo do when he finally got back to Spain?

EUGENE LYON: Well, he probably didn't sign on for any more trips to the Indies! But seriously, why do you ask?

SEÑORA FLORES: Perhaps he wrote other letters about the *Atocha* to relatives or friends.

EUGENE LYON: I doubt it, Señora Flores. After all, Lorenzo was just a seaman. I think our best bet would be to look at the account of Captain de Lugo, commander of the infantry force on the *Santa Margarita*. He survived, and his eyewitness report of the *Atocha's* sinking says it took place "east of the last key."

SEÑORA FLORES: I know that report well, Señor. Remember, I sent Mr. Fisher a transcript of the document some time ago.

EUGENE LYON: I remember. But I'm wondering if there is something else in the document that might have been missed. Why don't we look at it together one more time?

NARRATOR: After a considerable wait, a *portero* at the Archive of the Indies handed the two researchers a fragile bundle of documents.

EUGENE LYON: Well, here we go. This old-fashioned *procesal* script written without punctuation sure makes these documents hard to read. . . . Wait, here we are. . . . Hold everything! Take a look at this!

SEÑORA FLORES: Yes, that is the section.

EUGENE LYON: But look at what it says— "*veste del último cayo.*" It says *veste*,

not *este*! *West* of the last key, not east! The word must have been copied incorrectly during the transcription process. This means that Mel has been looking on the wrong side of the Marquesas! I'd better let him know right away!

NARRATOR: Meanwhile, back in Florida, Mel Fisher, his wife, Deo, and his son Dirk, were planning the search operation for the upcoming week.

DEO FISHER: Mel, didn't you say that Gene Lyon had hoped to send a report this week?

MEL FISHER: He was supposed to. I've been waiting to see what he'd come up with before doing any planning for this week's exploration. But I don't think we can wait any longer. What do you think, Dirk?

DIRK FISHER: If it were up to me, Dad, I would continue to work in the same area—east of the Marquesas Keys.

DEO FISHER: We're practically past the last reef in that location. In another week, there won't be anywhere else to look.

MEL FISHER: Don't I know it, Deo. Eleven years of exploration and no results! Gene Lyon is our last hope.

DEO FISHER: Gene, if you could hear me, I'd say, "Keep at it!"

NARRATOR: It was just then that the phone rang.

OPERATOR: This is the international operator. I have a collect call from a Mr. Eugene Lyon in Seville, Spain. Will you accept the charges?

MEL FISHER: Yes, operator, I'll accept them. Hello, Gene! I've been wondering what you were up to.

EUGENE LYON: Sit down, Mel. I've got some bad news . . . and some good news. The bad news is that you've been looking on the wrong side of the Marquesas for the last four months.

MEL FISHER: Great. So, what's the good news?

EUGENE LYON: The good news is that I think we've finally tracked down the information you've been looking for.

MEL FISHER: So . . . don't keep me in suspense!

EUGENE LYON: You need to look on the *west* side of the last key of the Marquesas. I hope it's what you're looking for, Mel. If it is, will you promise me you'll preserve the sites until marine archaeologists have a chance to examine the wrecks?

MEL FISHER: We've danced this dance before, Gene. You know I want to conduct the recovery operation professionally. But you have to understand that I've got the pressure of investment partners who want a financial return as soon as possible. I've made a lot of commitments to get financing for this operation.

EUGENE LYON: I'm coming to Florida within the next few weeks, Mel. I hope we can take up this issue again when I see you.

MEL FISHER: I hope we have a reason to take up the issue. See you then, Gene. And thanks!

DEO FISHER: What did Gene have to say, Mel?

MEL FISHER: He's got some revised information that suggests a new location for the *Atocha* and the *Santa Margarita!* Here, I wrote it down.

DIRK FISHER: Let me see it. *West?* West of the Marquesas Keys? Nobody's looked there!

MEL FISHER: Nobody until now. Outfit the *Southwind,* pronto, Dirk. We're going hunting! Today's the day!

DIRK FISHER: Aye, aye!

MEL FISHER: Deo, would you get in touch with our salvage lawyer? Tell him we might be putting in a claim.

DEO FISHER: Of course, but do you really think it's wise to move the whole operation based on a thirty-second telephone call? What proof did he give you?

MEL FISHER: Deo, you've got me there. Gene didn't offer any proof, but I'm sure he'll fill us in on all the details. Trust me—Eugene Lyon takes this history business very seriously. He researches, checks his facts, and always bases theory on evidence. If he says look west, we look west.

NARRATOR: Mel immediately shifted his operations to the west of the Marquesas. He searched during the fall and winter months without success. Then on June 1, 1971, a metal-detecting instrument called a magnetometer, used by Mel in his salvage operations, registered a strong contact. Mel and his divers found some silver coins, a musket ball, a galleon anchor, and three lengths of gold chains. More

finds were made during the summer, but nothing to indicate the *Atocha* or the *Santa Margarita* had been located. Still another year passed. Getting funding for the operation became more difficult, but Mel never gave up hope. Always an optimist, he gave T-shirts to the crew with his motto: "Today's the day!" and he sincerely believed it. Finally, in the spring of 1973, his luck began to change.

MEL FISHER: You bet our luck began to change! In one week in May, we hit something we dubbed the "Bank of Spain." On one day alone, fifteen hundred pieces of eight were brought up from the bottom! But I was convinced that the best was yet to come. And that Fourth of July, my hunch proved to be correct.

DIRK FISHER: Dad! Hey, Dad! One of the divers has brought up something that looks like a loaf of bread!

MEL FISHER: Loaf of bread? Why, that's no loaf of bread! That's a silver ingot.

DIRK FISHER: Whatever it is, it weighs a ton. Somebody help me get it over the side of the boat.

DEO FISHER: Look! Here come two more.

MEL FISHER: Quick, hand me something to wipe away the silver sulfide crust. Can anybody make out the marks? It looks like initials and Roman numerals.

NARRATOR: Mel immediately called in Gene Lyon.

Macmillan/McGraw-Hill

EUGENE LYON: Oh, what a thing of beauty! Those are the tally numbers and shipping identification marks you're looking at. Mel, I think this may be it—you may have found your treasure at last!

MEL FISHER: Is there any way to be sure, Gene?

EUGENE LYON: Well, theoretically, we should be able to match the tally number, the weight, and the silver fineness of each bar with the figures recorded in the ship manifests. These three bars are numbered 569, 794, and 4,584. If these ingots were carried on the *Atocha* or the *Santa Margarita,* we ought to be able to find confirmation in the microfilm copy of the manifests.

NARRATOR: Gene Lyon spent the next four days hunched over the microfilm reader in the Key West public library. Without success, he scanned the manifest of the *Margarita.*

EUGENE LYON: Mel, I've got some bad news. I've gone through every page of the manifest for the *Santa Margarita*—those three bars aren't listed in the documents.

MEL FISHER: You've still got the records of the *Atocha,* right? I'm not giving up hope yet. Keep at it, Gene, and think positive!

EUGENE LYON: I'll be back at the library when the doors open on Monday morning.

NARRATOR: On Monday, Gene carefully threaded the microfilm into the viewer and slowly began to turn the crank. The documents listing the treasure loaded on the *Atocha* at the port of Havana yielded no results; the bars were not listed in the manifest.

EUGENE LYON: Well, this is it. We're down to the last possibility—the records of the loading of the *Atocha* at the port of Cartagena. After this, I call it quits for the.... Whoa! There it is—*quatro mill quinientos e ochenta e quatro*: 4,584. It's the tally number of one of the silver bars! Now, does the silver fineness of the bar match what is recorded in the manifest? Let's see, it should be 2,380.... Bingo, another match! Fine, pure silver! And now for the last test. I'd better get over to Mel's office right away.

NARRATOR: Gene quickly made a copy of the manifest document page in the library's reader-printer, and then hurried over to Mel's office.

EUGENE LYON: Mel, take a look at this document!

MEL FISHER: Gene, you know I can't read a word of that funny-looking *procesal* script!

EUGENE LYON: Well, look at the spot I've circled. The bar number, 4-5-8-4, matches the tally number on the *Atocha's* manifest!

MEL FISHER: Great day in the morning! Does this mean what I think it means? Have we found the Big A at last?

EUGENE LYON: I think it does! But there's still one more test. We've got to weigh the bar and make sure that it matches the weight recorded in the manifest.

DEO FISHER: I'll track down an accurate freight scale and get it over to the office right away.

EUGENE LYON: While you do that, I'll work on converting the weight listed in the document as 125 marks and 3 ounces in Spanish measure. Dirk, maybe you can double-check my math.

DIRK FISHER: Based on my calculations, the bar should weigh exactly 63.58 pounds.

EUGENE LYON: That's what I come up with, too. Now we just have to wait until Deo returns with that freight scale.

MEL FISHER: Over sixty pounds of silver in that bar—and there are almost nine hundred more waiting to be found!

DEO FISHER: Here's the scale, Gene.

EUGENE LYON: And now for the acid test. Mel, why don't you set the weight at 63.6 pounds on the scale. Then Dirk and I can lift the bar up onto the weighing platform.

MEL FISHER: All right. Here goes.

NARRATOR: For a second, the balance arm of the scale swayed back and forth . . . it wavered . . . then it settled squarely in the middle.

EUGENE LYON: It matches; the weights match exactly! What a feeling. It's as though the silver master of the *Atocha* reached across three hundred and fifty years to shake my hand.

MEL FISHER: Well, I'd like to reach across a few feet and shake your hand, Gene! We couldn't have done it without you.

EUGENE LYON: Thanks, Mel, and don't forget Angeles Flores de Rodriguéz, my

colleague at the Archive of the Indies in Seville. For that matter, you owe a real debt of gratitude to Captain de Lugo.

MEL FISHER: I'll offer a toast in his honor, right after I call my salvage lawyer!

NARRATOR: For Mel Fisher, his partners, and employees, the next few years were some of the busiest and most stressful of their lives.

MEL FISHER: I'll say it was stressful. The three silver bars were just a beginning. It took us until May 1980 to find the actual site of the shipwrecked *Atocha!*

EUGENE LYON: You mean what we *thought* was the *Atocha*. But when we matched the numbers on the gold and silver bars we uncovered at the site with the 1622 ship documents, we discovered they were listed on the *Santa Margarita* manifest! We had located the *Santa Margarita,* not the *Atocha!*

DEO FISHER: And what a find that was! That wreck yielded over 140 pounds of gold and 1,670 pounds of silver.

MEL FISHER: But the best was yet to come! Five years later, on July 20, 1985, we found the "Mother Lode"— the resting place of the *Atocha's* main treasure mass! There were millions of dollars worth of gold, silver, emeralds, copper, and brass.

EUGENE LYON: The shipwrecks gave archaeologists a wealth of information. Portions of the *Atocha's* hull remained intact! The study of the galleon's construction is helping us fill a large void in our knowledge of European shipbuilding techniques in the early seventeenth century.

SEÑORA FLORES: As a researcher in Seville, I was able to gain valuable information about the trading routes of the Spanish Empire.

EUGENE LYON: I, too, reaped historical treasure. The cups and bowls, the chains, cannons, and navigational instruments found buried beneath the sand told us a great deal about life in the early seventeenth century.

NARRATOR: Part of the treasure that Mel Fisher recovered west of the Marquesas Keys now resides in a museum in Key West, Florida. The final financial estimate of the treasure's worth has been put at over $400 million. This was not achieved without sacrifice. Four people died during the search: a visitor to the salvage operation who fell overboard, a diver named Rick Gage, and Mel's son and his wife, Dirk and Angel Fisher, who drowned when their boat capsized in the middle of the night.

MEL FISHER: Some people say that buried treasure is cursed. I have never felt that way, even after I lost my son and daughter-in-law. There is great risk in hunting treasure, and as I've said before, treasure is worth what a person is willing to pay for it. Have I paid too much? I ask myself that question every day.

SEÑORA FLORES: I read in Seville that when the *Margarita* went down in 1622, Francisco Melián, the man chosen by the crown to recover the treasure, told his crew that the first man to find the wreck would be rewarded. A slave named Juan Bañon was lucky enough to find the first ingot in that silvery cargo, and for his success, he was given his freedom. For Juan Bañon, what was the treasure truly worth?

EUGENE LYON: Treasure means different things to different people. I have spent a lifetime studying old nautical records and Spanish colonial history. For me, treasure is knowledge. The culture of Spain, its language, and its customs changed half of the Western Hemisphere. Nearly four hundred years later, we are still enjoying the rich rewards of Hispanic traditions. Are cultures and history the ultimate treasure? You can exhaust a fortune. You can never exhaust the past.

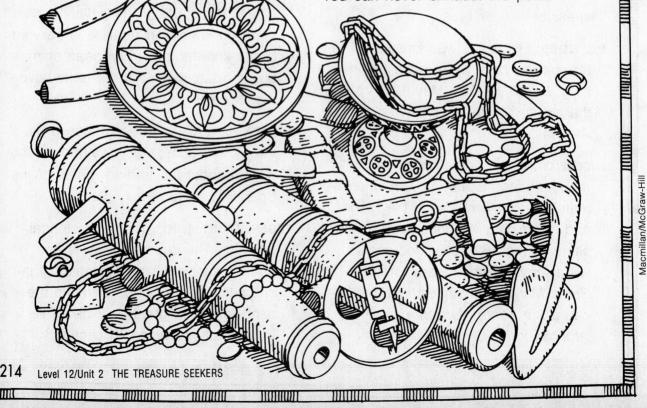

Macmillan/McGraw-Hill

Blocking Diagram

Arrange thirteen chairs, as shown. The narrator can use a music stand to hold the script.

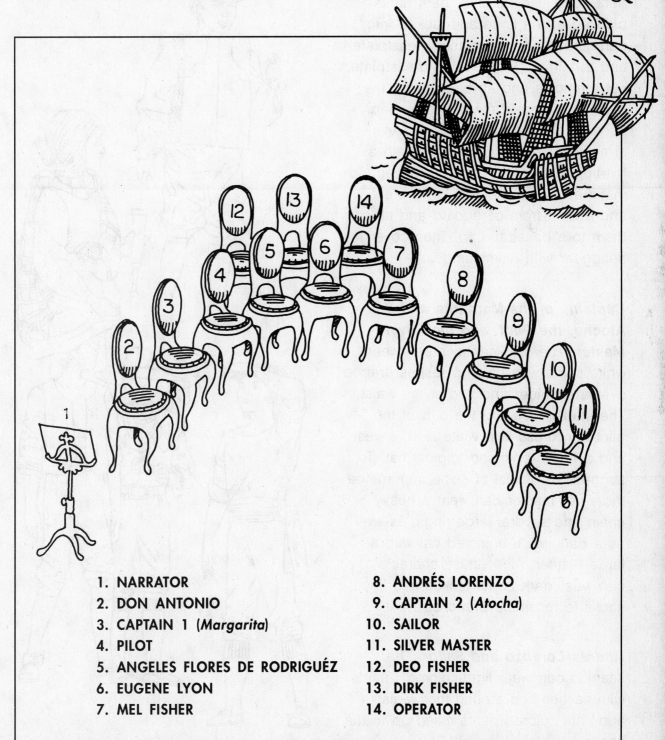

1. **NARRATOR**
2. **DON ANTONIO**
3. **CAPTAIN 1** (*Margarita*)
4. **PILOT**
5. **ANGELES FLORES DE RODRIGUÉZ**
6. **EUGENE LYON**
7. **MEL FISHER**

8. **ANDRÉS LORENZO**
9. **CAPTAIN 2** (*Atocha*)
10. **SAILOR**
11. **SILVER MASTER**
12. **DEO FISHER**
13. **DIRK FISHER**
14. **OPERATOR**

Costume Suggestions

Don Antonio The soldier can wear a dark, long-sleeved shirt, dark pants bloused at the knee and tucked into dark knee socks, a leather breastplate, and a helmet. To make the breastplate, cut armholes and an opening for the head in a large, brown grocery bag. Then slit the bag up the back. An armor design can be created with a felt-tipped marking pen on the bag. To make a Spanish helmet, cut a crest and a brim from cardboard and tape them to a baseball cap. Then cover the headgear with aluminum foil.

Captains of the Margarita and the Atocha, the Pilot, and the Silver Master The ship captains can wear white shirts with colorful sashes draped over a shoulder and tied at the waist. The student reading the part of the pilot can dress in a white shirt, a vest, and a broad-brimmed tropical hat. To suggest an official of some importance, the silver master can wear a heavy chain and several large rings, as well as a dark, wide-brimmed hat with a large feather. All of these characters can wear dark pants tucked into knee socks to resemble breeches.

Andrés Lorenzo and Sailor The seamen can wear light-colored T-shirts with sashes tied around their waists and light-colored pants rolled up to the knees.

Macmillan/McGraw-Hill

X Marks the Spot

On September 4, 1622—a calm and sunny day—the *Nuestra Señora de Atocha,* the *Santa Margarita*, and twenty-six other ships left Havana Harbor and sailed north to the Straits of Florida where the Gulf Stream's strong currents would propel them toward Spain. By the next morning, a hurricane had entered the Straits of Florida from the northeast. The fleet was on a collision course with destiny. In all, seven ships sank during the storm.

Early treasure hunters were able to locate some of the shipwrecks and recover a small percentage of the treasure. This reproduction of the Spanish Salvors Chart of 1623 shows the *Cabeza de los Martires* (Head of the Martyrs), so named because of the number of lives lost there. The large land mass shown is the southern tip of Florida, and the small circles represent the Florida Keys.

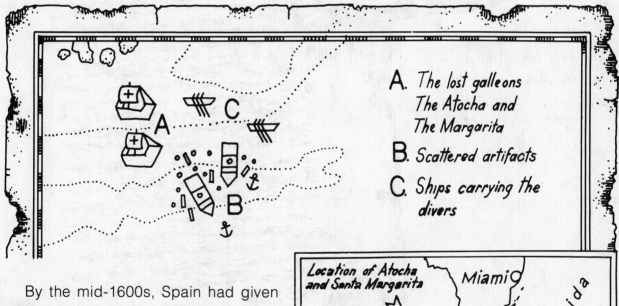

A. *The lost galleons The Atocha and The Margarita*

B. *Scattered artifacts*

C. *Ships carrying the divers*

By the mid-1600s, Spain had given up her attempt to recover the treasure. The precise locations of the *Atocha* and the *Margarita* were unknown until the mystery of their final resting places was finally unraveled by Mel Fisher and Eugene Lyon in 1971 and 1981. This map shows the area as we know it today.

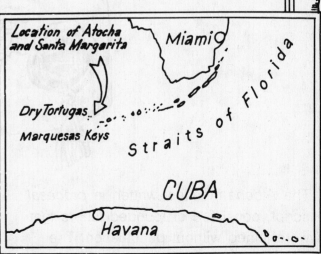

Location of Atocha and Santa Margarita

Miami

Dry Tortugas

Marquesas Keys

Straits of Florida

CUBA

Havana

Bar Number 4,584

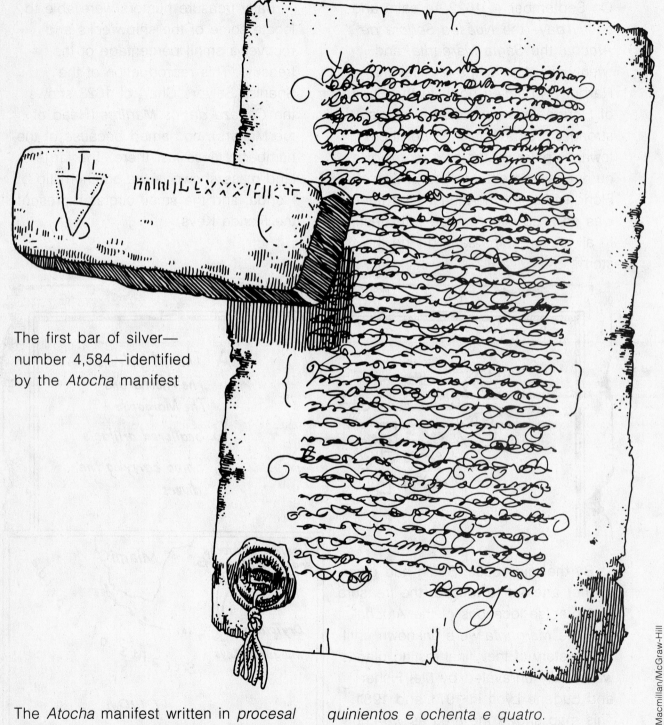

The first bar of silver—
number 4,584—identified
by the *Atocha* manifest

The *Atocha* manifest written in *procesal* script, consisted of rounded letters that were joined without punctuation. The number recorded here is *quatro mill quinientos e ochenta e quatro.* Deciphering and interpreting documents such as this manifest was Eugene Lyon's specialty.

· THE ·
TENNESSEE
TORNADO

BY SUSAN STRANE

The Times

CAST
WILMA PRESENT
MAMA
WILMA PAST
DOCTOR
MRS. HOSKINS
YVONNE
WOMAN
MAN
COACH GRAY

TEAMMATE 1
TEAMMATE 2
TEAMMATE 3
TEAMMATE 4
COACH TEMPLE
MAE FAGGS
JUDGE
YOUNG BOY

The News

TENNESSEE TORNADO

WILMA PRESENT: I was nicknamed the "Tennessee Tornado" by the press, but my friends and family back in my hometown of Clarksville, Tennessee, knew me as just plain Wilma Rudolph. There were twenty-two kids in my family, and I was number twenty. My daddy, Ed Rudolph, worked as a railroad porter. In his spare time, he did odd jobs for people around town. My mama, whose name was Blanche, cleaned houses to make extra money. Both of them worked hard to support our large family; still, when I think back on it, we had very little money. There were lots of things we did without, but one thing we did have plenty of was love. Born on June 23, 1940, I was a premature baby, tipping the scales at just four and a half pounds. Maybe that was why I was always sick when I was growing up.

Macmillan/McGraw-Hill

MAMA: Wilma, honey, sometimes I think you've had more than your fair share of being sick. Why, you're only three years old, and you've already had the measles, the chicken pox, the mumps, and I don't know how many colds!

WILMA PAST: Does that mean I'm special, Mama?

MAMA: Maybe it does, child. Here, now drink this down.

WILMA PAST: Oh, Mama, do I have to? I hate that stuff!

MAMA: Do you want to get well?

WILMA PAST: Yes!

MAMA: Then drink it and get under those covers. Go on now; swallow every last drop!

WILMA PRESENT: In spite of my mother's concoctions, I never had the strength that other kids had. Every cold I got seemed to last for weeks, and then it would develop into something else. When I was four, I had double pneumonia complicated by scarlet fever. That was one time Mama put her home remedies aside and called the doctor.

MAMA: She'll be all right, won't she, Doctor?

DOCTOR: She'll recover from the pneumonia and the scarlet fever, Mrs. Rudolph. But I'm afraid she contracted polio while she was ill. As a result, one of her legs is partially paralyzed. I'm sorry to have to tell you this, but I doubt that she'll ever walk again.

WILMA PAST: I *will* walk again. I will! I will!

MAMA: Yes, you will, child. We're going to fight this thing, you understand? Don't you worry, everything is going to turn out all right.

WILMA PRESENT: I started wearing a heavy metal brace to keep my leg straight. The brace went on as soon as I got up, and I wasn't allowed to take it off until I went to bed. When I was six, my mother and I started going to a hospital in Nashville for physical therapy. Twice each week, month after month, year after year—for four long years—I went for treatments. It was fifty miles each way in the back of a bus, which was the only place black people were allowed to sit. Back then, in the 1940s, there was still segregation in the South.

MAMA: There's only one seat left. You sit down, Wilma.

WILMA PAST: There are seats up front, Mama. It's not fair that you have to stand.

MAMA: No, it's not fair, and it's not right. Maybe someday things will be different. But until that time, you just hold up your head and don't let anybody get you down.

WILMA PRESENT: The treatments to strengthen my leg were painful. But even so, I looked forward to those trips to Nashville. I was getting out of Clarksville, seeing new things.

WILMA PAST: I like traveling, Mama. Someday, I'm going to break out of this brace, and I'm going to see lots of new places.

Macmillan/McGraw-Hill

WILMA PRESENT: I guess I had big dreams even then. Sometimes after one of these trips, I would inspect my leg to see if I could detect any change. For a long time, I didn't notice any improvement.

WILMA PAST: You've just got to be better by now, leg. That doctor works on you twice every week, and Mama massages you every night. There's got to be more to life than this. You hear me? Enough is enough!

WILMA PRESENT: Yes, I started to get angry. I began to fight back in a new way. It was almost like a competition—me against my illness—and I was determined to win, no matter what!

WILMA PAST: Mama, I'm seven years old now, and I can walk pretty well with my brace. You know how you and Daddy always say education is the most important thing? Well, I'm tired of being taught at home. I want to go to school with the other kids.

MAMA: Wilma, honey, I know you've been dreaming about it for a long time. And goodness knows you've got a strong will.

WILMA PAST: Same as you do, Mama!

MAMA: Well, we'll try it out.

WILMA PRESENT: I started school as a second grader. Despite all my brave talk, I must admit I felt terrified the first day I set foot in that school. Fortunately, my teacher was a warm, supportive person who sensed that I desperately needed to belong. She was in charge of the Brownies, and she urged me to join. That turned my life around. Fourth grade was another important year for me. I had a teacher named Mrs. Hoskins. My, she was strict! But she taught me how to think positively, and I grew to love her.

MRS. HOSKINS: Wilma! How are you going to learn anything if you don't pay attention? Save your dreaming for when you sleep!

WILMA PAST: Sorry, Mrs. Hoskins, I was just looking at Nancy's picture. I sure wish I could draw as pretty as that.

MRS. HOSKINS: Wilma, if you want to do something, do it. Don't daydream about it. *Do it!*

WILMA PRESENT: By the time I was ten, everyone in town was used to seeing me with that brace. To them, it was a part of me. But not to me. One Sunday, we all went to church, like always. But it was a day I'll never forget.

MAMA: Hurry along, now. Looks like everyone is already here, except us.

WILMA PAST: You all go ahead in. I'll be along in a minute.

YVONNE: Come on, Mama. The service is about to begin.

WILMA PRESENT: I waited a few minutes before I finally went in. I knew right away that people were staring at me. I could hear them buzzing as I walked down the aisle to where my family was sitting.

WOMAN: I do declare!

MAN: I can't believe what my eyes are seeing!

WOMAN: Just look at that!

YVONNE: Mama! Daddy! It's Wilma!

MAMA: Praise be! Wilma's walking down the aisle on her own two legs. Oh, happy, happy day!

WILMA PRESENT: I had walked in without the brace. After church, a lot of people came over to congratulate me.

MAN: That's tremendous, Wilma! You sure gave us a surprise!

YVONNE: You said you'd walk again, and you did it!

WILMA PRESENT: I just smiled and beamed and didn't say much. But looking back on it, I'd say it was one of the most important moments of my life. Over the next two years, I wore the brace off and on as I regained the full use of my leg. Then, when I was in the sixth grade, Mama packed up the brace and sent it back to the hospital. Now that I had achieved my first goal, I set a new one for myself. I was determined to become someone special. That fall, I entered seventh grade, which turned out to be another pivotal year in my life.

YVONNE: Wilma, it's hard for me to believe that you'll be going to Burt High School with me this fall!

WILMA PRESENT: For the kids I knew, everything revolved around Burt High School, where Clarksville's black students attended from seventh through twelfth grades. Athletics were very important in the school, and most kids went out for a sport. My sister Yvonne was on the girls' basketball team, and I made up my mind to follow in her footsteps.

WILMA PAST: Yvonne, do you think Coach Gray will give me a chance to play on the basketball team?

YVONNE: Wilma, what are you talking about? You don't know the first thing about basketball!

WILMA PAST: That's what you think! I've been watching all of you play for years. I've studied every move. I know which ones work and which ones don't. And I'm getting real tall. What do you say, Mama?

MAMA: Child, I'm not sure if you should go out for sports. What if you fall and get hurt? I can't bear to think of all those years of massage and therapy wasted.

WILMA PAST: I'll be okay, Mama. I know I can do it!

MAMA: Well, I guess there's no use trying to change your mind. Once you get set on something, there's no stopping you.

WILMA PRESENT: I made the team, but thinking back on it, I'm fairly sure that Coach Clinton Gray selected me because of my sister. I didn't play one single minute of a game that entire season—I was a real "bench-warmer," you might say. However, I wasn't wasting time. I watched and studied everything that happened on the court. I practiced every spare minute.

MAMA: Where you going, Wilma? It's almost dinner time.

WILMA PAST: I'm just going out in the yard, Mama. I want to shoot some baskets. When Coach Gray puts me in a game, I've got to be ready, don't I?

MAMA: I never did see anyone work so hard at a thing as you do, child.

WILMA PRESENT: My mother was right. I practiced until I was shooting and rebounding better than most of my teammates. But even after three straight years, I never really got to show what I could do. Oh, I did get into some games, but only when there were a few seconds left, and the team was either way ahead or behind. I didn't complain, but sitting on the bench was getting harder and harder! At the end of my ninth-grade season, Coach Gray proposed a new idea to the team, but to our surprise, it had nothing to do with basketball.

Macmillan/McGraw-Hill

COACH GRAY: Listen up, girls! I'm thinking of starting a girls' track team. It'll help you stay in shape for basketball. Would any of you like to go out for it?

WILMA PAST: Sure, Coach!

TEAMMATE 1: Sounds good to me!

COACH GRAY: Okay, we start on Monday.

WILMA PRESENT: I figured track would give me something to do after school between basketball seasons. As it turned out, running was pure enjoyment for me. I had no knowledge about the technical aspects of the sport or even about the work involved. But I was fast, and I won about twenty races that spring without any effort on my part. At that point, my sister gave me some friendly advice.

YVONNE: Gee, Wilma, maybe you ought to spend more time on running than on basketball. You ought to go with your strongest sport.

WILMA PAST: I love running, Yvonne, but it's just something to do in the spring. Basketball is still my favorite sport.

WILMA PRESENT: When basketball season started in my sophomore year, I felt my time had come.

WILMA PAST: Coach, I've been warming the bench for three seasons. I know I'm ready for a spot in the starting lineup. How about it?

COACH GRAY: Wilma, you're more annoying than a "skeeter" buzzing 'round my head, but you've worked real hard. All right, I'll give you a try.

WILMA PAST: Thanks, Coach. You won't be sorry!

WILMA PRESENT: Coach Gray made me a starting player—finally! The nickname that he gave me, "Skeeter," slang for mosquito, also stuck. I'll never forget my very best game that season. I scored thirty-two points and didn't miss a single shot or free throw.

COACH GRAY: You keep that up, Skeeter, and we'll make the championships this year.

WILMA PRESENT: Coach Gray's prediction was right. Our team did make it into the Tennessee High School Girls' Championships. We won a tough game in our first round, but then our smugness got the better of us. We were defeated by eight points in a game marked by sloppy ball handling and poor defense. After the game, I was crushed. Little did I know that it would turn out to be one of the most significant experiences of my entire life.

COACH TEMPLE: Excuse me, Wilma. I'd like to talk to you for a minute or two. My name's Ed Temple. I'm the coach for the Tigerbelles, the women's track team at Tennessee State University in Nashville.

WILMA PAST: Yes, sir. Say, weren't you one of the referees tonight?

COACH TEMPLE: Yes, I was. I do a lot of officiating so I can scout out new talent for my Tigerbelles. Based on what I saw tonight, I'd say you're definitely a new talent.

WILMA PAST: Thank you, Mr. Temple, but I don't know how anyone could think that after the way I played tonight!

COACH TEMPLE: Actually, Wilma, I'm thinking of another sport. With your height and long legs, you've got the makings of a sprinter. Have you ever considered competitive track?

WILMA PAST: Not really, sir. I do a lot of running after basketball season is over, but we don't have a real track team at Burt High. We don't even have a track. We jog outside and, when it rains, we run through the school.

COACH TEMPLE: Well, I know I can make a runner out of you. Just keep in mind what I've said, and we'll talk again sometime.

WILMA PRESENT: So there I was in 1956—a fifteen-year-old high school sophomore with a life that revolved around basketball, running, and my family. I'd never been so happy. As soon as basketball season ended, I put on my track shoes and started running. I ran every minute I could. I'd gotten the taste of winning and found I liked it.

COACH GRAY: Well, girls, next week is the big track meet at Tuskegee, Alabama.

WILMA PAST: Who's gonna be there, Coach?

COACH GRAY: You'll be competing against girls from all over the South. Only the best runners are invited.

TEAMMATE 1: Wow! That must mean we're pretty good.

COACH GRAY: You are, but I'd be kidding you if I didn't tell you that the competition is going to be tough, especially the girls from Atlanta, Georgia. They can practice all year round because of the warm climate there.

WILMA PAST: Don't worry, Coach. We'll make you proud of us!

WILMA PRESENT: When we got to the track, I saw that Coach Gray was right. The girls from Georgia really looked like runners. But I didn't pay much attention to them because, after my string of wins around Clarksville, I was feeling pretty cocky.

WILMA PAST: I think I can beat them. After all, I've won every single race I've ever been in.

TEAMMATE 1: I'll see you after the meet, Wilma. We're planning a big victory celebration.

WILMA PRESENT: So what happened? I didn't win a single race! I was totally devastated. My speed was no match for the training and experience of the other girls entered in the meet. I went home and moped around. Then somewhere along the line, I realized that I had learned a very important lesson: Nobody goes through life undefeated. If you can pick up after a crushing defeat and go on to win again, you're going to be a champion someday. But if losing destroys you, it's all over.

WILMA PAST: I've got to try to put it all back together. There's a lot more to track than running fast. I've got to learn the right way to run.

WILMA PRESENT: I acquired this sense of determination that I would never, ever give up no matter what else happened. I won the rest of the races I was entered in that season, but I never forgot Tuskegee. In fact, I remember thinking that anybody who had seen me lose so badly at that meet would have written me off. To my surprise, I was wrong.

COACH GRAY: Wilma, remember Ed Temple, the referee who's the women's track coach at Tennessee State? He's planning to come to Clarksville to talk with your folks.

WILMA PAST: He is? What about?

Macmillan/McGraw-Hill

COACH GRAY: I think he wants you to spend the summer at the university, learning some running techniques.

WILMA PRESENT: I rushed home to tell my mama and daddy.

MAMA: Wilma, honey, you're too young to be leaving home.

WILMA PAST: Mama, don't you see what a big break this is? If Coach Temple thinks I'm good enough, he might offer me a scholarship to the university. I could go to college!

WILMA PRESENT: While my parents talked it over with Coach Temple, I just sat tight and held my breath.

MAMA: Well, Wilma, you're the first one in this family who's ever had the chance to go to college. If running is going to do that, we just want you to put your mind to being the best you can be!

WILMA PRESENT: That summer of 1956 was no vacation for me. I learned that raw speed was not enough to win races. Coach Temple taught me breathing techniques, race strategies, and how to blast out of the starting blocks. It was hard work all right, but the hardest lesson of all was learning mental toughness.

COACH TEMPLE: Wilma, you're holding back when you run. I can see it.

WILMA PAST: Gee, Coach, I'm just a high school kid. Those girls on the senior team are older. Some of them are real track stars. I feel it would be disrespectful, almost, if I beat them.

COACH TEMPLE: Listen, Wilma, a track meet is not a popularity contest. Remember that! You're out there to win. So push for it!

WILMA PAST: I'll try, Coach.

COACH TEMPLE: You've got to do more than try, Wilma. You've got to change your mental attitude. I want you ready for the Amateur Athletic Union meet in Philadelphia, and that's only a few weeks away.

WILMA PAST: Coach, I'll be ready! I wouldn't miss it for anything. I've always dreamed of traveling.

WILMA PRESENT: We drove up to Philadelphia in a caravan of station wagons. I'd never been up North before. Everything in Philadelphia seemed so foreign to me. When we went to Franklin Stadium, I nearly fainted I was so intimidated.

WILMA PAST: I've never seen a stadium this big! I feel like a midget.

COACH TEMPLE: At six feet, you're some midget, Wilma!

WILMA PRESENT: The weeks of intensive training paid off. I won nine races, and our relay team captured the junior title.

COACH TEMPLE: You're coming along real well, Wilma. You've got a lot of potential.

WILMA PRESENT: Right after the AAU meet in Philadelphia, Coach Temple and I had a long talk.

Macmillan/McGraw-Hill

COACH TEMPLE: You have a good possibility of making the women's Olympic track team this fall, Wilma. I think you should give it a try.

WILMA PAST: That's a pretty big track meet, isn't it, Coach?

COACH TEMPLE: It's more than a track meet. The Olympics are the oldest competitive games in the world. They were first held in Greece around 3,000 years ago. Every four years, the best amateur athletes from all over the world are chosen to compete.

WILMA PAST: Did you say that athletes come from all over the world?

COACH TEMPLE: That's right. This year the games will be held in Melbourne, Australia. You're just sixteen, but you might make it . . . if you push hard enough.

WILMA PAST: After Philadelphia, I feel I can do anything!

WILMA PRESENT: We started the first leg of our journey to Melbourne a couple of weeks later. Coach Temple drove me and a group of Tigerbelles to the Olympic tryouts in Seattle, Washington. One of these college stars was a woman named Mae Faggs. Mae held all sorts of records in women's track, and she had won medals in previous Olympics. She took a special interest in me from the first day we met.

MAE: Wilma, I'm going to give you some tough advice. Stop trying to fit in with everybody else. Stop worrying if someone is going to like you or not if you win. Start running like an individual.

WILMA PAST: I'm just a high school kid. I don't want to cause any hard feelings.

WILMA PRESENT: But Mae wasn't about to let up. When the time came for the final qualifying heat in the 200-meter dash, she took me aside.

MAE: Listen, Wilma, do you want to make the United States Olympic team?

WILMA PAST: You bet I do!

MAE: Then listen to me. All you have to do in this race is stick with me. Put everything else out of your mind.

WILMA PRESENT: I remember the gun going off, and I remember taking off with a good start. When I looked up, I saw that I had actually passed Mae and was ahead of her! She pulled up, and we finished in a dead heat, breaking the tape at the same instant!

WILMA PAST: We did it! We did it!

MAE: We sure did! We're going to the Olympics! You know, Wilma, if you hadn't pulled back, you'd have beaten me in that race. I knew you had it in you, but I wondered when it would come out. Today it did.

WILMA PAST: I don't think I'll ever be afraid to challenge anyone again. Thanks, Mae.

WILMA PRESENT: When we got back to Tennessee State, people kept coming around to wish me well.

TEAMMATE 2: Congratulations, Wilma! We're all real proud of you!

TEAMMATE 3: Hey, Wilma, you sure put Tennessee State on the map!

TEAMMATE 4: Just wait till the Olympics. Then the whole world will know about it!

WILMA PRESENT: Back home in Clarksville, everyone was excited, too.

YVONNE: Wilma, you're famous! The newspaper says you're one of the fastest women in the whole world.

MAMA: I can't help remembering, child, that only a couple of years ago, you were going to Nashville for treatments on your leg. Now here you are going to Australia for the Olympics!

MAN: We sure are proud of you, Wilma. And we want you to go to Melbourne in style, so some of the merchants in Clarksville got together to get you this luggage and a new wardrobe to take along with our very best wishes.

WILMA PAST: Thank you all, very much. I'll never forget what you've done for me.

WILMA PRESENT: In October 1956, we flew to Melbourne, Australia. At first, I felt overwhelmed by all the people speaking different languages, but I soon realized we were all there for the same reason.

WILMA PAST: You know something, Mae? For the first time in my life, I feel I'm not being judged by the color of my skin. Here, judgments depend on performance.

MAE: Well, speaking of performance, we've got to start working on ours, especially our baton-passing. There's no question about it, our timing is off.

WILMA PRESENT: Passing the baton is one of the most important and most difficult things in running a relay. Split-second timing is an absolute necessity. In fact, a number of upsets have occurred in previous Olympic Games because of an error made during a handoff.

WILMA PAST: I sure do miss Coach Temple. He'd know what we're doing wrong.

MAE: Well, we'll just have to try to remember what he taught us and keep on practicing.

WILMA PRESENT: My very first Olympic race was three days into the games. It was the qualifying heat for the 200-meter race. I made it through the first heat, and moved on to the semi-finals where only the first- and second-place runners would advance. I came in third and was eliminated. I don't know what happened, except that I didn't run as fast as I should have. I felt terrible.

WILMA PAST: I can't eat or sleep. I've let everybody down. How will I ever be able to face them back home? I'm a failure.

MAE: I know how bad you feel, Wilma, but you've got another chance to show what you can do.

WILMA PAST: You're right, Mae. I've just got to do well in the relay.

WILMA PRESENT: Before the relay, Mae, as team captain, gathered us together to give us a pep talk.

MAE: Girls, I know we can do it if we give it all we've got! Let's make it into the top three and win ourselves a medal!

WILMA PAST: We've got to—for Coach Temple and everyone else back home.

WILMA PRESENT: There were teams from six countries in that relay race, and I must confess that no one was expecting much from us. Mae ran an excellent first leg keeping us tied for the lead. The second runner lost some ground to several teams before passing the baton to me. It was a clean pass and I got off well. I passed two runners on my leg, pulling us into third place. Our anchor runner held our position. We had done it! We had captured third place and bronze medals for ourselves and for the United States.

Macmillan/McGraw-Hill

MAE: Well, I think we can go home feeling mighty proud!

TEAMMATE 3: We sure surprised a lot of people today.

WILMA PRESENT: I was happy that I had salvaged something out of Melbourne, and I told myself a bronze medal wasn't all that bad for a sixteen-year-old from Tennessee. But as the Olympic Games ended, I could hear the voice of Mrs. Hoskins, my fourth-grade teacher.

MRS. HOSKINS: Wilma, if you want to do something, do it. Don't daydream about it. *Do it!*

WILMA PRESENT: Right then and there, I made a promise to myself.

WILMA PAST: Four years from now, wherever the Olympics are held, I'm going to be there, and I'm going to win a gold medal or two for the United States!

WILMA PRESENT: When I got home to Clarksville, I found Burt High School closed for the day so the students could attend a special assembly in my honor. When I walked out on stage, all the kids cheered and gave me flowers. After the assembly, I couldn't wait to see Coach Gray.

COACH GRAY: Congratulations, Wilma! You've come a long way. How do you feel?

WILMA PAST: Okay, but having to give that speech in the assembly scared me more than the Olympics! By the way, Coach, I heard there's a game tonight. I haven't played much basketball lately, but I'm in great shape. Can I play? Please?

COACH GRAY: Skeeter, you haven't changed a bit! Of course you can play!

WILMA PRESENT: A lot happened over the next few years. After high school, I entered Tennessee State University on a full athletic scholarship and joined Coach Temple's Tigerbelle track team. The 1960 Olympic trials were held the end of my sophomore year.

COACH TEMPLE: Are you all set Wilma? The 200-meter race is next.

WILMA PAST: I don't feel much like running today, Coach. But I'm ready to give it a try . . . and get it over with.

WILMA PRESENT: I remember when the race was over, I plopped down next to Coach Temple, and he was smiling.

COACH TEMPLE: Good race, Wilma. You're doing all right, aren't you?

WILMA PRESENT: Later, two of my teammates came running over.

TEAMMATE 2: Say, Wilma, why aren't you celebrating?

WILMA PAST: Celebrating? What for? I mean, I'm glad I made the Olympic team, but I made it once before, you know.

TEAMMATE 3: No, no, that's not what we mean. We're talking about your time—twenty-two point nine seconds.

TEAMMATE 2: It's a world record!

WILMA PAST: WHAT?

TEAMMATE 3: You mean nobody told you? You just set a record for the fastest 200 meters ever run by a woman!

WILMA PRESENT: I couldn't get over it, I'd set a world record, and I hadn't even felt like running! By the end of the trials, I'd qualified for three events—the 100 meters, the 200 meters, and the relay. Some of the other Tennessee State Tigerbelles also made the team. Best of all, Ed Temple was named coach of the United States Olympic Women's Track Team. After a three-week training session, we were off to Rome, Italy!

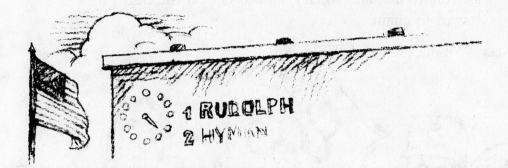

WILMA PAST: Coach Temple, I just love Rome, and this 100-degree temperature is perfect for me. It feels just like the weather in Tennessee.

COACH TEMPLE: You know, Wilma, it's a funny thing, but for the last two nights I've had the same dream. I keep seeing you with three Olympic gold medals around your neck.

WILMA PAST: I sure do hope your dream comes true!

WILMA PRESENT: But on the day before I was scheduled to run in my first race, disaster struck. It was a hot afternoon, and some of us were running through a sprinkler on a field of nice, soft grass.

TEAMMATE 2: This is a great way to cool off, isn't it?

TEAMMATE 3: Sure is, but we'd better get going. Practice starts in ten minutes, and you know how Coach Temple feels if anyone's late.

WILMA PAST: Okay. Just let me run through one last time. . . . Ow!

TEAMMATE 4: Wilma! What happened?

WILMA PAST: My ankle . . . I stepped in a hole and twisted my ankle. Ow! It hurts so much!

WILMA PRESENT: The trainer took one look and made a face; my ankle was swollen and discolored. He taped it up real tight and had me elevate it. I kept my leg up until the next morning—the day of the 100-meter final. Rumors were flying that I was out of the race. But when I put my weight on my foot, my ankle held up. I knew then I'd be able to run. That day, the stadium was jammed. For some reason, the fans had taken a liking to me, and when I walked out on the track, they started to chant.

ALL: Wil-ma! Wil-ma! Wil-ma!

WILMA PRESENT: The tension was building. I put everything out of my mind and concentrated on the race I had to run. Then we were off! My start was good; I came out second or third in the field. My ankle felt all right. When I reached fifty meters, I saw that I had left them all behind—and I was just beginning to turn on the speed. By seventy meters, I knew the race was mine; nobody was going to catch me. I had won my first gold medal!

COACH TEMPLE: That's number one, Wilma!

Macmillan/McGraw-Hill

WILMA PAST: Three days later, I ran in the 200-meter final.

ALL: Wil-ma! Wil-ma! Wil-ma! Go . . . go . . . go!

COACH TEMPLE: She's way ahead. She's going to do it!

TEAMMATE 3: Wilma did it again! She's got her second gold!

WILMA PRESENT: That left the relay. This was my chance to become the first American woman to win three Olympic gold medals. Everybody was talking about the teams from Russia, West Germany, and Britain. Well, we beat them *and* set a world's record in the process! The crowd went wild.

ALL: Wil-ma! Wil-ma! Hooray!

WILMA PRESENT: I had done it—the first American woman to win three gold medals. I had to share the moment with my family.

WILMA PAST:

Dear Folks,

Three Olympic gold medals—what a feeling! After the playing of "The Star Spangled Banner," I came away from the victory stand, and I was mobbed. People were pushing microphones into my face, pounding my back, and calling me the "Tennessee Tornado." I couldn't believe it. Finally, the American officials grabbed me and escorted me to safety. One of them told me that life would never be the same again.

WILMA PRESENT: That official was right! I was the darling of the press, but some animosity was developing toward me on the part of the other American women runners. The jealousy grew so intense that some of the Tigerbelles—girls I had been running with for years—were turning on me.

TEAMMATE 2: Listen to this. The paper says she has long, lissome legs and a pert charm.

TEAMMATE 3: How nice.

TEAMMATE 2: There's more. It says she makes all the other runners look like they're churning on a treadmill.

TEAMMATE 4: That means us, right?

TEAMMATE 2: No one talks about *us*. It's just Wilma, Wilma, Wilma. They forget that we ran the relay, too.

WILMA PRESENT: It all came to a head—literally—in London, where our team was participating in the British Empire Games. I had to appear at a banquet, and I looked a mess.

WILMA PAST: Oh, where are those hair rollers? I've got to meet Coach Temple in an hour and I look awful.

TEAMMATE 2: Gee, Wilma, I have no idea where they are.

TEAMMATE 4: Me, either.

TEAMMATE 3: Don't worry, Wilma. I'm sure they'll love you anyway.

WILMA PRESENT: When Coach Temple learned what had happened, he was furious. He called a team meeting, but as he discovered the next day, his lecture didn't have much effect. The Tigerbelles were entered in the women's relay. The stadium was packed with fans who wanted to see the fastest women's relay team in history, but my three teammates had something else in mind.

TEAMMATE 2: Let's just take it easy today, ladies.

TEAMMATE 3: Yeah! I'm feeling kinda tired.

WILMA PRESENT: They loped around the track just fast enough to keep us in the race. By the time I got the baton, the leading runner was forty yards ahead of me. Well, I was determined to win that race, so I poured on the speed. I caught up with the front runner at the tape—and won! The crowd went wild. So did Coach Temple.

COACH TEMPLE: When we get back to Tennessee State, you three are on probation!

WILMA PRESENT: From that point on, my teammates ran their best, but they shunned me when we were off the field. It was a relief when Coach Temple announced that we were going home. We landed at the Nashville airport, and home had never looked so good.

WILMA PAST: I never expected such a huge crowd, Coach.

COACH TEMPLE: Seems like everyone in Nashville is here to greet us—the governor, the mayor, television stations, marching bands. I've never seen anything like it.

WILMA PAST: It's great, Coach, but I just want to go home to my family in Clarksville.

WILMA PRESENT: In a few days, my folks joined me in a motorcade parade down the streets of my hometown. It was the most amazing event because the whole town—black and white—turned out to greet me.

WILMA PAST: Mama, do you realize this parade is the very first integrated event in Clarksville?

MAMA: And you made it happen, Wilma. Why, I never thought I'd live to see this day.

WILMA PRESENT: That night, for the first time in the history of Clarksville, black people and white people attended a banquet together. One of the featured speakers was County Judge William Hudson.

Macmillan/McGraw-Hill

JUDGE: Welcome, everyone. Wilma Rudolph has competed with the world and has brought home three gold medals. Not only that, she has inspired another victory right here at home. In working together to put on this banquet in her honor, I think we've learned a worthwhile lesson: If you want to get good music out of a piano, you have to play both the white and the black keys.

WILMA PRESENT: By the beginning of 1961, I'd completed my education, getting a degree in elementary education. I'd also received hundreds of invitations and honors. One of my proudest moments came when President Kennedy invited me, my mother, and Coach Temple to the White House. After returning from that Washington trip, I started to do some hard thinking.

WILMA PAST: I'm twenty-two years old, and I've won three Olympic gold medals. So where do I go from here, Coach?

COACH TEMPLE: What about the 1964 Olympics, Wilma?

WILMA PAST: I don't know. . . . I want to have a family, and I'd like to help kids like me make it. On the other hand, it would be exciting to compete again in '64. But if I did, I'd have to win at least three more gold medals, or else people would think I'm a failure.

COACH TEMPLE: I understand, Wilma, and remember this: If you lose in '64, that's what people will remember—the losses, not the three gold medals in 1960.

WILMA PRESENT: I had a lot to think about. Then, in 1962, a major meet was slated with the Soviet Union. I trained hard, for in the back of my mind was the thought that this might be the right time to end my career. I wanted to retire on top, even if it meant retiring earlier than I needed to. First came the 100 meters, and I won it easily. Then came the relay, an event the Russian team excelled at. When I got the baton for the final lap, the Russian runner was about forty yards ahead of me. I started picking up speed and closing on her.

COACH TEMPLE: That's the way, Wilma! Pour it on!

WILMA PRESENT: She saw me coming out of the corner of her eye, and I could tell she couldn't believe that I was there. Well, I caught her, passed her, and won the race. The crowd was on its feet, giving me a standing ovation, and I knew that it was time—time to retire, with the sweet taste of victory.

WILMA PAST: Whew! I thought I'd never finish signing autographs. I know I'll miss the running, but this day had to come sometime, didn't it, Coach?

COACH TEMPLE: It comes to all of us. You're a real champ, Wilma. You've opened lots of doors for lots of people. I'll always be proud of you. Are you okay? Do you want a lift back to the hotel?

WILMA PAST: I think I'd just like to sit here by myself for awhile. Thanks for everything, Coach.

WILMA PRESENT: I was untying my track shoes, when out from the shadows came a young boy who had been pushed aside by the crowd. He was clutching a scrap of paper and a pencil.

YOUNG BOY: Miss Rudolph . . . ?

WILMA PAST: Have you been waiting all this time? Come on over and sit down by me. Do you want to be a runner, too?

YOUNG BOY: Yes, and I dream about being in the Olympics some day. Miss Rudolph, . . . can I please have your autograph?

WILMA PAST: Son, I'll do better than that.

WILMA PRESENT: I took off my track shoes and signed my name on both of them. Then I handed them to the boy.

WILMA PAST: Here, these are for you. And let me tell you what someone once told me: If you want to do something, do it. Don't daydream about it. *Do it!*

BLOCKING DIAGRAM

Arrange sixteen chairs, as shown. The narrator, Wilma
Present, can use a music stand to hold the script.

1. WILMA PRESENT
2. DOCTOR
3. YVONNE
4. MAMA
5. WILMA PAST
6. COACH TEMPLE

7. TEAMMATE 2
8. TEAMMATE 3
9. TEAMMATE 4
10. WOMAN
11. MAN
12. MRS. HOSKINS

13. COACH GRAY
14. MAE FAGGS
15. TEAMMATE 1
16. JUDGE
17. YOUNG BOY

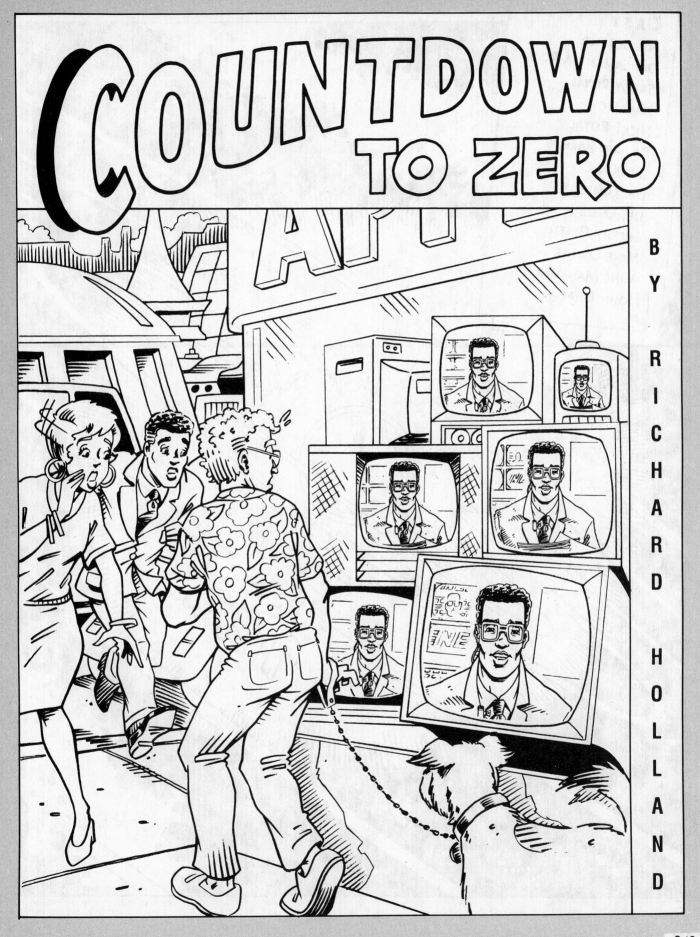

COUNTDOWN TO ZERO

BY RICHARD HOLLAND

CAST
NEWSCASTER
DR. SAMANTHA ROYAL
SANDY ROYAL
NARRATOR
NICKY ROYAL
DR. ART PARKER
DR. KILE
DR. GRAYBAR
DR. ORTIZ
SHERIFF GREEN
MINE OWNER
MINE MANAGER
JOHN BEEBE

DR. ROYAL: Sandy! Nicky! Better turn off the TV and get ready to leave for school!

SANDY: Okay, Mom. We're almost ready.

SOUND EFFECT: [*TV being switched off*]

NARRATOR: Sandy and Nicky, twelve-year-old twins of geophysicist Dr. Samantha Royal, were starting what they thought would be just another ordinary day. They had no idea that this day would mark the beginning of the most terrifying period in the earth's history.

DR. ROYAL: Here are your lunches, kids.

SOUND EFFECT: [*scratching on wood*]

DR. ROYAL: What's that scratching sound at the front door?

NICKY: I'll see.

SOUND EFFECT: [*door opening*]

NICKY: Hey, it's a cat!

SANDY: I recognize it. That's Bobby Sander's cat.

NICKY: Hmmm . . . that's funny. What's it doing way over here?

SANDY: Weird. We can drop it off at Bobby's house on our way to school.

NICKY: Hey, look at that! It looks like all the neighbors' cats are wandering up and down the street!

DR. ROYAL: That *is* strange. Well, we'd all better get going, or we'll be late.

SOUND EFFECT: [*door opening and closing; car starting*]

NARRATOR: The twins went off to school, and Dr. Royal went off to her lab without another thought about butterflies or cats. Her mind was on an important experiment that she and her colleague, Dr. Art Parker, had been working on for nearly four years. Now their work had reached a crucial stage.

DR. PARKER: Samantha, I think we're pretty close to fusing hepalite and tungasium to make artificial plasmonium.

SOUND EFFECT: [*clinking and clanking of lab equipment*]

DR. ROYAL: I think you're right, Art. I just hope Centripetal Corporation comes up with the grant money we need to complete our experiments.

DR. PARKER: They have to. How else will they get a substance as heavy as plasmonium for their moon anchors? Ever since mining natural plasmonium became illegal, they've been searching for a method to produce it synthetically.

SOUND EFFECT: [*knock and door opening*]

DR. KILE: Samantha! Art! Do you have a spare minute or two? Dr. Graybar would like you to come to the conference room.

DR. ROYAL: We can always find time for Dr. Graybar! What's up, Dr. Kile?

DR. KILE: It's the monarch butterfly problem. He's looking for some answers.

DR. ROYAL: But we're geophysicists, not biologists.

DR. KILE: Exactly what he needs.

DR. ROYAL: If you say so . . .

SOUND EFFECT: [*footsteps of three people*]

NARRATOR: Dr. Royal and Dr. Parker entered the conference room and found a group of distinguished scientists assembled there.

DR. GRAYBAR: Ah, yes. Welcome Dr. Royal, Dr. Parker. I think you know everyone here. We've been discussing a very serious matter. It seems that the monarch butterfly phenomenon is a manifestation of a more complex problem. Other species of animals have been exhibiting strange behavior, as well.

DR. ROYAL: Hmmm. That's interesting. Just this morning, my family noticed that all the neighborhood cats seemed to be wandering around as if lost.

DR. GRAYBAR: Exactly! I'm convinced there is a connection between the cats and the butterflies.

DR. PARKER: Really? Could you explain? I'm afraid you've lost me!

DR. GRAYBAR: Well, we know butterflies migrate using a form of internal radar tuned to the earth's magnetic field. Cats don't migrate, of course. But cats *have* been known to find their way home from hundreds of miles away using the same type of internal detection system.

DR. PARKER: Fascinating! Do you think there's been some kind of change in the magnetic field of the earth?

DR. GRAYBAR: That may be a possibility, but we don't know for sure. Centromagnetism is your area of expertise. That's why I asked you and Dr. Royal to attend this meeting.

DR. ROYAL: It could be disastrous if the earth's magnetic field changed even the slightest millibar.

DR. PARKER: Absolutely!

SOUND EFFECT: [*knock at the door*]

DR. ORTIZ: Dr. Graybar! Excuse me a moment, Dr. Graybar!

DR. GRAYBAR: Yes, Dr. Ortiz?

DR. ORTIZ: The National Weather Center in Washington just called. The sun . . . the sun rose forty-three point nine seconds too early this morning!

SOUND EFFECT: [*gasps from all*]

DR. GRAYBAR: This is even worse than we thought. If we don't come up with some answers quickly, I'm afraid that our planet will be facing serious consequences.

NARRATOR: The meeting concluded with an assignment of tasks. Each team of scientists began working at a frantic pace. Dr. Royal and Dr. Parker set about measuring the earth's magnetic field.

DR. ROYAL: Are the instruments set?

DR. PARKER: Yes. We've made all the satellite connections. I'm activating the laser-links from the poles.

SOUND EFFECT: [*hum and clicking of scientific instruments*]

DR. ROYAL: All right. Let's mark the position . . . in three . . . two . . . one . . . mark! What's the reading?

DR. PARKER: This is unbelievable!

DR. ROYAL: What is it, Art?

DR. PARKER: Magnetic north has moved three millibars to the east!

DR. ROYAL: That's impossible. Check again! Mark in three . . . two . . . one . . . mark! What's your reading now?

DR. PARKER: It's moved again! This time it's two millibars to the *west*!

DR. ROYAL: How can that be? Maybe the instruments are faulty.

DR. PARKER: No, I checked them thoroughly before we started. Samantha, there's no denying the fact that magnetic north is no longer constant! This must be why the butterflies are exhibiting such strange behavior.

DR. ROYAL: Imagine the potential effect on weather patterns! What will happen when the polar ice caps begin to melt?

DR. PARKER: The tides will surely be affected; the seasons, too.

DR. ROYAL: Since magnetic north keeps shifting, we have no way of predicting when these changes will occur.

NARRATOR: The world was to find out the next morning.

SANDY: Mom, it's time for school, but it's still so dark out.

DR. ROYAL: Well, the sun is coming up now. Come look out the window. Isn't it beautiful?

NICKY: Look! Look at that!

SANDY: The sun is going down again—like it's setting!

DR. ROYAL: This is incredible!

NICKY: Wait. It's coming back up again!

SANDY: Mom, how can we be having sunrise and sunset at the same time?

DR. ROYAL: I don't know—yet. Let's see if there is anything on the news.

SOUND EFFECT: [*TV being switched on*]

NEWSCASTER: Here's the latest Satellite News brief. This morning, millions of people witnessed an unbelievable sight: the sun rising twice in one morning. Scientists are at a loss to explain the phenomenon.

Macmillan/McGraw-Hill

NARRATOR: Within a few minutes, the phone lines were jammed. Police departments all over the country were flooded with calls from confused and frightened residents.

SOUND EFFECT: [*phone ringing*]

SHERIFF: Hello. Yes, this is Sheriff Green. Mr. Boynton! How are you this morning? What do you mean "Which morning?" Tuesday morning, of course. No, no, it's not Wednesday. Yes, it *is* a new day each time the sun rises. Yes, the sun did rise twice today, but it's still Tuesday. At least I think it's still Tuesday. No, I don't know who to ask. Best thing to do is to stay tuned to the local news satellite.

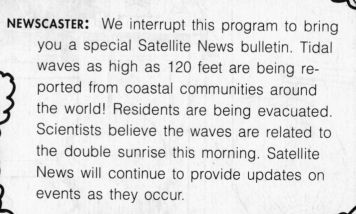

NEWSCASTER: We interrupt this program to bring you a special Satellite News bulletin. Tidal waves as high as 120 feet are being reported from coastal communities around the world! Residents are being evacuated. Scientists believe the waves are related to the double sunrise this morning. Satellite News will continue to provide updates on events as they occur.

NARRATOR: All over the world, scientists were meeting in an attempt to analyze the situation.

SOUND EFFECT: [*hum of many voices; banging of a gavel*]

DR. GRAYBAR: Will the meeting please come to order! Please come to order! Dr. Ortiz, you have the floor.

DR. ORTIZ: This double-sunrise phenomenon must be an optical illusion. I can find no other explanation for it.

DR. ROYAL: I know that as an astronomer you find it particularly difficult to believe, Dr. Ortiz. But it is not an optical illusion. It *did* happen.

DR. KILE: What do you think is causing it, Dr. Royal?

DR. ROYAL: I can't assign causality yet, Dr. Kile. But I do believe the earth is no longer spinning in a constant motion on its axis.

Macmillan/McGraw-Hill

SOUND EFFECT: [*hum of very excited voices; banging of a gavel*]

DR. GRAYBAR: Ladies and gentlemen, please! I am sure Dr. Royal has good reasons for making such a radical statement. I, for one, would like to hear them.

DR. ROYAL: Thank you, Dr. Graybar. According to our calculations—and I know this sounds incredible—the earth is wobbling.

DR. KILE: Wobbling? What in the world do you mean?

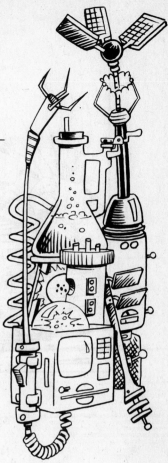

DR. ROYAL: Based on a series of measurements, Dr. Parker and I have discovered that the angle of the earth's tilt on its axis keeps varying. The earth is actually tilting back and forth one to three millibars every day. This means, of course, that the horizon line keeps fluctuating.

DR. PARKER: In other words, after the sun rises, the horizon moves up and covers it again, making it appear as if the sun is setting. When the earth tips down again, the sun appears to be rising a second time.

DR. ROYAL: We believe the unusual events that have occurred recently—the double sunrises, the tidal waves, the deviation in animal migratory patterns—have been caused by the earth wobbling.

DR. GRAYBAR: But *why* is the earth wobbling?

DR. ROYAL: We don't know yet. That's the next mystery to be solved.

NARRATOR: A few days later, while scouting around for rocks to include in their science-fair project, Sandy and Nicky stumbled onto what turned out to be an important clue.

SOUND EFFECT: [*footsteps walking over rocks and gravel*]

NICKY: What a great place to find unusual rocks! It's almost as good as the old quarry.

SANDY: It sure is. Hey, look at that pink glow! It seems to be coming from one of the rocks over there.

NICKY: Over where?

SANDY: Near that maglev track that leads to the old abandoned mine shaft! See? Come on—that would be a great sample to have.

SOUND EFFECT: [*footsteps running over rocks and gravel*]

NICKY: I've got my collection bag ready and waiting. Just drop it in.

SANDY: I can't, Nicky. It's too heavy!

NICKY: What do you mean it's too heavy? It's as small as a marble.

SANDY: You try picking it up. It won't budge. It weighs a ton!

NICKY: Sandy, look at your hand! It's glowing pink!

SANDY: Oh, no! It must be from this rock!

NICKY: Try wiping it off on the grass!

SANDY: I am! This pink stuff won't come off!

NARRATOR: Just then, the owner of the abandoned mine spotted the twins.

MINE OWNER: Hey! You kids! What are you doing? Get away from there! Don't let me catch you here again! Foster, get over here and help me move those rocks!

MINE MANAGER: Right away, boss!

NARRATOR: Terrified, the twins hurried home. Sandy tried to scrub the pink rock dust from her hand, but no matter what she used, her hand still glowed.

SOUND EFFECT: [*running water followed by opening and closing of a door*]

DR. ROYAL: Hi, I'm home!

SANDY: Mom! Mom! Look at my hand! I can't get this pink stuff off! Is it dangerous?

DR. ROYAL: Let me see it. How did this happen?

NICKY: Sandy touched a pink rock. I mean, it was glowing pink.

SANDY: Am I going to die?

DR. ROYAL: No, this is plasmonium dust. It's not toxic, and it'll wear off in a couple of days. You'll be fine, Sandy. But where on earth did you find plasmonium?

NICKY: We were near that abandoned mine looking for rocks for our science project.

DR. ROYAL: You mean the old Centripetal Corporation mine?

SANDY: Yes.

DR. ROYAL: Do you have the rock?

NICKY: No, it was too heavy to pick up. Besides, some men chased us away. They were really mean.

DR. ROYAL: Hmmm. There's something odd about all this. That mine has been shut down for over ten years. Listen, I don't want you two going back there. It's not a safe place.

SANDY: Okay, Mom. It *was* kind of spooky.

DR. ROYAL: Do you remember exactly where you found that rock?

NICKY: We found it right near one of the maglev tracks that comes out of the old mine shaft.

SANDY: Hold on a minute. I think I remember seeing a faded old sign that said shaft six.

DR. ROYAL: Thanks, eagle eye! I'd better call Art Parker right away.

SOUND EFFECT: [*dialing of telephone*]

DR. ROYAL: Hello, Art? Listen, I have a hunch that Centripetal Corporation is mining plasmonium again!

DR. PARKER: What makes you think so?

DR. ROYAL: Sandy and Nicky found a sample of the ore right outside Centripetal's so-called abandoned mine. Sandy's hand is still glowing pink.

DR. PARKER: Hmmm. Since the glow-life of plasmonium is eight days, that means the sample is fresh. Wasn't Centripetal mining from the earth's mantle before they were ordered to shut down?

DR. ROYAL: Yes, but they had pretty much exhausted the supply of plasmonium in the mantle. That's why they applied for a permit to mine in the earth's core.

DR. PARKER: Right, it's coming back to me now. That's when the International Earth Preservation Organization banned *all* mining of plasmonium to conserve the little that remained.

DR. ROYAL: That's correct. . . . Art, I have an idea.

DR. PARKER: What?

DR. ROYAL: Well, you know how desperate Centripetal has been for a plasmonium substitute for their moon anchors. . . .

DR. PARKER: Ye-e-s . . .

DR. ROYAL: Let's just suppose for a moment that they couldn't wait for our fusion experiments to yield results, so they started mining plasmonium from the earth's core—secretly, of course. Since plasmonium is earth's heaviest known substance, . . .

DR. PARKER: . . . if enough of it were removed from the core, it could cause the earth to become unbalanced!

DR. ROYAL: Exactly! I think we're on to something, Art. This could be . . .

SOUND EFFECT: [*loud rumble followed by crash of something heavy falling*]

SANDY: What's that?

NICKY: What's going on?

DR. ROYAL: Quick, turn on Satellite News.

SOUND EFFECT: [*TV being switched on*]

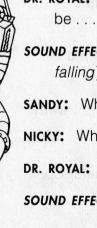

Macmillan/McGraw-Hill

NEWSCASTER: . . . have been recorded from coast to coast. Some of the earth tremors lasted for as long as three minutes. Others were only a few seconds in duration. Fortunately, no casualties have been reported, but in some areas, property damage has been extensive. Stay tuned for exclusive Satellite News coverage.

DR. PARKER: [*muffled voice*] Samantha, Samantha!

DR. ROYAL: Art, Art, are you still there? Are you all right?

DR. PARKER: Wow! Yes, I'm okay. How about you and the kids?

DR. ROYAL: We're all right, too. This is getting to be very serious. We've got to do something—fast.

DR. PARKER: You'd better report your suspicions about Centripetal Corporation to Dr. Graybar.

DR. ROYAL: I will—right away.

SOUND EFFECT: [*telephone receiver being replaced*]

NARRATOR: Dr. Graybar was shocked by what Dr. Royal had to say. The next morning, he called an emergency meeting of the IEPO—the International Earth Preservation Organization. The member countries were immediately linked by satel-vision.

DR. PARKER: As you all know, Dr. Royal and I have concluded that the earth is wobbling because it's out of balance. Now we have a hypothesis to explain this phenomenon.

DR. ROYAL: We have reason to believe that Centripetal Corporation is mining plasmonium from the earth's core.

DR. KILE: But Centripetal's license to mine plasmonium was canceled ten years ago. You yourself were on the inspection team, Dr. Royal.

DR. ROYAL: That's true. But inspections at the mine site were stopped more than a year ago. Now, if they *have* been mining from the core in this past year, they could have removed as much as 250 trillion qwarnels of plasmonium.

DR. PARKER: This would explain why the earth is unbalanced, and why the earth's magnetic field keeps changing.

DR. ORTIZ: What evidence do you have to back up this notion?

DR. ROYAL: Yesterday my children found a small sample of plasmonium ore near Centripetal Corporation's abandoned mine.

DR. KILE: Do you have the sample?

DR. ROYAL: Regrettably, no. It was much too heavy for them to lift. And when the people from Centripetal saw the children, they chased them off.

DR. ORTIZ: Now Dr. Royal, you can't expect us to take the word of children when the future of the nation . . .

DR. KILE: The earth!

DR. GRAYBAR: The universe!

DR. ORTIZ: Yes! When the future of the entire universe is at stake.

DR. ROYAL: I myself saw the plasmonium dust on my daughter's hand. The situation is critical. According to my calculations, if the earth tilts another nine millibars, the planet will go hurtling out into space!

DR. PARKER: And it will only take the removal of another two million qwarnels of plasmonium to make that happen. So you see, Centripetal must be investigated immediately.

DR. ORTIZ: Just the same, I think we must study the problem a little while longer.

DR. KILE: I agree with Dr. Ortiz. We must not be too hasty. After all, Centripetal Corporation did give us over two hundred million dollars for scientific research last year.

DR. GRAYBAR: Dr. Royal, we need concrete evidence. It would not be responsible to accuse Centripetal without proof.

NARRATOR: Unable to convince the organization to take immediate action, Dr. Royal and Dr. Parker went back to their lab and pondered the problem.

SOUND EFFECT: [*footsteps followed by door opening and closing*]

DR. ROYAL: Art, we can't just sit by and let Centripetal Corporation destroy the entire world.

DR. PARKER: But Dr. Graybar is right. We can't accuse them of mining plasmonium without concrete evidence, Samantha.

DR. ROYAL: Then we'll have to get the evidence!

DR. PARKER: How? We can't go marching up to them and say we'd like to take a little tour of their abandoned mine.

DR. ROYAL: No, we can't. What we can do is figure out a way to get into the mine. If we find any traces of glowing plasmonium in the mine shafts, we'll have our proof.

DR. PARKER: But how will we know where to search? There are hundreds of shafts in Centripetal's mine.

DR. ROYAL: I still have a map of that mine from when I served on the inspection team. Let's go back to my house and take a look in my files.

SOUND EFFECT: [*door opening and closing; car starting*]

NARRATOR: As the two scientists headed for Dr. Royal's house, the owner of Centripetal Corporation met with the manager of the mine.

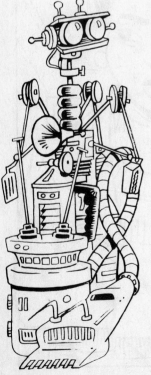

MINE MANAGER: Those kids were a little too interested in that pink rock. You know, boss, I think I recognized them. Their mother is that scientist, Samantha Royal. Remember her? She was on the inspection team that kept us shut down for ten years.

MINE OWNER: Do I ever remember! But we managed to outfox them, didn't we, Foster? We didn't do any plasmonium mining, but we kept all the *equipment* in running order. Nothing illegal about that!

MINE MANAGER: Yeah! And then when they finally decided it was safe to stop inspections after ten years, we were able to get right back in business—quietly, of course!

MINE OWNER: Right. We've been very careful. So don't worry about those kids—or their mother. They don't know anything.

MINE MANAGER: Say, boss—off the record—you don't think our mining has anything to do with this earth-wobbling thing, do you?

MINE OWNER: Nah! People have been mining for years, and the earth has never wobbled.

MINE MANAGER: But they were mining in the earth's mantle. We've gone into the core.

MINE OWNER: Don't worry, I tell you. Besides, we only need to keep going for another month or so. Another two million qwarnels of plasmonium, and we'll all be able to retire—very comfortably.

MINE MANAGER: Yeah, we'll be rich, all right. Very rich!

MINE OWNER: It probably wouldn't hurt to beef up security, just in case anyone starts to get nosy.

MINE MANAGER: Should I post a guard at the northeast end of the mine?

MINE OWNER: No, that might make it look as if we have something to hide. We can't do anything that might arouse suspicion. Let's just make sure that everything looks as if it hasn't been disturbed for the last ten years. And, for Pete's sake, check to see that there's no more plasmonium ore lying around!

NARRATOR: Meanwhile, Dr. Royal and Dr. Parker examined the company's maps and developed a plan.

SOUND EFFECT: [*crackle of paper unfolding*]

DR. ROYAL: Let's see. Sandy said she thought she found the rock that was glowing pink near shaft six.

DR. PARKER: Uh-huh. Four . . . seven . . . six! Here it is, in the northeast quadrant.

DR. ROYAL: Art, I'm fairly certain that's where Centripetal had proposed to dig into the earth's core.

DR. PARKER: Well, Samantha, I'm convinced. I'd say there isn't a minute to lose. The sooner we look into this, the better.

DR. ROYAL: It's still fairly early; how about going right now? I'll just leave a note for the kids.

SOUND EFFECT: [*start-up noise of computer followed by clicking of keyboard*]

DR. ROYAL: Let's see now . . .

Dear Sandy and Nicky,

Dr. Parker and I are going to take a look at Centripetal Corporation's mine. There's a frozen pizza and some veggies in the fridge. If I'm not back by eight o'clock, call Aunt Holly and ask her to come over. See you in the morning.

Love you,
Mom

Macmillan/McGraw-Hill

NARRATOR: Dr. Royal left the note on the kitchen counter, where Sandy and Nicky would be sure to see it. Then she and Dr. Parker headed out to the mine.

SOUND EFFECT: [*door closing; car starting*]

NARRATOR: As they drove away, Dr. Royal had no way of knowing that a sudden gust of wind caused by closing the door had blown the note off the counter. The paper fell to the floor and came to rest under the refrigerator.

DR. ROYAL: Let's park down the road from the mine and walk the rest of the way.

SOUND EFFECT: [*car stopping; two doors closing quietly*]

DR. PARKER: So far, so good. There doesn't seem to be anyone around.

NARRATOR: The two made their way to the northeast quadrant and found the tracks leading to shaft six. There was an old wooden door with a padlock on it blocking the entrance.

DR. PARKER: This doesn't look as if it's been used in the past ten years, let alone the past year.

DR. ROYAL: That's true. This wood is so old, it's rotting away. I wonder how sturdy it is. . . .

SOUND EFFECT: [*crack of breaking wood; creaking hinges*]

DR. PARKER: It broke right off its hinges.

DR. ROYAL: That's what you call a lucky break! And we'd might as well make the most of it.

DR. PARKER: Go ahead. I'm right behind you. Look! Shine the flashlight along the wall down there. Hmmm. There's certainly no pink glow. Just a lot of dusty rocks.

DR. ROYAL: Look here. It's the high-speed elevator they built when they applied for permission to mine the core. Come over here on the platform and take a look at the control panel. See, they installed stops down to minus twenty.

DR. PARKER: I doubt if they ever got around to wiring it up.

NARRATOR: As he spoke, Dr. Parker absentmindedly pushed one of the buttons.

SOUND EFFECT: [click]

DR. ROYAL: The light went on!

DR. PARKER: Let's see what happens if I press minus three.

SOUND EFFECT: [whirring and hum of an elevator]

DR. ROYAL: We're moving! What's going on here?

DR. PARKER: It's working—and it doesn't even squeak. Samantha, this elevator has been used very recently. I'm sure of it.

SOUND EFFECT: [elevator hum stopping; door sliding open]

NARRATOR: At minus three, the elevator stopped and the door slid open. Suddenly, the two scientists were bathed in a glow of pink light.

DR. ROYAL: Art! This is it!

DR. PARKER: Plasmonium! Tons of it! This must be their loading dock!

NARRATOR: Dr. Royal took a microcamera out of her pocket and began filming while Dr. Parker took a tiny rock sample and put it into his backpack. They were both very conscious of the need to work quickly.

DR. ROYAL: That should do it. We've got our proof now!

DR. PARKER: Right. Let's go back up. Hurry!

SOUND EFFECT: [*hum of elevator coming to a sudden stop*]

DR. ROYAL: It stopped. How come the door isn't opening?

DR. PARKER: I don't know. Here, let's try this lever. Give me a hand.

DR. ROYAL: It won't budge. It seems to be jammed!

SOUND EFFECT: [*static*]

DR. PARKER: The lights are flickering, too! There may be a short in the wiring.

DR. ROYAL: Or maybe they turn off the power at night.

DR. PARKER: Uh-oh! *None* of the buttons are working now.

DR. ROYAL: We're stuck!

DR. PARKER: I don't see any way out of here.

DR. ROYAL: I'm afraid there's only one way. In my note, I told the twins where we were going. When they realize I'm not back, I'm sure they'll get help. There is one hitch, though.

DR. PARKER: What's that?

DR. ROYAL: I said I'd see them in the morning. That's several hours from now!

DR. PARKER: Well, let's just hope there are no earth tremors between now and then.

NARRATOR: No sooner were the words out of Dr. Parker's mouth, than they heard a sound that made their blood run cold.

SOUND EFFECT: [*rumble that gets louder and louder*]

DR. PARKER: What is that?

DR. ROYAL: It sounds like the mine is collapsing!

SOUND EFFECT: [*bumping noises as elevator car shakes*]

DR. PARKER: Hang on!

NARRATOR: Meanwhile, at Samantha's house, the twins had finished their dinner and were taking a break from their homework.

SANDY: I don't understand it. Mom *always* lets us know if she's going to be home late.

NICKY: I know. I called the lab. No one answers. I tried Dr. Parker, too, but he's not home, either. I'm worried.

SANDY: Me, too. Let's check Mom's appointment book. Maybe that'll tell us something.

NARRATOR: The children went into their mother's office.

NICKY: I feel funny about this. You know we're not allowed in here when Mom's not home.

SANDY: I know, but this is special.

SOUND EFFECT: [*papers rustling*]

SANDY: Look at this!

NICKY: Hey, it's a map of the Centripetal mines.

SANDY: And someone's drawn a circle around shaft six. That's where we found the plasmonium.

NICKY: Are you thinking what I'm thinking?

SANDY: I sure am! We'd better call Sheriff Green right away.

NARRATOR: After hearing what Sandy and Nicky had to say, Sheriff Green was also concerned.

SHERIFF: Listen, kids, I'll drive over to the mine and take a look around.

NICKY: Please, Sheriff, let us go with you.

SHERIFF: No, no, it's much too late. . . .

SANDY: But we can show you exactly where we found the plasmonium ore.

SHERIFF: Hmmm . . . well, I suppose that would be a help. All right; I'll come by and pick you up in a few minutes.

NARRATOR: Just a short time later, they were following the same route Dr. Royal and Dr. Parker had taken that afternoon.

NICKY: Look! There's Mom's car. So she *is*. . . . What's that?

SOUND EFFECT: [*rumbling starts as Nicky speaks; gets louder and louder through the following speeches*]

SANDY: Oh, no!

SHERIFF: [*loudly*] This is zero-five-one calling Homebase. Zero-five-one calling Homebase. SOS! Do you read?

SOUND EFFECT: [*rumbling starts to get softer, then slowly fades away*]

NARRATOR: Within hours of the sheriff's call to headquarters, news of the trapped scientists had been picked up by Satellite News. Soon, reporters as well as rescue crews were on the spot.

NEWSCASTER: This is Bob Fredrickson for Satellite News reporting live from the Centripetal Corporation mine where Dr. Samantha Royal and Dr. Art Parker are trapped in a collapsed mine shaft. It is believed that last night's earth tremor caused the cave-in.

NARRATOR: Among those riveted to Satellite News were two people who had a very *personal* interest in what was going on—the owner and the manager of the Centripetal Corporation mine!

MINE MANAGER: How did Royal and Parker get in there, anyway?

MINE OWNER: I don't know. But we'd better hope they don't get out. Would you turn up the volume so I can hear this interview?

NEWSCASTER: [*slightly louder*] With me now is John Beebe, a member of the rescue team. John, how is the rescue operation progressing? Is it going as quickly as was hoped?

BEEBE: Well, Bob, the answer to that is yes and no. We're making good progress because the new laser-drivers we're using can cut through anything. What's slowing us down is the type of rock that has to be moved.

NEWSCASTER: What do you mean?

BEEBE: Well, some of the rocks we've encountered are unbelievably heavy. Even with our megalifters, we're limited in the number of rocks that can be moved at one time.

NEWSCASTER: What kind of rocks are they?

BEEBE: I really wouldn't know, Bob. But they're very unusual. They glow pink. Kind of pretty, actually.

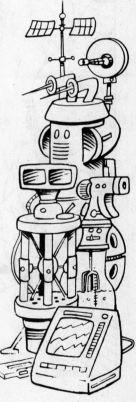

NEWSCASTER: I understand that the . . .

SOUND EFFECT: [*hum of excited voices*]

NEWSCASTER: Uh-oh, something seems to be happening here. The sun is setting—and it's only eight o'clock in the morning! Excuse me, sir. Sir?

DR. GRAYBAR: Yes?

NEWSCASTER: Aren't you Dr. Graybar of World Science Laboratories?

DR. GRAYBAR: Yes, I am.

NEWSCASTER: Can you explain why the sun is going down at this hour of the day?

DR. GRAYBAR: I would say that the earth has suddenly tipped again. This is very serious. I'm sure there will be severe consequences. And I might add that Dr. Royal and Dr. Parker predicted this.

NEWSCASTER: Thank you, Dr. Graybar and Mr. Beebe. Now, back to our studio.

NARRATOR: A few minutes later, the head of the rescue operation came running out of the mine shaft with the news that the tipping of the earth had created a deep crevice that allowed rescuers to reach the trapped scientists.

MINE MANAGER: Boss! There's another news bulletin coming on. Quick! Something must have happened at the mine.

NEWSCASTER: This is Satellite News interrupting our regular programming to bring you this fast-breaking bulletin. It's expected that rescuers will be reaching Dr. Royal and Dr. Parker very shortly.

BEEBE: We've got 'em!

NEWSCASTER: Can you see Dr. Parker and Dr. Royal?

BEEBE: Yes! Yes! They're bringing them out!

SOUND EFFECT: [*cheering*]

SANDY/NICKY: Mom! Mom!

NEWSCASTER: Excuse me, Dr. Royal, Dr. Parker, do you have a few words for our Satellite News viewers?

DR. ROYAL: Sandy! Nicky!

SANDY: Mom! Are you all right?

NEWSCASTER: Ummm . . . excuse me . . .

NICKY: Are you okay, Mom? How about you, Dr. Parker?

DR. ROYAL: Well, we're a little bruised and very hungry, but otherwise I think we're okay.

DR. PARKER: And from what the sheriff told us, it's thanks to you two that we're here at all!

NEWSCASTER: Dr. Royal, Dr. Parker, you're glowing pink!

DR. ROYAL: That's because we're covered with plasmonium dust. Centripetal Corporation has secretly been mining plasmonium from the earth's core.

MINE MANAGER: Boss! Boss! Did you hear that?

MINE OWNER: Don't worry, Foster. They can't prove a thing. All the evidence has been buried in the cave-in!

NEWSCASTER: That's a strong accusation, Dr. Royal. Do you have any proof?

DR. ROYAL: See this camera? It tells the whole story.

MINE OWNER: I'm afraid that does it for us, Foster.

NARRATOR: In the days that followed, there was still a great deal to be done.

SOUND EFFECT: [*hum of many voices; banging of a gavel*]

DR. GRAYBAR: I've called this meeting because our problems are not over. The earth *must* be returned to its normal position. And it must be done *now,* before there is another earth tremor.

DR. ORTIZ: To accomplish that, plasmonium must be replaced in the earth's core. But how?

DR. KILE: Dr. Royal and Dr. Parker have been working on the production of artificial plasmonium. Perhaps we should ask them if they have any ideas.

DR. ROYAL: You're correct, Dr. Kile. We have managed to create a synthetic plasmonium in our laboratory by fusing hepalite and tungasium. We think it's a viable technique, but our research has not been tested in the field.

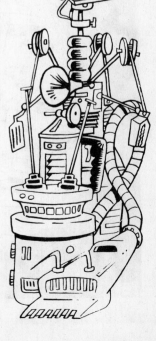

DR. GRAYBAR: You will have that opportunity now. It's our only hope.

NARRATOR: The crevice in the Centripetal mine that had been created by the last earth tremor was found to extend well beyond the earth's mantle. Did it go as far as the core? No one knew for sure, but they would soon find out.

NEWSCASTER: [*very quietly*] This is Bob Fredrickson of Satellite News on location in the mountains that surround the Centripetal Corporation mine. From where I'm standing, I can see the mine directly below me. I'm told that the mine crevice has been filled with hepalite and tungasium. Scientists are now ready to detonate a thermofusion explosion that they hope will result in the formation of plasmonium. This synthetic plasmonium will, in turn, be forced into the earth's core. The whole world is watching and waiting during this countdown to zero!

NEWS

DR. PARKER: T minus thirty seconds and counting.

NEWSCASTER: Thirty seconds to the most important moment in the life of this planet.

DR. ROYAL: T minus ten seconds and counting. Nine . . . eight . . . seven . . . six . . . five . . . four . . . three . . . two . . . one . . . zero . . .

SOUND EFFECT: [*very loud explosion that continues for a few seconds; then more softly as the narrator speaks*]

NARRATOR: There was a tremendous roar. The earth shook as never before. After several minutes, there was silence. When the dust and debris settled, a huge crater could be seen where the Centripetal Corporation mine had once been. It was several minutes before anyone dared speak.

DR. GRAYBAR: What is the position of the sun?

DR. PARKER: Thirty-eight millibars northeast.

DR. ORTIZ: Exactly where it should be!

DR. ROYAL: It worked!

SOUND EFFECT: [*cheering and congratulations*]

NEWSCASTER: This is Bob Fredrickson for Satellite News. It's 8 A.M., the day after Countdown to Zero, as it's now being called. And now a report from the science desk. The first swarms of monarch butterflies were seen in Mexico yesterday, where scientists expected them to resume their normal migration patterns. The sun rose only once this morning, and I know I speak for all of us when I say that we certainly are glad!

DR. ROYAL: Sandy! Nicky! Better turn off the TV and get ready to leave for school!

SANDY/NICKY: Okay, Mom!

SOUND EFFECT: [*TV being switched off*]

BLOCKING DIAGRAM

Arrange eleven chairs, as shown. The narrator
and the newscaster can use music stands
to hold their scripts.

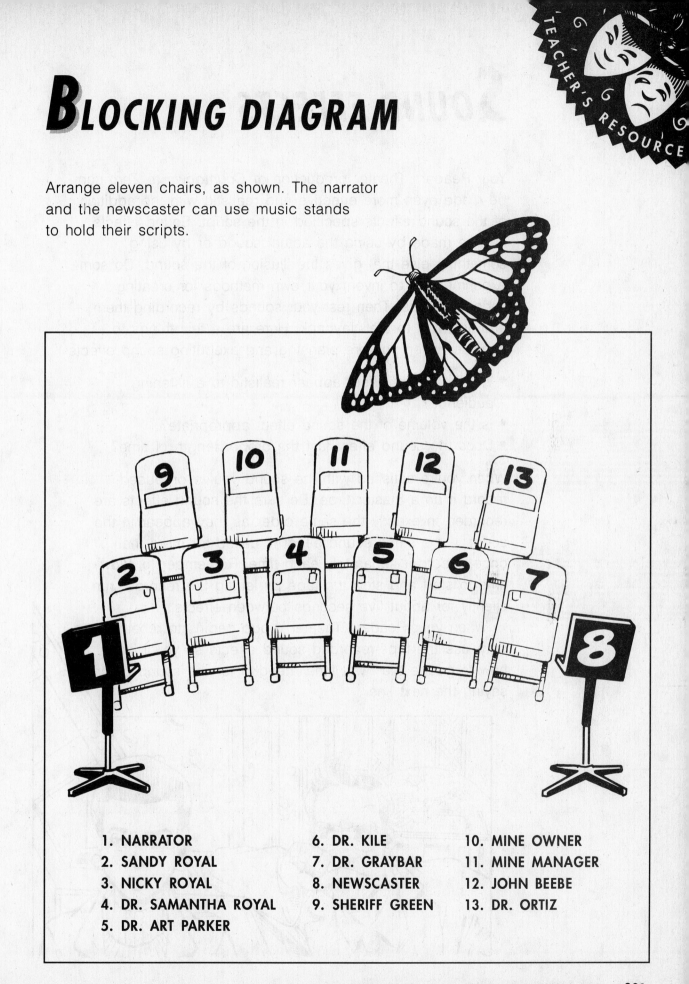

1. NARRATOR
2. SANDY ROYAL
3. NICKY ROYAL
4. DR. SAMANTHA ROYAL
5. DR. ART PARKER
6. DR. KILE
7. DR. GRAYBAR
8. NEWSCASTER
9. SHERIFF GREEN
10. MINE OWNER
11. MINE MANAGER
12. JOHN BEEBE
13. DR. ORTIZ

SOUND EFFECTS

Your Readers Theater production of *Countdown to Zero* can be made even more effective and realistic with the addition of the sound effects specified in the script. Sound effects can be made by using the actual sound or by using something else that gives the illusion of the sound. Do some experimenting to invent your own methods for creating various sounds. Then test your sounds by recording them and listening to the playback. Here are a few things to consider when you are planning and executing sound effects:

- Will the sound effect appear realistic to a listening audience?
- Is the volume of the sound effect appropriate?
- Does the sound effect last the proper length of time?

When you're satisfied with the sound you've produced, record it on a master tape. Be sure the sound effects are recorded in exactly the same order as they appear in the script. If the same sound effect is called for more than once, record it separately each time. Remember to allow time to start and stop the tape by letting the recorder run silently for about five seconds between effects.

When your Readers Theater group begins to rehearse the play, use the tape-recorded sound effects so you'll know how to gauge the "wait time" needed for the sound before saying the next line.

Macmillan/McGraw-Hill

CREATING SOUND EFFECTS

TV being switched on and off Record the click of a light switch, or a TV with the volume turned down. Or make a clicking sound with the tongue against the roof of the mouth.

scratching on wood Scratch on a wooden desk, table, or door.

door opening and closing Experiment with several doors and record the one that sounds the best.

knock at door Knock on a wooden door.

car starting; car stopping; car doors opening and closing You'll need the help of an adult to record a car engine starting. The sound of the motor being turned off followed by the opening and closing of the doors will signal that the car has stopped.

clinking and clanking of lab equipment Place silverware or other metal items in a box and rummage through them.

footsteps Record actual footsteps (the microphone should follow the walkers). The walkers should wear shoes, not sneakers, and walk on a bare floor. Decide in advance the pace at which each person should walk. To make the sound of receding footsteps, the microphone should remain in place instead of following the walker.

gasps; hum of excited voices Use your classmates. Rehearse them so that they sound natural; for example, they shouldn't gasp in unison!

banging of a gavel Sharply rap a wooden block on a desk or table.

dialing of telephone; phone being hung up Lift a telephone receiver. Depress the switch and dial. Then hang up.

phone ringing Tape the real thing for this sound.

footsteps walking or running over rocks and gravel Fill a bowl half full of a flake-type cereal and hold it close to the mike. Press two fingers in the flakes in a walking or running rhythm. For two people walking or running, double the bowls and the number of fingers.

running water Record the real thing, or pour water from a pitcher into another container that already has about an inch of water in it.

rumbling Put a handful of dried beans or macaroni in a small, deflated balloon. Then inflate the balloon and shake it. For a rumbling that gets louder and then fades away, begin with the volume of your tape recorder on *low,* increase it slowly to *loud,* then decrease slowly to *off.*

crash of something heavy falling Drop a heavy book or box on a desk.

muffled voice over the telephone Cup your hands together and place them over your nose and mouth. Speak naturally into your cupped hands.

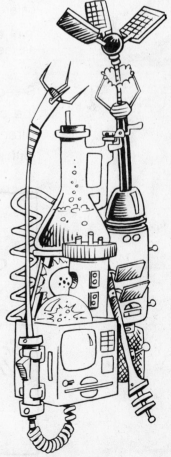

crackle of paper unfolding Prepare a sheet of notebook paper by folding it in half several times. As you record, unfold it close to the microphone.

computer Use the real thing, or record a hair dryer from a distance while typing on an electric typewriter.

crack of breaking wood Break several sticks.

creaking hinges Find a door that squeaks and record the sound while opening or closing it.

click of a light switch Use the real thing, or make a clicking sound with the tongue against the roof of the mouth.

whirring and hum of elevator Run a hair dryer at a distance. Keep it running as the readers speak. When the elevator is supposed to stop, turn off the hair dryer.

door sliding open Record a real elevator door opening. The sound made by a sliding cabinet or closet door could also be used.

static Crumple a piece of cellophane near the mike, or turn a radio dial to the far end and record the static noise.

bumping noises Hit an elbow against a door, or wrap a block of wood in a towel and knock it on a table.

papers rustling Rub two sheets of notebook paper together near the microphone.

cheering and congratulations Use your classmates. Ask them to say different things, such as *Yea* and *That's great*.

loud explosion Inflate a paper bag and pop it. At the same moment as the pop, create a rumbling sound. Let it fade slowly.

Select a studio director who can use hand signals to cue the sound-effects person and the readers. Both the studio director and the sound-effects person should have scripts with the sound effects highlighted.

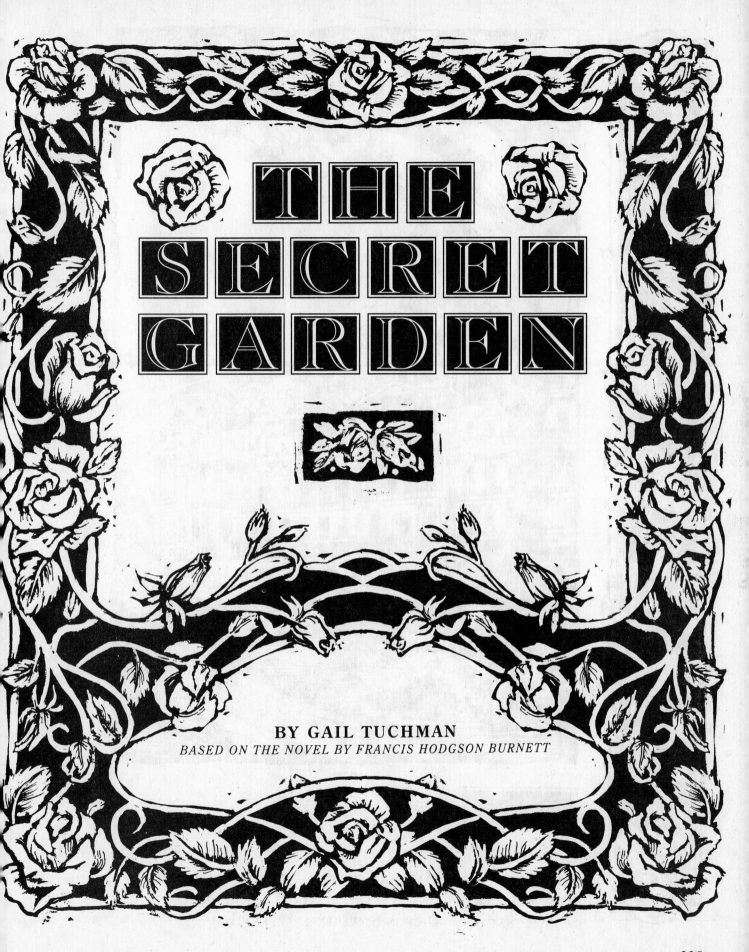

THE SECRET GARDEN

BY GAIL TUCHMAN
BASED ON THE NOVEL BY FRANCIS HODGSON BURNETT

Macmillan/McGraw-Hill

CAST

NARRATOR	MARTHA SOWERBY	ARCHIBALD CRAVEN
MRS. MEDLOCK	BEN WEATHERSTAFF	COLIN CRAVEN
MARY LENNOX	DICKON SOWERBY	DOCTOR

ACT I

NARRATOR: Mary Lennox was born in India in the 1890s. As a young child, she was cared for by an Indian servant, or ayah, who always gave Mary her own way in everything. As she grew up, inactivity left her pale and languid, and her ayah's catering made her as selfish as any tyrant who ever lived. Shortly after Mary's tenth birthday, an epidemic of cholera broke out in India, and people began dying like flies. It was in this strange and sudden way that Mary was left without parents or an ayah to care for her. And because she had no other relatives, she was sent to Yorkshire, England, to live with her uncle, Archibald Craven. Mrs. Medlock, her uncle's housekeeper, met Mary in London, and together they traveled to Mr. Craven's ancestral home, Misselthwaite Manor.

[*Display transparency of Misselthwaite Manor* (page 315).]

MRS. MEDLOCK: I may as well tell you something about where you are going. The house is six hundred years old, and it's on the edge of the moor. There's near a hundred rooms in it, though most of them's locked up tight. There's pictures and fine old furniture and a big park round it with gardens and trees—but there's nothing else. Well, what do you think of it?

MARY: Nothing. I know nothing about such places.

MRS. MEDLOCK: Don't you care?

MARY: It doesn't matter whether I care or not.

MRS. MEDLOCK: You're right. It doesn't. Your uncle is not going to trouble himself about you. That's sure and certain. He never troubles himself about no one. He's got a crooked back which set him wrong. He was a sour young man, and he got no good of all his money and big place till he married. His bride was a sweet, pretty thing. He'd have walked the world over to get her a blade o' grass she wanted. When she passed away . . .

MARY: Oh! Did she die?

MRS. MEDLOCK: Yes, and it made him stranger than ever. He won't see people, and most of the time he goes away. When he's home, he shuts himself up in the West Wing. You needn't expect to see him, and you mustn't expect there will be people to talk to. You'll have to play about and look after yourself. You'll be told what rooms you can go into and what rooms to keep out of. There's gardens enough, but when you're in the house, don't go poking about.

MARY: I shall not want to go poking about!

NARRATOR: When they arrived at the manor, Mary was led upstairs.

[*Display transparency of Mary's room (page 316).*]

MRS. MEDLOCK: Well, here you are! This room and the next one are where you'll be. You must keep to them. Don't you forget that!

NARRATOR: The next morning when Mary opened her eyes, she saw a young housemaid kneeling at the grate kindling a fire. Outside her window, Mary could see a great stretch of treeless land.

MARY: What is that? It looks like an endless, dull, purplish sea.

MARTHA: That's the moor. Does tha' like it?

MARY: No. I hate it!

MARTHA: That's because tha'rt not used to it. In time tha' will like it. I just love it. It's not bare. It's covered wi' growin' things as smells sweet. It's fair lovely in spring an' summer when the gorse an' broom an' heather's in flower. Mother raised twelve o' us in a cottage on the moor, an' the young ones still tumble about an' play out there all day. I wouldn't live away from the moor for anythin'.

MARY: In India, my ayah never spoke with me in this way. Are you to be my servant?

MARTHA: I'm to do the housemaid's work up here an' wait on you a bit, but you won't need much waitin' on.

MARY: Who will dress me?

MARTHA: Canna' tha' dress thysen!

MARY: What do you mean? I don't understand your language.

MARTHA: That's Yorkshire tha'rt hearin'. I mean, can't you put on your own clothes?

MARY: No, I never did in my life. My ayah always dressed me.

MARTHA: Well, it's time tha' should learn. It'll do thee good to wait on thysen a bit. My mother always said she couldn't see why grand people's children didn't turn out fools—what with bein' washed an' dressed an' took out to walk as if they was puppies!

NARRATOR: Mary suddenly felt so horribly lonely and far away from everything she understood that she began sobbing. But something friendly in Martha's Yorkshire speech had a good effect on her, and after a bit she stopped crying.

MARTHA: It's time for thee to wrap up warm an' run out an' play.

MARY: Who will go with me?

MARTHA: You'll go by yourself. My twelve-year-old brother, Dickon, goes off on the moor by himself and plays for hours. He's got a pony an' sheep on the moor that knows him, an' birds come an' eat out of his hand. However little there is to eat, he always saves a bit o' his bread to coax his pets.

MARY: Your Dickon sounds interesting. I should like to meet him.

MARTHA: Tha' might. Now, here's your coat an' hat. If tha' goes round that way, tha'll come to the gardens. There's lots o' flowers in summertime, but there's nothin' bloomin' now. One of the gardens is locked up, and no one has been in it for ten years. Your uncle had it shut when his wife died so sudden. It was her garden, an' he locked the door an' dug a hole an' buried the key.

MARY: A garden no one has been in for ten years! I wonder what it looks like. Can any flowers still be alive? How could a garden be shut up? How curious indeed. . . .

NARRATOR: Mary buttoned her coat and went outside. She spent many hours wandering through different gardens with ivy-covered walls. Suddenly, she stopped and looked more closely at one of the high stone walls.

[*Display transparency of the ivy-covered wall* (page 317).]

MARY: Martha mentioned a locked-up garden. I wonder if this could be the one. This wall looks as if it encloses a place on the other side. I can see the treetops above the wall and a beautiful bird on one of the branches! Perhaps he lives in the mysterious garden and knows all about it. I wonder why my uncle buried the key. If he liked his wife so much, why did he hate her garden?

NARRATOR: As Mary walked back toward the manor, she saw an old gardener. He took no notice of her, and so at last, she spoke to him.

MARY: There's no door into the garden on the other side of that wall. There are trees there, and a bird with a red breast is sitting on one of them and singing.

BEN: That's the robin. He comes when I whistle to him.

Macmillan/McGraw-Hill

MARY: He's so pretty and cheerful. Does he always come when you call him?

BEN: Aye, that he does. I've knowed him ever since he was a fledgling when he come out of the nest in the garden. He was too weak to fly back over the wall for a few days an' we got friendly. When he went over the wall again, the rest of his brood was gone. He was lonely, an' he come back to me.

MARY: I'm lonely, too.

BEN: I'm Ben Weatherstaff, an' I'm lonely mysel' except when the robin is with me. He's the only friend I've got.

MARY: I have no friends at all. I've never had anyone to play with.

BEN: Tha' an' me are a good bit alike. We was both wove out of the same cloth. We're neither of us good-lookin' an' we're both of us as sour as we look. We've got the same nasty tempers, both of us, I'll warrant.

NARRATOR: Mary turned away from Ben and spoke to the robin.

MARY: Would you make friends with me, robin? Would you?

BEN: Why, tha' talked to the robin almost like Dickon talks to his wild things on the moor. The robin lives in the garden over the wall among the old rose trees.

MARY: Rose trees? I should like to see them. Where is the door? There must be a door somewhere.

BEN: There was a door ten year' ago, but there's no door anyone can find now. Don't you poke your nose where it's no cause to go. Get you gone to play, for I've no more time.

NARRATOR: Each day Mary grew more curious about the locked garden. As she walked and ran in the wind, the fresh air blown over the moor filled her lungs. It whipped red color into her cheeks, brightened her eyes, and gave her an appetite she'd never known before. One night during a storm, she was sitting with Martha.

[*Display transparency of Mary's room (page 316).*]

MARY: Why does Mr. Craven hate the garden?

MARTHA: Mrs. Medlock said it's not to be talked about. There's lots o' things in this place that's not to be talked over—by Mr. Craven's orders. But for the garden, he wouldn't be like he is. It was Mrs. Craven's garden that she had made when first they were married. They used to tend the flowers them-selves, an' him an' her used stay there hours an' hours, readin' an' talkin'.

MARY: What happened to her? Mrs. Medlock said she died.

MARTHA: There was an old tree with a branch bent like a seat on it, an' she made roses grow over it, an' she used to sit there. But one day when she was sittin', the branch broke an' she fell on the ground an' was hurt so bad that next day she died. The doctors thought Mr. Craven would die o' sadness. That's why he hates the garden. No one's never gone in since, an' he won't let anyone talk about it.

MARY: I feel sorry for him. Wait . . . listen! What was that? Did you hear someone crying? It sounded like it came from one of the corridors.

Macmillan/McGraw-Hill

MARTHA: No, no. It's the wind. Sometimes it sounds as if someone was lost on the moor an' wailin'. Or it's Betty Butterworth, the scullery maid who's had the toothache all day.

NARRATOR: The next night, Mary heard the crying sound again.

MARY: There *is* someone crying! There *is*!

[Display transparency of the ivy-covered wall (page 317).]

NARRATOR: A few days later, Mary went outside with a skipping rope that Martha's mother had sent her. Spring was coming and the earth was rich and ready for things to grow. Mary skipped alongside the ivy-covered wall near the locked-up garden and looked at the treetops. The robin chirped and hopped about to greet her.

MARY: You do remember me! Just look how close you let me come! You are prettier than anything else in the world.

NARRATOR: Mary watched the robin hop over to a small pile of freshly turned-up earth to look for a worm.

MARY: What a deep hole! Maybe a dog was digging here. Why, there's something sticking out of the soil. A . . . key! Perhaps it's the key to the garden! If I could find the door, I could open it and see what's inside the walls and what happened to the old rose trees. I must find that hidden door!

NARRATOR: The next day Mary went again to the walk beside the walled-in garden. The robin was there, swaying on a long branch of ivy. He greeted her with a chirp.

MARY: Hello, friend robin. Since you showed me where the key was yesterday, perhaps you will show me the door today.

NARRATOR: The robin flew to the top of the wall and sang. Suddenly a gust of wind waved the branches of the trees and swayed the ivy hanging from the wall. As the ivy trails swung to and fro, Mary spotted the tarnished knob of a door hidden under the leaves. With trembling hands, she drew the key from her pocket and inserted it into the keyhole.

MARY: The key fits! It fits!

NARRATOR: Mary took a long breath as she held back the curtain of ivy and slowly pushed the door open. Then she slipped through it and shut it tight behind her. She looked about, breathing fast with excitement, wonder, and delight. Mary was standing *inside* the secret garden.

[*Display transparency of the barren garden (page 318).*]

MARY: How still it is! How still! No wonder it's still. I am the first person who has spoken in here for ten years. It's the sweetest, most mysterious-looking place I've ever seen. I wonder if anything is alive. I don't see even a tiny bud anywhere, but I'm *inside* the wonderful garden, and I can come through the door under the ivy anytime. I've found a secret place all my own!

NARRATOR: Suddenly Mary saw some little pale-green points poking up out of the black earth.

MARY: It isn't a completely dead garden! There are living things here. I'll dig and weed until everything can breathe. I shall come every day to my secret garden and make it live again.

Macmillan/McGraw-Hill

ACT II

[*Display transparency of Mary's room* (page 316).]

NARRATOR: That night Mary was so excited that she could hardly wait to talk with Martha.

MARY: Martha, does Dickon know about plants?

MARTHA: Why, Dickon can make a flower grow out of a brick wall. Mother says he just whispers things out o' the ground.

MARY: I wish . . . I wish I had a little spade. This is such a big, lonely place. If I had a spade, I might make a little garden.

MARTHA: Aye. And why not? Mother said diggin' an' rakin' would make tha' happy. I'll ask Dickon to bring thee some garden tools an' seeds.

MARY: Oh, thank you, Martha!

[*Display transparency of the ivy-covered wall* (page 317).]

NARRATOR: A few days later, Mary saw a boy sitting under a tree near the greenhouse. He was playing a wooden pipe, while squirrels, pheasants, and rabbits drew near to listen. When he saw Mary, he spoke to her in a low piping voice.

DICKON: Don't tha' move. It'll flight 'em. I'm Dickon, and I know tha'rt Miss Mary. I'll get up slow because if tha' makes a quick move, it startles 'em. A body 'as to move gentle an' speak low when wild things is about.

MARY: Did you get the garden tools and seeds?

DICKON: Aye. Sit thee on the log an' I'll tell thee what all the seeds will look like when they flower—an' how to plant 'em an' watch 'em an' feed an' water 'em. Where is tha' garden?

MARY: Can you keep a secret? It's a great secret, and I don't know what I should do if anyone found it out. I believe I should die!

DICKON: I'm keepin' secrets all the time. If I couldn't keep secrets from the other lads—secrets about fox cubs an' birds' nests—there'd be naught safe on the moor. Aye, I can keep secrets.

MARY: I've found a garden. Actually, I've stolen it. It isn't mine. It isn't anybody's for that matter. Nobody wants it and nobody cares for it and nobody ever goes into it. Perhaps everything is dead in it already. I don't know, and I don't care! Nobody has any right to take it from me when I care about it and they don't.

DICKON: Eh-h-h! Where is it?

MARY: Come with me and I'll show you. The door is hidden over here under the ivy. Here it is. Just a moment, and I'll have it unlocked.

NARRATOR: Mary turned the key and the two children walked through the little wooden door.

[*Display transparency of the barren garden (page 318).*]

DICKON: Eh! It is a strange, pretty place! It's as if a body was in a dream.

MARY: Will you help me make it come alive?

DICKON: I'll come every day if tha' wants, rain or shine. It'll be the best fun I ever had in my life—shut in here an' wakenin' up a garden.

MARY: Dickon, you're as nice as Martha said. You make the fifth person I like. I never thought I should like five people.

DICKON: Only five folk tha' likes? Who is the other four?

MARY: Your mother and Martha and the robin and Ben Weatherstaff. Does tha' like me?

DICKON: Eh, that I does! I like thee wonderful an' so does the robin, I do believe.

NARRATOR: When Mary returned to the house that afternoon, Martha was waiting for her.

MARTHA: Your uncle wants to see you in his study. Mother met him on the moor this mornin'. She said somethin' as put him in the mind to see you before he goes away tomorrow.

NARRATOR: Mary's heart began to thump as she changed her dress, brushed her hair, and followed the waiting Mrs. Medlock down the corridor, in silence. This was to be her first meeting with her uncle since she arrived at the manor. She hardly knew how she would be received by this man she'd heard so much about.

[*Display transparency of Mr. Craven's study (page 319).*]

MRS. MEDLOCK: This is Miss Mary, sir. I'll come back for her when you ring.

MR. CRAVEN: Come in, Mary. Are you well, child? Do they take good care of you?

MARY: Yes, sir.

MR. CRAVEN: You are very thin.

MARY: I am getting fatter.

MR. CRAVEN: I forgot you. I intended to send you a governess.

MARY: Please—please don't make me have a governess, yet.

MR. CRAVEN: That's what Martha's mother said. She thought you ought to get stronger before you had a governess.

MARY: Martha's mother knows all about children. I want to play outdoors. It makes me feel strong when the wind blows over the moor. I skip and run and look to see if things are beginning to stick out of the earth. I don't do any harm.

MR. CRAVEN: Don't look so frightened. You could not do any harm, child. You may do what you like. I am your guardian, though I am a poor one. I can't give you time and attention because I'm ill, but I wish you to be happy. Martha's mother thought you needed fresh air and freedom and running about, so play as much as you like. Is there anything you want? Toys, books, dolls?

MARY: Might I—might I have a bit of earth?

Macmillan/McGraw-Hill

MR. CRAVEN: Earth! What do you mean?

MARY: To plant seeds in—to make things grow—to see them come alive.

MR. CRAVEN: A bit of earth? You can have as much earth as you want. You remind me of someone else who loved the earth and things that grow. When you see a bit of earth you want, take it, child, and make it come alive.

MARY: May I take it from anywhere—if it's not wanted?

MR. CRAVEN: Anywhere. You must go now because I'm tired. I shall say good-bye to you now for I'll be away all summer.

NARRATOR: That night Mary was awakened by heavy rain and wind—and a sound that she had heard before.

MARY: I hear crying again. And this time I'm going to find out where it's coming from.

NARRATOR: As Mary walked from corridor to corridor, the faint crying sound led her on until she reached a large, heavy door. Slowly she pushed the door open and saw a boy with a thin face, the color of ivory, lying in a huge bed. Tears ran down his face. Mary tiptoed silently across the big room.

[*Display transparency of Colin's room (page 320).*]

COLIN: Who are you? Are you a ghost?

MARY: No. Are you one?

COLIN: No. I am Colin Craven. Who are you?

MARY: I am Mary Lennox. Mr. Craven is my uncle.

COLIN: He is my father.

MARY: Your father! No one ever told me he had a son.

COLIN: Come here. You *are* real. Where did you come from?

MARY: From my own room. I heard crying. Why were you crying?

COLIN: Because I couldn't go to sleep and my head ached.

MARY: Did no one ever tell you I had come to live here?

COLIN: They daren't. I should have been afraid you'd see me, and I won't let people see me or talk about me.

MARY: Oh, what a strange house this is! Everything is a kind of secret. Rooms are locked up and gardens are locked up—and you! Have you been locked up?

COLIN: No. I am ill, and I have to stay in bed. It tires me to be moved out of this room. My father doesn't want to see me, although sometimes he comes when I'm sleeping. My mother died when I was born, and it makes him miserable to look at me.

MARY: He doesn't want to see the garden again, either.

COLIN: What garden?

MARY: Oh! Just—just a garden your mother used to like. Have you been here always?

COLIN: Nearly always. I was at the seashore once, but people stared at me. I used to wear an iron thing to keep my back straight, but a doctor came from London and said it was stupid. He told them to take it off and keep me out in the fresh air. I hate fresh air. . . . Wait! I just realized something—we are cousins! How old are you?

MARY: I am ten, and so are you.

COLIN: How do you know that?

MARY: When you were born, the garden door was locked and the key was buried, and it has stayed locked up for ten years.

COLIN: What garden door was locked? Who did it? Where was the key buried?

MARY: No one will talk about it. I think they have been told not to answer questions.

COLIN: I would make them tell me. If I were to live, this place would someday belong to me. They would have to tell me.

MARY: Do you think you won't live?

COLIN: I don't suppose I shall. Ever since I remember anything, I have heard people say I shan't. At first they thought I was too little to understand, and now they think I don't hear. But I do. I don't want to live, but I don't want to die, either. I think about it until I cry and cry. I want to see the garden, and I want the key dug up. The servants here must do as I say, so I will make them take me there!

MARY: Oh, don't—please don't do that! If you tell anyone, it will never be a secret again. If no one knows but us, it will become *our* secret garden. I promise I shall look every day for the key to the garden door.

COLIN: I like the idea of a secret garden. You must look for the key and then come chat with me every day.

NARRATOR: Mary visited Colin again the next day and told him about Dickon and the moor. As the two cousins were talking and laughing, Colin's doctor and Mrs. Medlock walked in.

DOCTOR: What is this? I'm afraid there has been too much excitement, and excitement is not good for you, my boy.

MRS. MEDLOCK: But he does look rather better, sir.

DOCTOR: You must not talk too much, Colin; you must not forget you are ill, and you must not forget you're very easily tired.

COLIN: I *want* to forget all that. Mary helps me forget.

DOCTOR: Very well, but you must remember to stay calm during these visits. Mary, Colin is in very delicate health. He must avoid any upsets or excitement.

MARY: All right, Doctor. I understand.

NARRATOR: For a week it rained, and Mary and Colin spent hours in his room reading splendid books and talking. On the first sunny day, Mary went to the garden and found Dickon. She immediately told him about Colin.

[*Display transparency of the awakening garden (page 321).*]

MARY: When I talk with Colin, I have to be very careful in what I say about the secret garden. I want to get to know him first. He's not like you, Dickon. I don't know yet, *for sure*, if he can be trusted with the secret.

DICKON: Don't thee worry! It'll all be right. See how these has pushed up, an' these an' these? Here's a whole clump o' crocuses burst into purple an' orange an' gold.

NARRATOR: Mary and Dickon ran all around the garden. Leaf buds were swelling on rose branches that had seemed dead. The children put their noses close to the earth and sniffed its warm spring perfume. They dug and pulled and laughed and watched the robin building a nest.

MARY: When we first came here, everything seemed dull and gray. Now the gray wall is changing. It's as if a green mist were creeping over it.

DICKON: Aye, an' it'll be greener an' greener till the gray's all gone. Can tha' guess what I was thinkin'? I was thinkin' that if Colin was out here he wouldn't be thinkin' how sick he feels. He'd be watchin' for buds to break on the rosebushes. He'd likely be healthier. I was wonderin' if we could get him to come out here an' sit under the trees.

MARY: I've been thinking about that, too, just as I've wondered if he could keep a secret. Do you think we could bring him here without anyone seeing us? You could push his chair as if we were going for a stroll in the big gardens.

DICKON: Us'd be just two children watchin' a garden grow, an' he'd be another. Two lads an' a lass just lookin' at the spring-time. It'd be better than doctor's stuff.

NARRATOR: It was late afternoon when Mary returned to the house. Colin was furious because she hadn't visited him earlier.

[*Display transparency of Colin's room (page 320).*]

COLIN: Why did you go out instead of coming to talk to me? You are a selfish thing!

MARY: Well, so are you! You're the most selfish person I ever saw.

COLIN: I'm not as selfish as you because I'm ill. I'm sure there is a bump coming on my back, and I'm going to die.

MARY: You're not! You just say that to make people feel sorry for you. I don't believe it!

COLIN: Get out of the room!

MARY: I'm going, Colin, and I won't come back!

NARRATOR: But Mary did go back to Colin's room later that night when Mrs. Medlock came to fetch her.

MRS. MEDLOCK: Miss Mary, please come with me! Colin's worked himself into hysterics, and he'll do himself harm. No one can do anything with him. You come and try. He likes you.

NARRATOR: Mary put on her dressing gown and followed a worried Mrs. Medlock. She could hear Colin's tantrum all the way down the corridor.

MARY: Colin, stop this! I hate you! Everybody hates you! You'll scream yourself to death, and I wish you would. If you scream another scream, I'll scream too. And I can scream louder than you, and I'll frighten you!

COLIN: I can't stop! I felt a bump. I felt it. I shall have a crooked back like my father, and then I shall die.

MARY: You didn't feel a thing. Half that ails you is temper and hysterics. It was only a hysterical bump. There's nothing the matter with your horrid back. Turn over and let me look at it! There's not a single bump there. There's not a bump as big as a pin, and if you say there is again, I shall laugh!

COLIN: Do you think . . . I could . . . live to grow up?

MARY: You probably will, if you do as you are told and not give way to your temper. And you must get out in the fresh air.

COLIN: I'll go out with you, Mary, and Dickon can push my chair. Take my hand—as a kind of making up.

ACT III

NARRATOR: The garden had reached the time when it seemed as if more beauty was bursting out of the earth every day. Quite suddenly it came into Mary's mind that this was the right moment to tell Colin about finding the garden.

MARY: Colin, can I trust you? I trusted Dickon because the moor animals and birds trust him. Can I trust you—for sure—*for sure?*

COLIN: Yes—oh, yes!

MARY: Dickon will come to visit you tomorrow, but that's not all. The rest is better. I found a hidden door under the ivy on the wall. It opens into the secret garden!

COLIN: Oh! Mary! Shall I see it?

MARY: Of course you shall! I found the key and got in weeks ago, but I daren't tell you because I was afraid I couldn't trust you—*for sure!* But that's changed now. Since the doctor has given permission for you to go out with Dickon and me, we will take you to the garden tomorrow!

NARRATOR: That night, Colin was so excited he could hardly sleep. Soon after breakfast, he was helped into his wheelchair. Dickon pushed it slowly and steadily while Mary walked alongside. When they got to the garden door, Mary checked to make sure nobody was watching. Then quickly she opened the door, and Dickon pushed the chair through with one strong, steady, splendid push. Colin looked round and round as Dicken and Mary had done.

[*Display transparency of the awakening garden (page 321).*]

MARY: The garden's different from when I first saw it. Little green leaves are covering all the gray. The flowers are beginning to bloom, and the trees are showing pink.

DICKON: An' a pink glow o' color is creepin' all over thee, too, Colin—over tha' face an' neck an' hands an' all.

COLIN: The sun feels warm upon my face—like a hand with a lovely touch. I shall get well! I shall! And I shall live forever and ever and ever!

DICKON: I'll push tha' chair round the garden.

COLIN: I feel like I'm being taken around the country of a king and queen and showed all its mysterious riches. Why look, that's a very old tree over there, isn't it? There's not a single leaf on it. It looks quite dead.

DICKON: Aye. But roses has climbed all over it, an' they will hide every bit o' the dead wood when they're full o' leaves an' flowers. It won't look dead then. It'll be the prettiest of all.

COLIN: It looks as if a big branch had been broken off.

DICKON: It's been done many a year. Eh! Look at the robin!

NARRATOR: As Colin watched the robin, Mary whispered to Dickon.

MARY: It's lucky that the robin came by. I was afraid Colin might ask more about the old tree. We can never tell him how it broke!

COLIN: I'm going to see everything grow here. I'm going to grow here myself. Look! Who's that peering at us over the wall from the top of the ladder? Does he know who I am?

NARRATOR: Ben Weatherstaff stared and gazed and gulped a lump down his throat. He answered in a shaky voice.

BEN: Aye. That I do—wi' tha' mother's eyes starin' at me out o' tha' face. Tha'rt the poor bent lad.

COLIN: I'm not bent! I'm not!

NARRATOR: Colin's anger filled him with strength. He tore the coverings off his legs and shouted.

COLIN: Dickon, come here this minute! Hold my arms!

MARY: He can do it! He can!

COLIN: Just look at me!

DICKON: Why, he's standin' as straight as I am! He's as straight as any lad i' Yorkshire!

NARRATOR: Ben choked and gulped and suddenly tears ran down his wrinkled cheeks as he struck his hands together.

BEN: The lies folks tell! Tha'lt live to be a man yet. Bless thee!

COLIN: This is my garden. And you mustn't dare say a word about it! Come down from that ladder so I can talk to you. You will have to be in on our secret now.

NARRATOR: While Mary brought Ben Weatherstaff in through the hidden door, Colin tried to walk.

COLIN: I'm going to walk to that tree, and when I want to sit, I will sit, but not before. Everyone thought I was going to die. But I'm not.

BEN: Tha' die? Tha's got too much pluck in thee. Sit thee down on the ground a bit, young master.

COLIN: What work do you do in the gardens?

BEN: Anythin' I'm told to do. I'm kep' on by favor—because tha' mother liked me.

COLIN: My mother? This was her garden, wasn't it?

BEN: Aye, it was that, and she was very fond of it.

COLIN: It's my garden now, and I'm fond of it. I shall come here every day, but it's to be a secret. Dickon and Mary have made it come alive, and now you can come to help.

BEN: I've come here before when no one saw me. The last time was about two year' ago.

COLIN: But no one's been in it for ten years! There was no door!

BEN: I come over the wall, but the rheumatics held me back the last two year'. Mrs. Craven was so fond of the garden. She says to me, "Ben, if ever I'm ill or if I go away, you must take care of my roses." When she did go away, the orders was no one was ever to come here. But I come over the wall, and I did a bit o' work once a year. She gave her order first.

COLIN: I'm glad you did it. You'll know how to keep the secret.

BEN: Aye. I'll know. An' twill be easier for a man wi' rheumatics to come in at the door.

NARRATOR: On the grass near the tree, Mary had dropped her trowel. Colin stretched out his hand for it.

COLIN: Mary, let me have that trowel so I can dig in the earth.

BEN: I can get thee a rosebush to plant.

COLIN: Good! I want to do it before the sun goes down.

BEN: Here, lad. Mind the thorns. Set the plant in the earth thysel'.

NARRATOR: Colin's thin white hands shook as he set the rose in the hole that Dickon had helped him dig.

COLIN: It's planted! And the sun is only slipping over the edge. Help me up, Dickon. I want to be standing when it sets. That's part of the beauty.

NARRATOR: There *was* beauty in the garden, and it seemed to intensify in the months that followed. One day, Colin called Mary, Dickon, and Ben Weatherstaff together under the old tree.

[*Display transparency of the garden in bloom* (page 322).]

COLIN: Since I've been in the garden, I've had a strange feeling of being happy, as if something were pushing and drawing in my chest and making me breathe fast. Everything here makes me happy—the leaves and trees, the flowers and birds, the foxes and squirrels, and all of you. Beauty is all around us. The beauty in this garden has made me stand up and know I'm going to live to be a man. The beauty in this garden will push and draw me and make me grow strong so that I can walk and run like other children.

NARRATOR: Colin began to exercise, eat, laugh, and grow stronger, and Mary began to change, too. Her hair became thick and healthy-looking, and she had a bright color and lost her sour look. Like Colin and Mary, everything in the secret garden thrived and bloomed. The eggs in the robin's nest hatched, and the fledglings took their first flight.

COLIN: I wish my father would come home so I could show him the garden!

NARRATOR: While the secret garden was coming alive, Archibald Craven was wandering in faraway places. One day, he sat beside an icy mountain stream and looked at a mass of blue flowers—forget-me-nots.

MR. CRAVEN: It seems so long ago that I used to look at such flowers. They're so lovely. . . . I almost feel as if—as if I were coming alive again. Last night, I had a dream that my precious wife, Lilias, was calling me back to the garden. How strange it is that this morning I received a letter from Martha's mother suggesting I come home. Some secret force is drawing me home. I must go back to Misselthwaite at once! I've been filled with such terrible sorrow for ten years, but I want to do something now to set things right. I'll try to find the key to the garden and open the door. I must, though I don't know why.

NARRATOR: Upon his arrival at the the manor, Mr. Craven went directly to the garden. Mary and Colin were having a race, and when Archibald Craven got to the garden door—at that precise moment—Colin burst through the door at full speed, almost into his father's arms!

MR. CRAVEN: Good heavens! Who . . . who are you?

COLIN: Father, I'm Colin. Can you believe it? I hardly can myself.

MR. CRAVEN: You're in the garden. In the garden!

COLIN: It was the garden that did it—and Mary and Dickon and Ben and the robin. I'm going to live forever, Father. Aren't you glad?

MR. CRAVEN: Take me into the garden, my boy, and tell me all about it.

Macmillan/McGraw-Hill

NARRATOR: Mr. Craven held his son and Mary as they told him all about the secret garden. A little while later, Mrs. Murdock and Martha stood at the windows and gaped as they watched the master of Misselthwaite striding across the lawn. He had not looked this way in ten years. On one side of him skipped the young girl from India, flushed and happy. And on his other side, with his head up in the air and his eyes full of laughter, walked Master Colin—as strongly and steadily as any boy in Yorkshire!

locking iagram

Arrange eight chairs, as shown. The narrator can use a music stand to hold the script.

1. NARRATOR
2. DOCTOR
3. ARCHIBALD CRAVEN
4. COLIN CRAVEN
5. MARY LENNOX

6. DICKON SOWERBY
7. MARTHA SOWERBY
8. MRS. MEDLOCK
9. BEN WEATHERSTAFF

Macmillan/McGraw-Hill

ostume uggestions

Narrator This performer does not need a special costume, but a jacket and string tie for a boy reader or a long skirt for a girl could help the performer feel more in character.

Mrs. Medlock As housekeeper at Misselthwaite Manor, this character can wear a long dark skirt and blouse. A brooch or large pin could be used to fasten a velvet ribbon at the neck.

Mary Lennox Mary can wear a dark blouse and a mid-calf skirt or jumper. Dark tights and a large hair bow would also be appropriate.

Martha Sowerby As parlor maid, Martha can wear a blouse and a long skirt covered by a white apron. This character can pin a doily or lace hanky on her head to simulate a maid's cap.

Ben Weatherstaff A long-sleeved work shirt, wool vest, worn-looking pants with suspenders, cap, and boots would be fine for this character.

Dickon Sowerby Dickon can be dressed like Ben, with knickers instead of pants. Knickers can be made by tucking pant legs into knee socks and "blousing" the pants at the knee.

Archibald Craven and the Doctor

These readers should have a somber appearance; dark pants and jackets, white shirts, and black cravats are suggested.

Colin Craven

For the scenes that take place inside the house, Colin can wear a long-sleeved white shirt or smock that resembles a nightshirt. The garment should be large enough to conceal his clothes. When the scene shifts to the garden, the performer can remove the shirt to reveal knickers, a sport coat, and bow tie.

 **Backdrops**

Backdrops for *The Secret Garden* can be created by reproducing the following transparency patterns on acetate and having students color them with markers. Position an overhead projector out of the sight lines of the audience. Following the cues in the script, project the transparencies onto a light-colored wall or screen behind the cast.

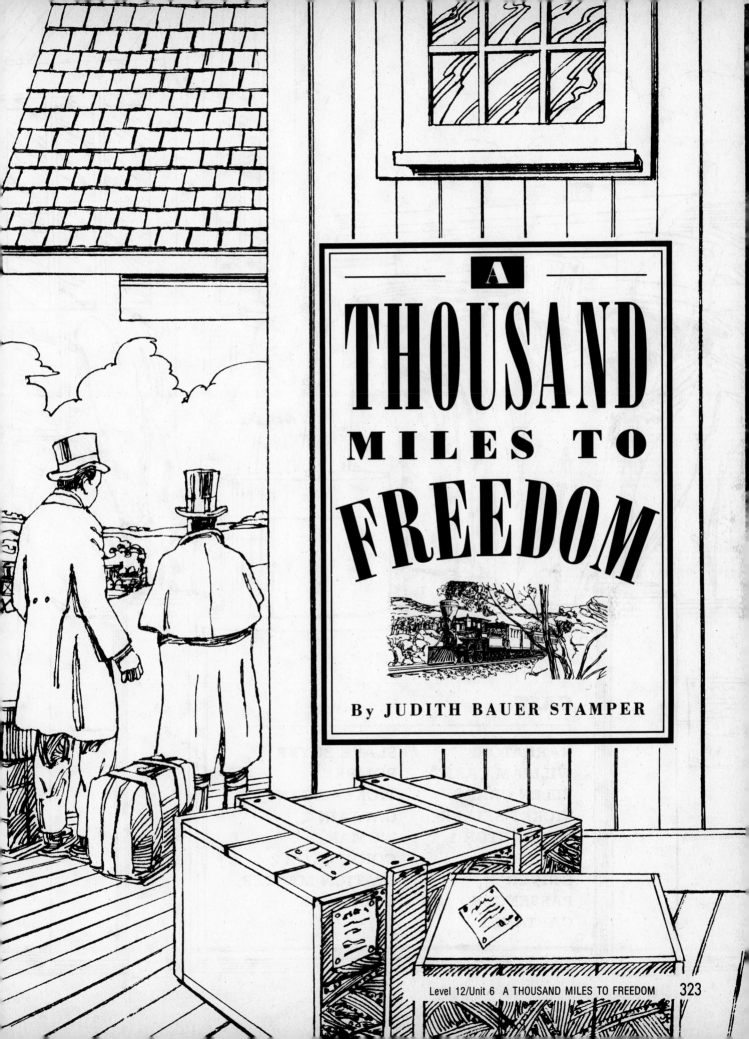

A THOUSAND MILES TO FREEDOM

By JUDITH BAUER STAMPER

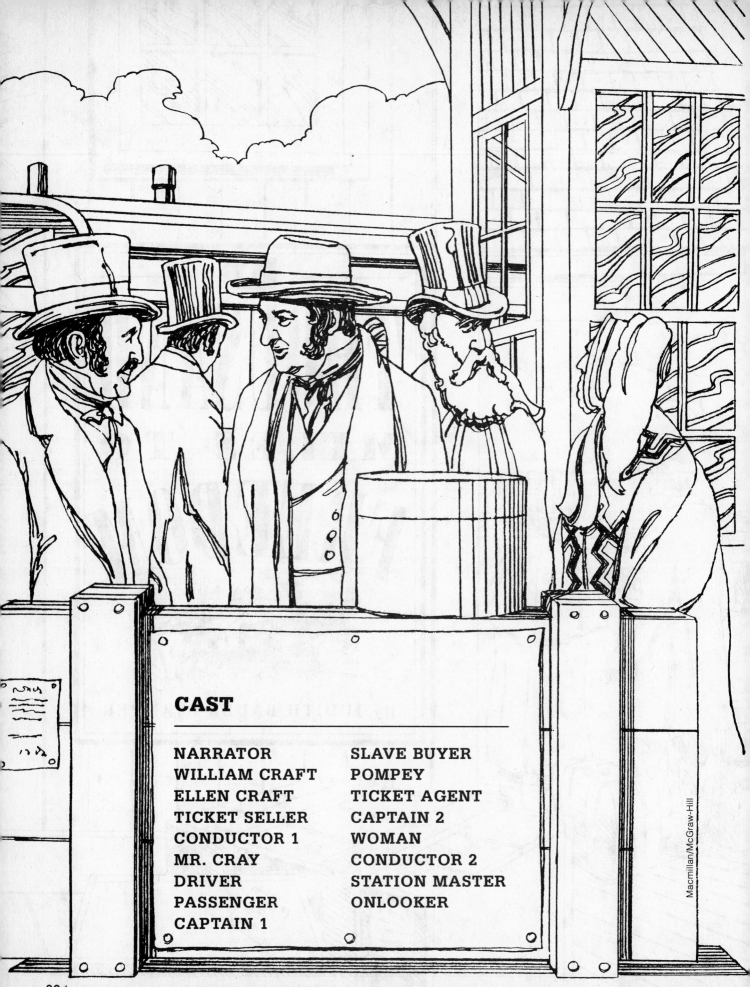

CAST

NARRATOR	SLAVE BUYER
WILLIAM CRAFT	POMPEY
ELLEN CRAFT	TICKET AGENT
TICKET SELLER	CAPTAIN 2
CONDUCTOR 1	WOMAN
MR. CRAY	CONDUCTOR 2
DRIVER	STATION MASTER
PASSENGER	ONLOOKER
CAPTAIN 1	

Macmillan/McGraw-Hill

Sunday, December 17, 1848   Macon, Georgia

NARRATOR: It was a still December night in the year 1848. On the grounds of a fine plantation in Macon, Georgia, a light burned in a small cabin near the main house. Inside, a young couple talked. Ellen Craft gave every appearance of being white, with her fair skin and straight hair, so like her father. However, as the daughter of a black woman, she was obliged by law to follow her mother's condition. And so she was as much a slave as her mother—and as her husband, William Craft. As the couple spoke, their voices were hushed, not due to the lateness of the hour, but rather to the subject of their discussion.

WILLIAM: Ellen, listen! I got a plan, and I think it'll work!

ELLEN: A plan for our escape, William? What is it? Tell me!

WILLIAM: You'll pretend to be white, and I'll travel with you as your manservant.

ELLEN: But no white lady travels alone with a male slave.

WILLIAM: That's so. But you won't be a white *lady*. You'll dress yourself up as a young white gentleman—a sickly gentleman needing help. We'll take the train north, to Philadelphia and freedom!

ELLEN: Oh, William, we don't dare! Pretending to be white would be hard enough, but I could never act the part of a white gentleman for a journey of a thousand miles.

WILLIAM: Ellen, listen to me. Think of what'll happen if we don't dare. We'll belong to our masters forever—slaves to be bought and sold.

ELLEN: I think of nothing else! If we had children, they'd be the master's property, too. They could be torn away from us at any time. I could not bear it! . . . You're right, William. We must dare. Let us get the things we need for the disguise; with God's help, I will try to carry out the plan.

NARRATOR: William Craft was what was called a town slave. Trained in woodworking, his master hired him out to a cabinetmaker, a Mr. John Knight. William's wages went to his master, but he was allowed to keep the money that he made by working overtime. It was with these savings that the couple planned to finance their flight to freedom. Over the next few days, William went to different parts of town at odd times to purchase the articles they needed: a coat, a shirt, a hat, boots, and a pair of dark-green spectacles for Ellen. He couldn't find trousers small enough, so Ellen carefully stitched them herself. At last, the disguise was assembled.

Macmillan/McGraw-Hill

WILLIAM: We're ready. All that needs doing is to get visiting passes for a few days over Christmas. Most likely your mistress won't refuse—with you being her favorite slave and all.

ELLEN: I'll say I want to visit my dying old aunt for Christmas.

WILLIAM: And I'll ask Mr. Knight if I can go with you. He's a mighty suspicious man, but since I've never asked for a pass before, maybe he'll say yes. . . . If no one 'spects us back till after Christmas, they won't be looking for us till we're safe in Philadelphia. I surely pray we get those passes.

NARRATOR: The next day, William returned to the cabin with the precious paper in his pocket. He showed it to Ellen.

ELLEN: And here is mine!

WILLIAM: It's a wonder, Ellen. These papers are life or death to us, and we can't even read 'em.

ELLEN: Cannot read. . . . Oh, William, our plan will never work. I just remembered something I heard my mistress say. Travelers must write their names in a book when staying in a hotel, as well as at the Custom House in Charleston, South Carolina. And I can neither read *nor* write my name. We are lost, William, we are lost!

NARRATOR: Sitting in their little room that night, Ellen and William were on the verge of despair. All at once, Ellen raised her head, a smile replacing her tears.

ELLEN: William, it has come to me. You'll bandage my right hand and bind it up in a sling. Then it would seem right for me to ask someone at the hotel to write my name for me!

WILLIAM: Yes! That'll do it!

ELLEN: Perhaps, too, I should bind some herb poultices under my chin with strips of cloth. The bandages will add to my sickly appearance and hide the fact that I have no beard.

WILLIAM: We'll make you look like you're sufferin' from a mighty bad toothache!

NARRATOR: William and Ellen worked all through the night reviewing their plans and making their preparations. As a personal maid in the big house, Ellen had learned much. Though she could not read or write, she was as well-spoken as her mistress. As a house servant, she often overheard conversations about trips up North. She had stored in her mind information that might someday prove helpful to her and to William. Now that day had finally come.

Macmillan/McGraw-Hill

Thursday, December 21, 1848

**From Macon, Georgia
To Savannah, Georgia**

NARRATOR: Shortly before dawn, William cut Ellen's hair.
Then he helped her on with the disguise.

WILLIAM: Hold still while I fasten this bow tie. You surely
do make a most respectable gentleman. People'd never
guess a slave is hiding behind those spectacles and
bandages.

ELLEN: I hope you're right, William. I fear the next few days
may be worse than the twenty-two years I've spent as a
slave.

WILLIAM: It's time to blow the candle out now. Hold my
hand, and let us pray for success. Think of it—freedom
for Christmas!

NARRATOR: A few moments later, they rose and stood together in breathless silence. What if someone had been
about the cabin listening and watching their movements? William took his wife by the hand, stepped to
the door, drew it open, and peeped out. Though there
were trees surrounding the cabin, the foliage scarcely
moved. In fact, everything appeared to be as still as
death.

WILLIAM: [*whispering*] Come, my dear. I will latch the door
behind us one last time.

ELLEN: Now that the hour has finally come, I am so afraid.

WILLIAM: Me, too, Ellen. I've never been so scared. Every inch of this thousand miles seems like a mountain. But we've got to go on! There's no turning back now!

ELLEN: You are right, William. I'm ready now. We must have faith that God is on our side.

NARRATOR: They stepped out as softly as moonlight upon the water and tiptoed cautiously across the yard into the street. They scarcely breathed for fear of waking the sleeping household.

WILLIAM: This is where I leave you, Ellen, for we cannot be seen together in Macon. Do you remember what you must do?

ELLEN: Yes. From this moment, I must act as Mr. William Johnson, on my way to Philadelphia to seek medical advice. My slave, William, is along to attend me. I will go to the train station now and buy our tickets to Savannah, Georgia.

WILLIAM: And I'll board the last car with the other slaves. I'll look for you on the platform in Savannah.

NARRATOR: They walked separately, in different directions, to the railway station. Ellen felt both excitement and fear. Pretending to be free, she suddenly felt free—but real freedom was still a thousand miles away. As she walked into the red-brick station, she reminded herself of all the gestures a young, white gentleman might use—flicking lint from a coat lapel or hooking his thumbs in his vest pockets. Then she squared her shoulders and walked up to the ticket window.

ELLEN: Two tickets to Savannah, please. One for myself and one for my slave.

TICKET SELLER: Here you are, sir. Have a pleasant journey.

ELLEN: I thank you kindly, sir.

CONDUCTOR 1: A-l-l aboard!

Macmillan/McGraw-Hill

NARRATOR: From his seat in the car at the end of the train, William watched Ellen board one of the front carriages. Then, in amazement and horror, he saw Mr. Knight, the cabinetmaker for whom he worked, rush across the train platform. He began looking suspiciously at the passengers in each of the carriages.

WILLIAM: It's Mr. Knight! Why would he be looking for me so soon?

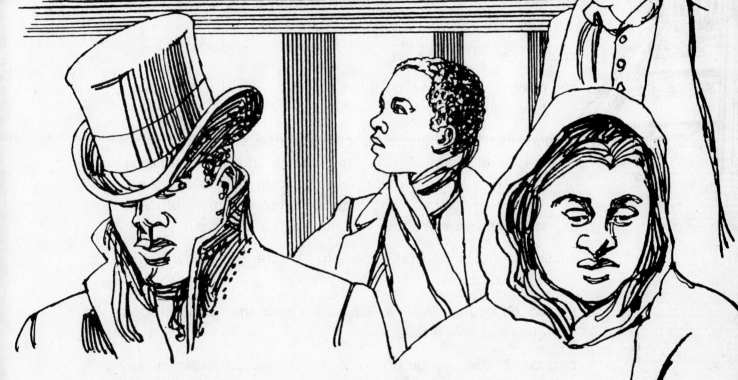

NARRATOR: Mr. Knight moved from one car to another, coming closer and closer to where William sat. With a pounding heart, William shrank into a corner and turned his face away from the door.

CONDUCTOR 1: A-l-l aboard!

NARRATOR: William expected to be grabbed from his seat at any moment. Suddenly, the train's whistle blew and the wheels began to turn. Mr. Knight jumped down from the train onto the platform as the train began to pick up speed. Only then did William sit up in his seat and begin to breathe more freely. But he might not have breathed quite so freely had he known that at this very moment, in another carriage, "Mr. Johnson" was also facing a fearful encounter.

MR. CRAY: It's a very fine morning, sir.

NARRATOR: It was Mr. Cray speaking. He was a friend of Ellen's master, and he had taken a seat next to "Mr. Johnson"! Fearful that Mr. Cray might recognize her voice, Ellen pretended not to hear.

MR. CRAY: [*in a louder voice*] It's a very fine morning, sir.

NARRATOR: Again, he did not receive an answer.

MR. CRAY: I will make him hear! [*loudly*] It's a very fine morning, sir!

ELLEN: Yes . . . yes, it is.

MR. CRAY: Poor fellow, he must be deaf. I shall not trouble him anymore.

NARRATOR: "Mr. Johnson" breathed a little easier, but was very glad when Mr. Cray got off the train several stops later. Finally, as evening fell, the train pulled into the Savannah station. "Mr. Johnson" stepped down off the train and saw William waiting on the platform.

WILLIAM: You must find a carriage, master. I'll follow behind with the bags.

ELLEN: Of course, William. There's a carriage at the station entrance. We'll take it.

DRIVER: Might you be going to the Charleston steamer, sir?

ELLEN: Yes, I am.

DRIVER: Right this way, then. Let me help you, sir. I can see that you are not well. Your slave can ride up on top.

ELLEN: I thank you, sir.

NARRATOR: The carriage took William and Ellen through the streets of Savannah to the steamer bound for Charleston, South Carolina. Soon after boarding, "Mr. Johnson" retired to his cabin to avoid encountering the other passengers. William followed behind with the bags. The minute the door shut behind them, Ellen pulled off her spectacles and hugged her husband.

Macmillan/McGraw-Hill

ELLEN: Oh, William, what a trial. When Mr. Cray sat down beside me, it was all I could do to keep myself from jumping off that train! But we did it, William. They believed me!

WILLIAM: I was sure we'd be caught when I saw old Mr. Knight come looking through the carriages. But as neither man recognized you, I do believe we've got a chance!

ELLEN: William, did you hear the others talking as we boarded? They think it odd that I retired so early. Perhaps you had better warm some flannel cloths and liniment by the stove where all are sure to notice you.

WILLIAM: The smell alone will make it mighty clear you're ill.

NARRATOR: The passengers certainly did take notice of William.

PASSENGER: What is that you've got there?

WILLIAM: Opodeldoc liniment, sir, for my master's rheumatism.

PASSENGER: It stinks enough to kill or cure twenty men! Away with it, or I reckon I'll throw it overboard!

NARRATOR: Satisfied that he had accomplished his purpose, William took the cloths and the opodeldoc back to his master's cabin. He waited a few minutes and then went back on deck, where he met the ship's captain.

WILLIAM: Begging your pardon, sir. Where do slaves sleep, sir?

CAPTAIN 1: Slaves? We have no sleeping accommodations set aside for your kind on this ship. You can sleep standing up for all I care!

NARRATOR: Sc William paced the deck for several hours, and then found some cotton sacks in a warm spot near the funnel. He dozed there, waiting for morning, when he would assist his master in preparing for breakfast.

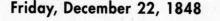

Friday, December 22, 1848   **From Charleston, South Carolina
To Wilmington, North Carolina**

NARRATOR: At breakfast, "Mr. Johnson" was seated beside the captain in the ship's dining room.

CAPTAIN 1: Good morning, sir. How are you feeling today?

PASSENGER: I do hope your rheumatism is improved this morning?

ELLEN: Thank you both. I passed a comfortable night.

NARRATOR: Since "Mr. Johnson" had one arm in a sling, William cut his master's food and then went out.

CAPTAIN 1: You have a very attentive slave, sir, but you had better watch him like a hawk when you get North. He seems all very well here, but he may act quite differently there. I've known many a gentleman who have lost their slaves among them cutthroat abolitionists.

NARRATOR: Before "Mr. Johnson" could speak, a man sitting across the table joined the conversation.

SLAVE BUYER: Sound doctrine, Captain, very sound. I would not take a slave North under no consideration. If you do, he's as good as gone. He'll run away the first chance he gets. Now, stranger, if you've a mind to sell that slave, I'm your man. Just mention your price, and if it isn't out of the way, I will pay for him right here and now in hard silver dollars. What do you say, stranger?

ELLEN: I thank you for your offer, but I don't wish to sell, sir. I cannot get on well without him.

SLAVE BUYER: You will have to get on without him if you take him up North. I can tell you as a friend, he'll leave you the minute he crosses Mason and Dixon's line.

ELLEN: I think not, sir. I have great confidence in William's fidelity.

SLAVE BUYER: Fidelity! Fidevil! You use a word like "fidelity" for a slave! It always makes me mad to hear a man talking about fidelity in slaves. There ain't a one of 'em who wouldn't take off if he had half a chance!

CAPTAIN 1: Excuse me, gentlemen, we are approaching Charleston. I am sure you all will want to go out on deck.

ELLEN: Thank you, Captain, but I fear the sea air is too much for my constitution to bear. If you'll excuse me, sir, I'd best retire to my cabin.

NARRATOR: Ellen walked slowly back to the cabin, shaking with anger. William was waiting by the door for her return.

WILLIAM: I could hear that slave buyer a-shouting clear out on deck. What'd he say?

ELLEN: He offered to buy you, William! Thank goodness we're pulling into port. It looks as if we've made it to Charleston, South Carolina.

WILLIAM: Just look at that crowd on the wharf. That could mean trouble for us. It's possible someone in that crowd might recognize me. We'd better wait until things clear out 'fore leaving the ship.

ELLEN: I pray our absence hasn't been discovered. If it has been, they may have telegraphed for someone to stop us on shore.

NARRATOR: William and Ellen waited until all the other passengers had gone ashore. When they saw that no one lingered on the wharf, they took a carriage from the steamer to a hotel that Ellen had heard about. While "Mr. Johnson" rested, William took his master's boots out on the back steps to polish them. While he was sitting there, one of the hotel slaves engaged him in conversation.

POMPEY: Where you headed, brother?

WILLIAM: Philadelphia.

POMPEY: Philadelphia! I hear there're no slaves in Philadelphia.

WILLIAM: I heard the same.

POMPEY: I surely do wish I was going with you! How you getting there?

WILLIAM: We're taking the steamer from Charleston to Philadelphia.

POMPEY: That's what you think—that steamer don't run in the winter, brother. You know, a few weeks back, they found a runaway slave hiding on board. They whipped him good and sent him back to his master.

WILLIAM: Poor soul! Well, I guess my master will know another way to Philadelphia.

POMPEY: I hope when you get there, you stay!

WILLIAM: Thank you, brother. I best be going now.

NARRATOR: When William returned to the room with the well-shined boots, he told Ellen what he had learned.

WILLIAM: We gotta change our plans, Ellen. It may be just as well for us. Since that runaway slave was found, I got a suspicion they're going to check all the slaves mighty carefully.

ELLEN: I heard a passenger describing another way—the Overland Mail Route. We'd have to take a steamer to Wilmington, North Carolina, and a train from there to Philadelphia.

WILLIAM: We're all right then! We should leave right after dinner.

NARRATOR: Upon leaving the hotel, William and Ellen took a carriage to the Charleston Custom House office. There "Mr. Johnson" would buy the tickets through to their final destination, Philadelphia—but not without obstacles.

ELLEN: Two tickets to Philadelphia, please. One for me and one for my slave.

TICKET AGENT: Just a minute, sir. . . . Hey you, come over here!

WILLIAM: You talking to me, sir?

TICKET AGENT: Of course I'm talking to you! Do you belong to this gentleman?

WILLIAM: Yes, sir, I do.

TICKET AGENT: That's all right then. Now, sir, I wish you to register your name here and also the name of your slave. You'll also have to pay a dollar duty on him.

ELLEN: Here is the dollar, sir. But, as you can see, I cannot write because of my bandaged arm. Would you kindly register the names for me?

TICKET AGENT: Regulations forbid me from doing that, sir! Either you register the names yourself or you'll not pass through my station.

NARRATOR: The man spoke so harshly that he attracted the attention of other passengers in the Custom House. It was a tense moment. Ellen found herself scarcely breathing. Just then, a passenger who had sat at breakfast with "Mr. Johnson" stepped forward. He patted "Mr. Johnson" on the shoulder and then turned to the ticket agent.

PASSENGER: See here, sir! Mr. Johnson is well known to me, and I will vouch for him. Anyone can see that he is unwell. There is no reason to treat him so unkindly.

TICKET AGENT: I am simply following the rules, sir.

CAPTAIN 2: What is all this commotion about? I'm the captain of the steamer bound for Wilmington. We're about to leave, and these passengers must board. I will register the gentleman's name and assume the responsibility upon myself. Your full name, sir?

ELLEN: William Johnson.

CAPTAIN 2: William Johnson and slave. There, it's done. Everything is in order now, Mr. Johnson.

ELLEN: Thank you, Captain. You have my deepest gratitude, sir.

CAPTAIN 2: I'm sure the ticket agent intended no disrespect, Mr. Johnson. They have to be very vigilant in Charleston; otherwise, those blamed abolitionists might make off with any number of slaves.

ELLEN: I am sure you are right, Captain. I am sure you are right.

NARRATOR: "Mr. Johnson" trembled at their narrow escape. How close they had come to being sent back! He could only imagine what other troubles might lie ahead.

**Saturday, December 23, 1848   From Wilmington, North Carolina
                                   To Washington, D.C.**

NARRATOR: William and Ellen reached Wilmington on the third morning of their journey. There they boarded a train that took them to Richmond and then on to Fredericksburg, Virginia. Outside Fredericksburg, they boarded a steamer bound for Washington, D.C. During the trip, "Mr. Johnson" met many white people whose kindness posed great danger. One man presented him with his business card. "Mr. Johnson" quickly put it in a pocket for he couldn't risk holding it upside down while pretending to read it! Two young ladies offered their shawls to make a pillow for the ailing gentleman. Evidently, the disguise was convincing. However, "Mr. Johnson" could never let down his guard. There was no way to know when danger might strike—or in what form.

WOMAN: Oh, my goodness, there goes my slave Ned. That's him, over there!

ELLEN: Madam, I fear you are mistaken. That's my slave William!

NARRATOR: The woman paid no attention to "Mr. Johnson's" protests.

WOMAN: You, Ned, come here to me, you runaway!

ELLEN: I assure you, madam, that you are mistaken!

NARRATOR: "Mr. Johnson's" blood ran cold. What would he do if the woman continued to insist that William was her Ned? Would he be asked to produce ownership papers?

WOMAN: Come closer, Ned. I know it's you, you rascal!

WILLIAM: Excuse me, missus. I'm William.

NARRATOR: The woman looked closely at William and then turned to "Mr. Johnson."

WOMAN: Oh, I do beg your pardon, sir. I was so sure he was my Ned! But indeed you were right. I was mistaken.

NARRATOR: "Mr. Johnson" breathed a sigh of relief. Their luck had held once again. If only it would last a little longer.

Macmillan/McGraw-Hill

Sunday, December 24, 1848

**From Washington, D.C.
To Baltimore, Maryland**

NARRATOR: In Washington, William and Ellen hurried off to catch the train for Baltimore. They arrived in Baltimore on the evening of December 24. They had reached the most perilous stop on their long journey.

ELLEN: Baltimore frightens me more than I can say, William. I should be happy that it's the last southern port we have to travel through. But I am more anxious than ever.

WILLIAM: We got good reason for being fearful. The guards are everywhere on the lookout to keep slaves from crossing into Pennsylvania where they'd be free. But I can't believe we'll fail—not when we're so near our goal!

NARRATOR: William helped his master into the train. Then he made his way to the Negro car in the back. Suddenly, he felt someone tapping his shoulder.

CONDUCTOR 2: Where are you going?

WILLIAM: To Philadelphia, sir.

CONDUCTOR 2: What are you going there for?

WILLIAM: I'm traveling with my master, sir. He's in a carriage up front, sir.

CONDUCTOR 2: Well, I calculate you had better get him out, and be mighty quick about it because the train will soon be starting. It's against railroad rules to let any man take a slave past here, unless he can satisfy them in the office that he has a right to take him along.

NARRATOR: William ran back to the carriage where he had left Ellen. Fortunately, "Mr. Johnson" was sitting quite alone.

WILLIAM: How're you feeling, master?

ELLEN: Much better, thank you. I'm glad we're getting on so nicely.

WILLIAM: I'm afraid we're not getting on quite so well as we'd hoped.

ELLEN: What do you mean? Is something the matter?

WILLIAM: Mr. Johnson, sir, we gotta go into the station and prove I'm your slave.

ELLEN: [*whispering*] Prove that you're my slave? But I have no proof! Oh, William, we've come so far! Is it possible that we're doomed after all to hopeless bondage?

WILLIAM: [*whispering*] Ellen, now's the time we gotta call up our faith and courage. We'd best go in . . . and quickly.

NARRATOR: The two terror-stricken fugitives entered the station office. They both knew that their very existence was at stake; with this encounter, they would sink or swim. The office was crowded with travelers full of Christmas cheer. William and Ellen made their way to the station master's window. He eyed them suspiciously, but somehow Ellen managed to kept her head up and her voice firm.

ELLEN: Do you wish to see me, sir?

STATION MASTER: Yes. I hear you're traveling with a slave. It's against railroad rules, sir, to allow any person to take a slave out of Baltimore into Philadelphia, unless he can satisfy us that he has a right to take him along.

ELLEN: Why is that?

STATION MASTER: Because, sir, if we should allow any gentleman to take a slave past here into Philadelphia, and
should that gentleman not be the slave's owner, and
should the proper master come and prove that his slave
escaped on our railroad—then we would have to pay
what the slave was worth. That's why!

ELLEN: I understand, sir, but . . .

STATION MASTER: Now, do you, or do you not, have proof that this is your slave?

ELLEN: I do, sir, but I do not have it with me.

NARRATOR: Their conversation had attracted the attention of the other passengers, who seemed to sympathize with "Mr. Johnson" because he looked so ill. Seeing their reaction, the station master became more polite.

STATION MASTER: Do you have some acquaintance in Baltimore who could assure us that this slave is your property?

ELLEN: Alas no, sir, I do not. I bought tickets in Charleston to pass us through to Philadelphia, and therefore you have no right to detain us here in Baltimore.

STATION MASTER: Well, sir, right or not, I shan't let you go through without proof that this is your slave!

NARRATOR: For a few minutes, there was total silence in the office. Ellen and William looked at each other. Neither dared speak a word for fear of making some blunder that would give them away. They knew that the railroad officers had the power to throw them into prison. Then they would be taken back to punishment and a life of slavery. They felt as though they were suspended over a pit by the thinnest of threads. Then suddenly, a large man pushed to the front of the crowd and approached the station master's window.

ONLOOKER: Where's your Christmas spirit, station master? Can't you see that this poor gentleman is sick. Have a heart. Let him go on to Philadelphia.

STATION MASTER: That's easy for you to say, sir. It's not you who's taking the responsibility.

NARRATOR: Just then the bell rang for the train to leave. It came with the sudden shock of an earthquake. The office door opened; the conductor of the train stepped in. Every eye was fixed intently on the drama at the station master's window.

STATION MASTER: Conductor, did these two come with you on the train from Washington?

CONDUCTOR 2: They surely did, sir! Going up to Philadelphia to see a special doctor, I understand. All right, everyone, we're ready to pull out.

NARRATOR: "Mr. Johnson" appealed to the station master once again.

ELLEN: Please allow me to board that train, sir. I am feeling faint and very weak.

STATION MASTER: I really don't know what to do. . . . Oh-h-h, I calculate it's all right. Clerk, inform the conductor to let this gentleman and his slave pass. As he is not well, it's a pity to stop him here. We will let him go.

ELLEN: Thank you, sir. Thank you! And a very Merry Christmas to you and your family.

Monday, December 25, 1848

**From Baltimore, Maryland
To Philadelphia, Pennsylvania**

NARRATOR: William and Ellen boarded the train seconds before it pulled out of the station. Ellen collapsed into her seat. The train traveled on into the night, carrying them closer and closer to their final destination. Early on Christmas morning, the train pulled into the Philadelphia station. Before it even stopped, William leaped onto the platform and ran to get Ellen.

ELLEN: We are safe, William! Safe and free!

WILLIAM: Glory be, Ellen! We have been granted freedom for Christmas!

NARRATOR: The abolitionist William Lloyd Garrison recounted the Craft's harrowing escape in his newspaper, *The Liberator.* In 1850, two years after their flight to freedom, Ellen and William Craft moved to England for fear that if they stayed in the United States, they might be forced to return to their former masters under the provisions of the soon-to-be-enacted Fugitive Slave Act. With the assistance of a friend, William wrote a book titled *Running a Thousand Miles for Freedom,* which recounted the true story of their daring escape. The Crafts and their two children lived in England for eighteen years. They returned to the United States after the Civil War and bought a former plantation near Savannah, Georgia. There they established a school for black children and adults.

Blocking Diagram

Arrange sixteen chairs, as shown. The narrator can use
a music stand to hold the script.

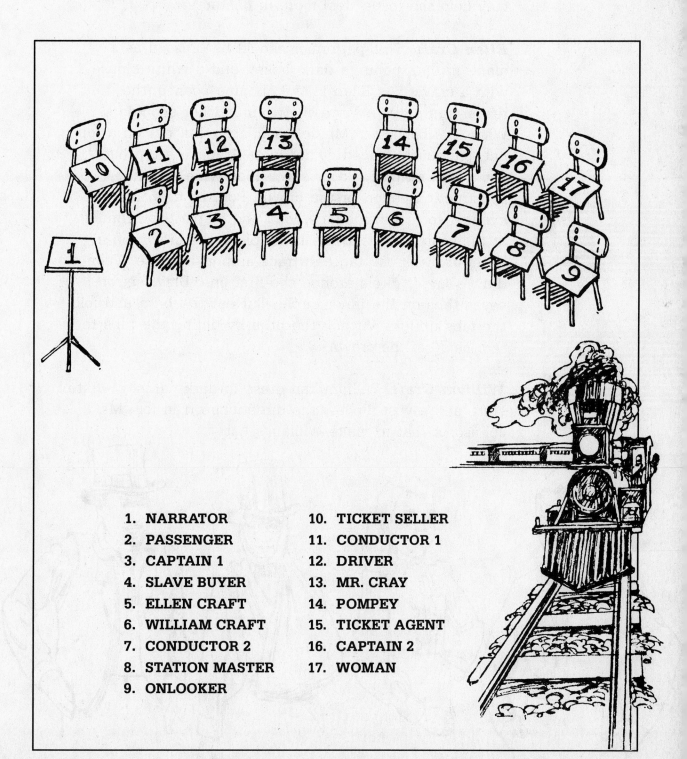

1. **NARRATOR**
2. **PASSENGER**
3. **CAPTAIN 1**
4. **SLAVE BUYER**
5. **ELLEN CRAFT**
6. **WILLIAM CRAFT**
7. **CONDUCTOR 2**
8. **STATION MASTER**
9. **ONLOOKER**

10. **TICKET SELLER**
11. **CONDUCTOR 1**
12. **DRIVER**
13. **MR. CRAY**
14. **POMPEY**
15. **TICKET AGENT**
16. **CAPTAIN 2**
17. **WOMAN**

Costume Suggestions

Narrator Although this role does not call for a special costume, a bow tie for a boy or a long skirt for a girl may help the reader feel more in character.

Ellen Craft This performer should be dressed as a man—in dark pants, a dark jacket, and a white blouse with a cravat. As Ellen in the opening scenes, the reader can drape a large shawl around her shoulders. When she becomes "Mr. Johnson," she can put on a top hat, previously placed at her feet. To make a top hat, cut a long strip of six- or seven-inch-wide black construction paper for the crown. Roll the strip into a cylinder to fit the reader's head and staple the cylinder at the seam. To make the brim, place the crown on a sheet of black oak tag and trace around its base. Then draw a larger circle around the first one. Draw six or seven tabs on the inner circle. Cut out the brim and fold the tabs upright. Attach the brim by gluing the tabs to the inside of the crown.

William Craft William can dress in dark pants, a white shirt, and a vest. Follow the directions given for "Mr. Johnson's" hat to make William's hat.

Macmillan/McGraw-Hill

Mr. Cray, Passenger, Slave Buyer, and Onlooker
The basic costumes for these readers can consist of long
pants, shirts, and jackets. An additional item such as a
cravat, string tie, vest, or hat will help individualize
each outfit.

Railroad Employees These performers can wear dark
pants, white shirts, and dark jackets. A cap with the
employee's job designation would help differentiate the
various characters.

Captain 1 and Captain 2 Light pants, dark jackets,
and blue caps with nautical insignias on the front would
be appropriate for the captains.

Driver and Pompey These readers can wear jeans,
work shirts, and suspenders.

Woman A long dress, or a frilly blouse and a long skirt,
would be fine for this character. An umbrella decorated
to resemble a parasol can be placed near her chair.

A Perilous Journey

Ellen and William Craft's thousand-mile flight to freedom took place more than one hundred and forty years ago. Their route and means of transportation are illustrated on this 1848 map.

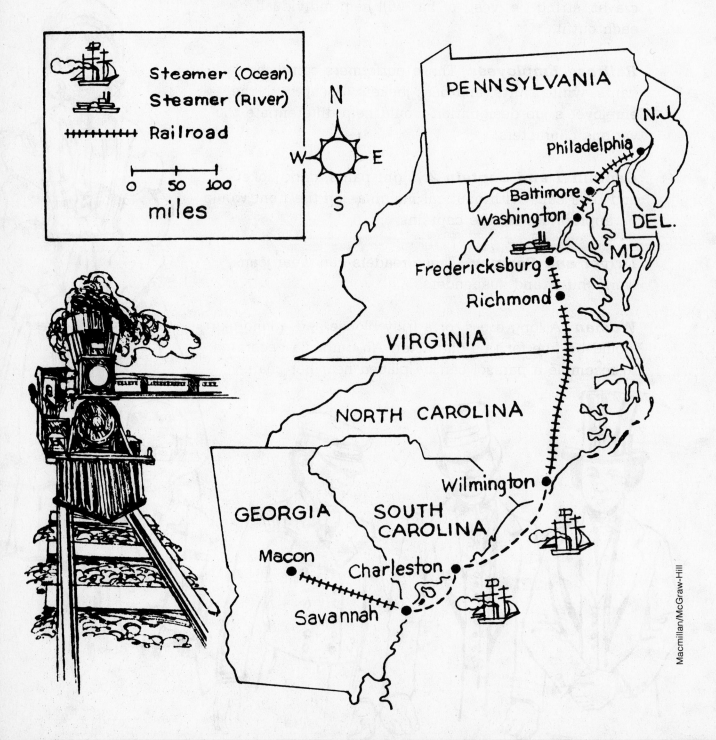

Readers Theater Plays

After your students have participated in a Readers Theater production or two, many may be motivated to write a Readers Theater script of their own. The following ten student resource pages are designed to help guide them through this process.

In addition to developing writing skills, creating a Readers Theater script is also a useful way to extend students' study of story elements. In creating any Readers Theater script, students must solve the problem of conveying action and changes in time and place in a script that is read rather than acted with costumes, scenes, and props. The transformation of narrative into drama also challenges students to closely examine elements of character, motivation, plot, and setting. If students are adapting a story, they must determine what to include and what to omit. If they are writing an original play, they face a different set of decisions: how to invent a story line that incorporates dramatic tension and how to make characters believable. If the play is based on historical events, students should determine what research is required to ensure historical accuracy.

Before students begin writing their own Readers Theater plays, you may find it helpful to explore with them the differences between narrative and drama. One way to do this is to obtain a copy of *The Secret Garden,* by Frances Hodgson Burnett or *Tom Sawyer,* by Mark Twain (sources are listed in the Bibliography on page xii).

Read portions from one of these selections and invite comparisons with the Readers Theater version found in this book. You may wish to assist students in evaluating the relative merits of telling the story in each form. What is gained in each case? What is lost? In making these comparisons, focus on the role of the narrator in providing transitions from one setting to another and in describing action that cannot be conveyed through dialog in the Readers Theater version. Point out examples of how descriptions and other elements of the narrative are transformed into dialog, and how some characters in the play may seem more real because of the words they speak.

After students grasp the major differences between stories and scripts, introduce the following Readers Theater writing-process worksheets to guide them through the process of creating their own Readers Theater plays. Students can work individually, in small cooperative-writing groups, or as an entire class when writing a script.

If your students choose to adapt a folk tale or legend, suggest that they read several versions of the story before they begin the writing process. If students decide to adapt a story or a book, a reading followed by group discussion will ensure that all students are familiar with the story plot, characters, and setting. If students choose to write an original play, they will need to create the plot, characters, and setting themselves.

Getting Started

Stop a minute to think about the Readers Theater productions in which you've participated. As a member of a Readers Theater group, you may have thought that you too could write a play for others to read. Writing a play is not that complicated if you follow a series of steps that take you from finding an idea for a play through writing the final script.

FINAL SCRIPT
DIALOG
CHARACTERS
SETTING
PLOT
PLAY IDEA

GETTING AN IDEA FOR A PLAY

At one time or another, every writer has asked the question, "What should I write about?" One of the most important steps in writing a play is coming up with an idea that will work. A play is like any other story—it generally grows from real-life *experiences* combined with input from your imagination. If you take a little time to think about your experiences, you'll find dozens of things that could be used in a play. Here are a few real-life experiences that can provide good sources for ideas:

- personal experiences you've had at home, at school, or just about anywhere
- experiences that have happened to friends, family members, or others you know
- things you've read in books, newspapers, and magazines
- things you've seen in television programs and movies
- things you've read about in history books

Macmillan/McGraw-Hill

Besides real-life experiences, the other ingredient that goes into creating an idea for a play is your *imagination*. Your imagination is different from that of anyone else—it's one of the things that makes you unique! No one else will imagine exactly the same things in the same way. Your imagination enables you to start with a real-life experience and then transform it into something that no one else could think of.

A Friend's Experience: Last year, my friend's class put on a school play. He told me that the star was so concerned about his role that, in his view, everyone else's part was unimportant.

Imagination: Suppose someone was so serious about a role in a play that his or her behavior became annoying to everyone in the family. What kinds of problems might arise? How would the family deal with these problems?

Get together with a partner or a small group. Brainstorm at least one idea for each source listed on page 188. In each case, add a comment about how your imagination might allow you to treat the idea in an original way. Use another sheet of paper to record your ideas. To help you get started, one possibility has been done for you.

THE PLOT

A play is made up of related events that tell a story. This series of events is called the plot. A good plot will keep you asking, "What's going to happen next?"

Most plots consist of three parts:

- A situation, in which the characters and the setting are introduced
- A conflict, which involves the characters in an attempt to solve some problem. The problem might involve only the characters or may be a struggle against some outside force, such as nature.
- A resolution, or solution, to the conflict

Macmillan/McGraw-Hill

When you're trying to think of plot ideas, remember that all three parts of the plot do not need to be the same length. In most plays, the basic situation is introduced in a page or two. Similarly, the resolution is often presented very concisely. Usually, the majority of events spelled out in the plot focus on the conflict.

Here's a possible plot outline for the incident involving a girl preparing for a starring role in a play, which was mentioned on the "Getting Started" page.

Situation: Jenny has just learned that she will play Dorothy in a school production of The Wizard of Oz. She is thrilled with the role and is determined to do an outstanding job. The same week, her younger brother, Alan, announces that he will be playing a tree in a kindergarten production scheduled for Earth Day.

Conflict: Although Jenny's parents are pleased with her announcement, they treat her role about the same as they treat Alan's. This baffles and upsets Jenny, who feels her part is much more significant. A number of incidents occur involving preparations for both productions in which the children express their annoyance with each other.

Resolution: Finally their mother, who has tried to mediate the disagreements between Jenny and Alan, takes out a photo album and shows pictures of a kindergarten play from some years earlier in which Jenny played one of seven rabbits. The photos and subsequent discussion help Jenny recall how she felt when she was Alan's age. Jenny realizes that any role, regardless of size, is important.

Look again at the list you made when you read the "Getting Started" page. From the list, choose your favorite play idea. Then write a plot outline based on the idea you've chosen. Your outline should include a summary of the situation, the conflict, and the resolution. Write your plot outline on another sheet of paper.

CREATING CHARACTERS

Anyone who appears in a play is called a character. Usually characters are people; however, in fantasies or fables, animals and elements of nature such as flowers or a river can have speaking parts. When writing a play, it is important to try to make your characters different from one another. These differences can help you create a conflict and keep the play action moving forward.

Think about the stories and books you've read. In these works, writers can tell readers about the characters. In some instances, the writer may stop the action to describe what a character is like or why a character is behaving in a certain way.

Macmillan/McGraw-Hill

A play is different. The only way information can be shared about characters is through dialog, the words spoken by the characters. Through dialog, the audience learns what the different characters are like. What does this mean to you, as the writer? It means you must have a clear idea of each character in your mind as you write your play. It also means you will want to carefully choose the words said by your characters to make sure they fit your view of each character's personality. One way to get a clear idea of each personality is to write *character sketches*. A character sketch is a description of a character's appearance, personality, and relationship to the other people in the story. Here, for example, is a character sketch of Jenny's brother Alan.

Alan is a five year old boy who can be adorable one moment and infuriating the next. He looks like most boys his age, except he has bright red hair and a grin that makes him look like a jack-o-lantern because of his three missing teeth! Usually, Alan is a great little brother-- he's funny, friendly, and smart. But sometimes he can be a real pain, especially when he feels that not enough attention is being paid to him. Then he whines, fusses, and tattles on his older sister Jenny. Life with Alan can be difficult at times because no one can predict what he will be like from one minute to the next.

Look back at the plot you have outlined for your play. Then make a list of the main characters you'll need to create. Write a short character sketch for each. Remember that the more information you include, the easier it will be to invent dialog for your character. Keep these sketches handy as you work on your play to remind you of what each person is like. This will help you write believable dialog for your play.

A READERS THEATER SCRIPT

Writing a play is different from writing a story. One important difference you've already discovered is the exclusive use of dialog in a play. Another important difference is in the format. In a script, the characters' names appear on the left followed by a colon (:). The dialog appears on the right side of the page. A third important difference is the use of a narrator in many Readers Theater plays. A narrator can be used to describe a scene, identify changes in setting, or describe important actions that cannot be written as dialog.

Study the following example based on the play idea described in preceding pages. Pay special attention to the part of the narrator.

Narrator: Alan was in the living room with his parents, busily working on his tree costume for the kindergarten play. At that moment, Jenny came in the front door, reading from her script.

Jenny: "Goodness, Toto! This doesn't look anything like Kansas!" Oh, hello, everyone. I was just rehearsing one of my big scenes.

Alan: We were just making my costume. It's for my big scene.

Macmillan/McGraw-Hill

Jenny: You mean as a tree? He doesn't seem to understand, does he mother?

Mother: Understand what, dear?

Jenny: What it means to have a real part in a play.

Alan: I do have a real part! I'm a tree, and that's more real than a girl whose best friend is a talking scarecrow!

Jenny: Oh, right! And what will you do, make tree noises? A real character is when you have lines like, "There's no place like home!"

Father: That's a good line, all right. But Alan has lines of his own to memorize.

Alan: I'll say I do. Just listen to this! "I help make the oxygen you need to breathe."

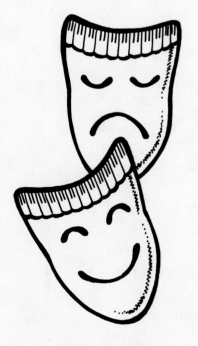

Use the dialog above to discuss these questions in your Readers Theater group.

- How might a story about this incident be told? How is the script different from a story version?
- What is the purpose of the narrator's speech?
- Is the dialog appropriate for the characters?
- What do you think the characters will say next?

Create a scene for your play in which several important characters interact. Use your character sketches as a guide in writing dialog for the characters you've chosen. Use the narrator to describe actions that are not part of the dialog or to establish the setting.

Ready, set, write!

Use the following checklist as a guide in planning and writing your play. After you complete each step, put a check in the box.

Prewriting

☐ Brainstorm ideas for a play.
☐ Outline the plot.
☐ Decide on the setting.
☐ Write the character sketches.

Drafting

☐ Write a first draft of your play. If you work in a group, one person can record the dialog as the group dictates it.
☐ Set up your script using play format. Place the characters' names on the left and the dialog on the right. Skip a line between speakers.
☐ Use the narrator to describe any action that cannot be written as dialog and to tell about changes in time or setting.
☐ Think of a title for your play.

Revising

☐ Make sure the events in your play follow one another in logical order.
☐ Check to see that you have included all the information the audience will need to make sense of the play.
☐ Add or eliminate characters, as needed.
☐ Read your play aloud. Rewrite any dialog that does not sound natural.
☐ Add expressions that help bring your characters to life.
☐ Add humorous dialog, if appropriate.

Macmillan/McGraw-Hill

PROOFREADING

☐ Correct all mistakes in spelling, grammar, punctuation, and script form.

☐ Ask someone else to proofread your script for errors you may have missed.

PUBLISHING

☐ Make a final draft of the script. It should be neat and easy to read. If possible, prepare it on a typewriter or a word processor. Check to make sure that you have made all corrections.

☐ Make a copy for each member of the cast.

When your script is finished, it's time to begin rehearsing. At this point, try not to think of your play as finished. During rehearsals, you may find some places where changes could improve the play. When you're satisfied, plan a performance to share your work with an audience. Don't forget to step forward and take a curtain call for all your hard work as author!

Young Soul

First, feel, then feel, then
read, or read, then feel, then
fall, or stand, where you
already are. Think
of your self, and the other
selves . . . think
of your parents, your mothers
and sisters, your bentslick
father, then feel, or
fall, on your knees
if nothing else will move you,

then read
and look deeply
into all matters
come close to you
city boys—
country men

Make some muscle
in your head, but
use the muscle
in your heart

—Imamu Amiri Baraka
(LeRoi Jones)

About the Teeth of Sharks

The thing about a shark is—teeth,
One row above, one row beneath.

Now take a close look. Do you find
It has another row behind?

Still closer—here, I'll hold your hat:
Has it a third row behind that?

Now look in and . . . Look out! Oh my,
I'll never know now! Well, goodbye.

—John Ciardi

He ate and drank the precious Words

He ate and drank the precious Words—
His Spirit grew robust—
He knew no more that he was poor,
Nor that his frame was Dust—

He danced along the dingy Days
And this Bequest of Wings
Was but a Book—What Liberty
A loosened spirit brings—

—Emily Dickinson

Manners

For a Child

of 1918

My grandfather said to me
as we sat on the wagon seat,
"Be sure to remember to always
speak to everyone you meet."

We met a stranger on foot.
My grandfather's whip tapped his hat.
"Good day, sir. Good day. A fine day."
And I said it and bowed where I sat.

Then we overtook a boy we knew
with his pet crow on his shoulder.
"Always offer everyone a ride;
don't forget that when you get older,"

my grandfather said. So Willy
climbed up with us, but the crow
gave a "Caw!" and flew off. I was worried.
How would he know where to go?

But he flew a little way at a time
from fence post to fence post, ahead;
and when Willy whistled he answered.
"A fine bird," my grandfather said,

"and he's well brought up. See, he answers
nicely when he's spoken to.
Man or beast, that's good manners.
Be sure that you both always do."

When automobiles went by,
the dust hid the people's faces,
but we shouted "Good day! Good day!
Fine day!" at the top of our voices.

When we came to Hustler Hill,
he said that the mare was tired,
so we all got down and walked,
as our good manners required.

—Elizabeth Bishop

FROM WHITMAN

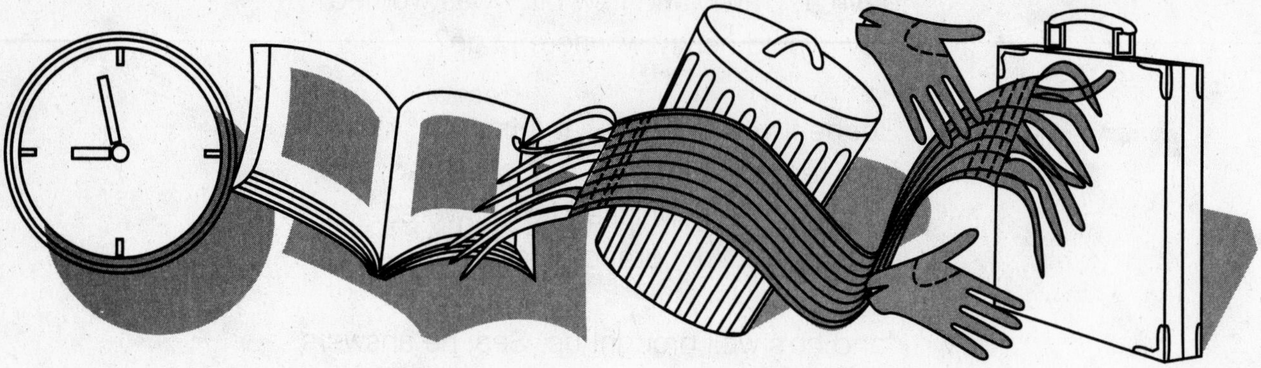

When I go to school
I see
women & men running
to catch a bus.
I see
teachers
with their sunglasses
and long black raincoats,
their red nail polish
and gold jewelry.
I see
crossing guards with a
white banner helping
children.
I see
my building super
putting garbage bags in
garbage cans
with
his gray gloves
and blue jacket.

I see
other children going to school.
They have their lunchboxes
and bookbags.
I see
people with
briefcases and suits
talking to their
friends
with their red
skirts and high-heel shoes.
I see
people from all over the world
talking in different languages
with white scarves
around
their heads.
When I get to school
I see
things that become
a part of me.

—Consuelo Posloncec

So small a thing
This mummy lies,
Closed in death
Red-lidded eyes,
While, underneath
The swaddled clothes,
Brown arms, brown legs
Lie tight enclosed.
What miracle
If he could tell
Of other years
He knew so well;
What wonderment
To speak to me
The riddle of
His history.

—*Myra Cohn Livingston*

My Horse, Fly Like a Bird

My horse, fly like a bird
To carry me far
From the arrows of my enemies,
And I will tie red ribbons
To your streaming hair.

—*Virginia Driving Hawk Sneve*
adapted from a Lakota
warrior's song to his horse

ITHACA

When you start on your journey to Ithaca,
then pray that the road is long,
full of adventure, full of knowledge.
Do not fear the Lestrygonians
and the Cyclopes and the angry Poseidon.
You will never meet such as these on your path,
if your thoughts remain lofty, if a fine
emotion touches your body and your spirit.
You will never meet the Lestrygonians,
the Cyclopes and the fierce Poseidon,
if you do not carry them within your soul,
if your soul does not raise them up before you.
Then pray that the road is long.
That the summer mornings are many,
that you will enter ports seen for the first time
with such pleasure, with such joy!
Stop at Phoenician markets,
and purchase fine merchandise,
mother-of-pearl and corals, amber and ebony,
and pleasurable perfumes of all kinds,
buy as many pleasurable perfumes as you can;
visit hosts of Egyptian cities,
to learn and learn from those who have knowledge.

Always keep Ithaca fixed in your mind.
To arrive there is your ultimate goal.
But do not hurry the voyage at all.
It is better to let it last for long years;
and even to anchor at the isle when you are old,
rich with all that you have gained on the way,
not expecting that Ithaca will offer you riches.

Ithaca has given you the beautiful voyage.
Without her you would never have taken the road.
But she has nothing more to give you.

And if you find her poor, Ithaca has not defrauded you.
With the great wisdom you have gained, with so much experience,
you must surely have understood by then what Ithacas mean.

—*C. P. Cavafy*

Pegasus in Pound

Once into a quiet village,
    Without haste and without heed,
In the golden prime of morning,
    Strayed the poet's winged steed.

It was Autumn, and incessant
    Piped the quails from shocks and sheaves,
And, like living coals, the apples
    Burned among the withering leaves.

Thus, upon the village common,
    By the school-boys he was found;
And the wise men, in their wisdom,
    Put him straightway into pound.

Then the sombre village crier,
    Ringing loud his brazen bell,
Wandered down the street proclaiming
    There was an estray to sell.

And the curious country people,
    Rich and poor, and young and old,
Came in haste to see this wondrous
    Wingèd steed, with mane of gold,

Thus the day passed, and the evening
    Fell, with vapors cold and dim;
But it brought no food nor shelter,
    Brought no straw nor stall, for him.

Patiently, and still expectant,
          Looked he through the wooden bars,
Saw the moon rise o'er the landscape,
          Saw the tranquil, patient stars;

Till at length the bell at midnight
          Sounded from its dark abode,
And, from out a neighboring farm-yard,
          Loud the cock Alectryon crowed.

Then, with nostrils wide distended,
          Breaking from his iron chain,
And unfolding far his pinions,
          To those stars he soared again.

On the morrow, when the village
          Woke to all its toil and care,
Lo! the strange steed had departed,
          And they knew not when nor where.

But they found, upon the greensward
          Where his struggling hoofs had trod,
Pure and bright, a fountain flowing
          From the hoof-marks in the sod.

From that hour, the fount unfailing
          Gladdens the whole region round,
Strengthening all who drink its waters,
          While it soothes them with its sound.

—*Henry Wadsworth Longfellow*

The Song of Wandering Aengus

I went out to the hazel wood,
Because a fire was in my head,
And cut and peeled a hazel wand,
And hooked a berry to a thread;
And when white moths were on the wing,
And moth-like stars were flickering out,
I dropped the berry in a stream
And caught a little silver trout.

When I had laid it on the floor
I went to blow the fire aflame,
But something rustled on the floor,
And some one called me by my name:
It had become a glimmering girl
With apple blossom in her hair
Who called me by my name and ran
And faded through the brightening air.

Though I am old with wandering
Through hollow lands and hilly lands,
I will find out where she has gone,
And kiss her lips and take her hands;
And walk among long dappled grass,
And pluck till time and times are done
The silver apples of the moon,
The golden apples of the sun.

—William Butler Yeats

At the Top of My Voice

When I stamp
The ground thunders,
When I shout
The world rings,
When I sing
The air wonders
How I do such things.

—Felice Holman

Instead of Gentle Human Beings

Instead of gentle human beings,
why weren't my forefathers
like rock, elm, deer
which apparently don't distinguish
and never say,
"Don't quit this grove
in which you've already learned
where the cold wind comes from,
where the warm wind goes."

—Carlos Germán Belli
translated by Cheli Duran

En vez de humanos dulces

En vez de humanos dulces,
por qué mis mayores no existieron
cual piedra, cual olmo, cual ciervo,
que aparentemente no disciernen
y jamás a uno dicen:
"no dejes este soto,
en donde ya conoces
de dó viene el cierzo, a dó va el noto."

—Carlos Germán Belli

Another Mountain

Sometimes there's a mountain
that I must climb
even after I've climbed one already
But my legs are tired now
and my arms need a rest
my mind is too weary right now
But I must climb before the storm comes
before the earth rocks
and an avalanche of clouds buries me
and smothers my soul
And so I prepare myself for another climb
Another Mountain
and I tell myself it is nothing
it is just some more dirt and stone
and every now and then I should reach
another plateau and enjoy the view
of the trees and the flowers below
And I am young enough to climb
and strong enough to make it to any top
You see the wind has warned me
about settling too long
about peace without struggle
The wind has warned me
and taught me how to fly
But my wings only work
After I've climbed a mountain

—Abiodun Oyewole

The Wall of China

Who ever had
Such a whale of a plan
As the Emperor
Chin Shih Huan?

To build a wall
As long as the land,
And as high as a hill
Was what he planned.

The wall he built
Was straight and bent,
Camels and elephants
On top of it went,

But the steps so narrow
Three would pack—
That was to keep
The Tartars back.

Not many Tartars
With bow and arrow
The steps could mount
That were so narrow.

—*Padraic Colum*

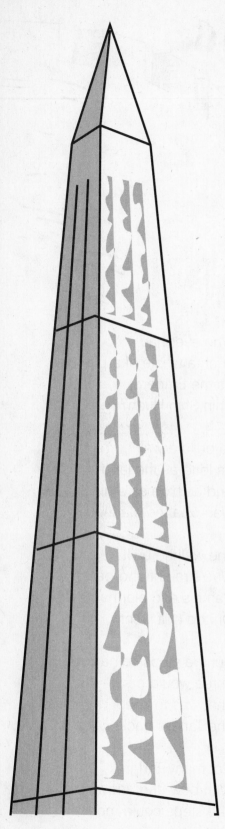

HATSHEPSUT'S
OBELISK

Now my heart turns to and fro,
In thinking what will the people say,
They who shall see my monument in after years,
And shall speak of what I have done. . . .
In order that my name may endure in this temple,
For eternity and everlastingness,
They are each of one block of hard granite,
Without seam, without joining together! . . .
Lo, the god knows me well,
Amun, Lord of Thrones-of-the-Two-Lands;
He made me rule Black Land and Red Land as reward,
No one rebels against me in all lands.
All foreign lands are my subjects,
He placed my border at the limits of heaven,
What Aten encircles labors for me.
He gave it to him who came from him.
Knowing I would rule it for him.
I am his daughter in very truth,
Who serves him, who knows what he ordains.
My reward from my father is life-stability-rule . . .
 eternally like Re.

—Queen Hatshepsut

From the Most Distant Time

Majestic, from the most distant time,
The sun rises and sets.
Time passes and men cannot stop it.
The four seasons serve them,
But do not belong to them.
The years flow like water.
Everything passes away before my eyes.

—*The Emperor Wu of Han*
translated by Kenneth Rexroth

The Clock Ticks

get up get up
clatter a cup

spoon stir
toaster pop

stoke up
down the drain

door knob
click lock

clip clop
walk the block

books to school
wheels to work

rush clack
lurch slack

hup stop
out all out

clip clop
walk the block

into the building
into the box

going up
to the top

open shut
button press

window blind
lights on

read spell
file write

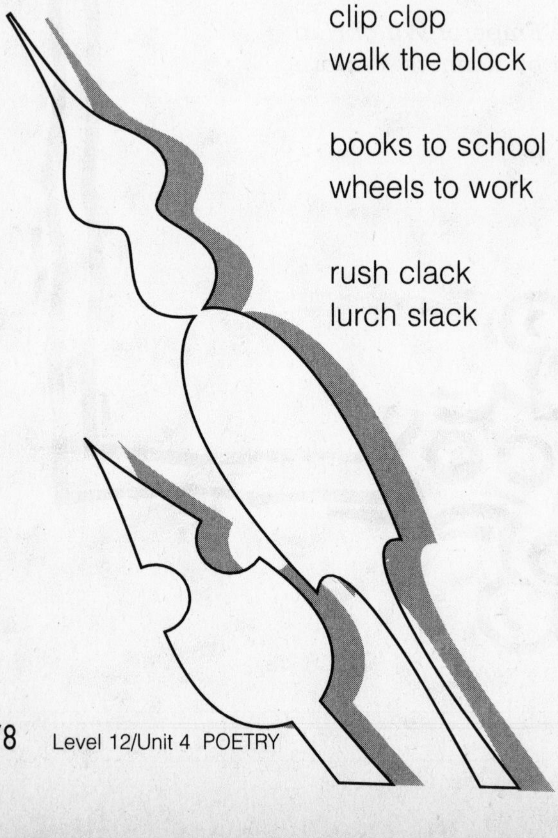

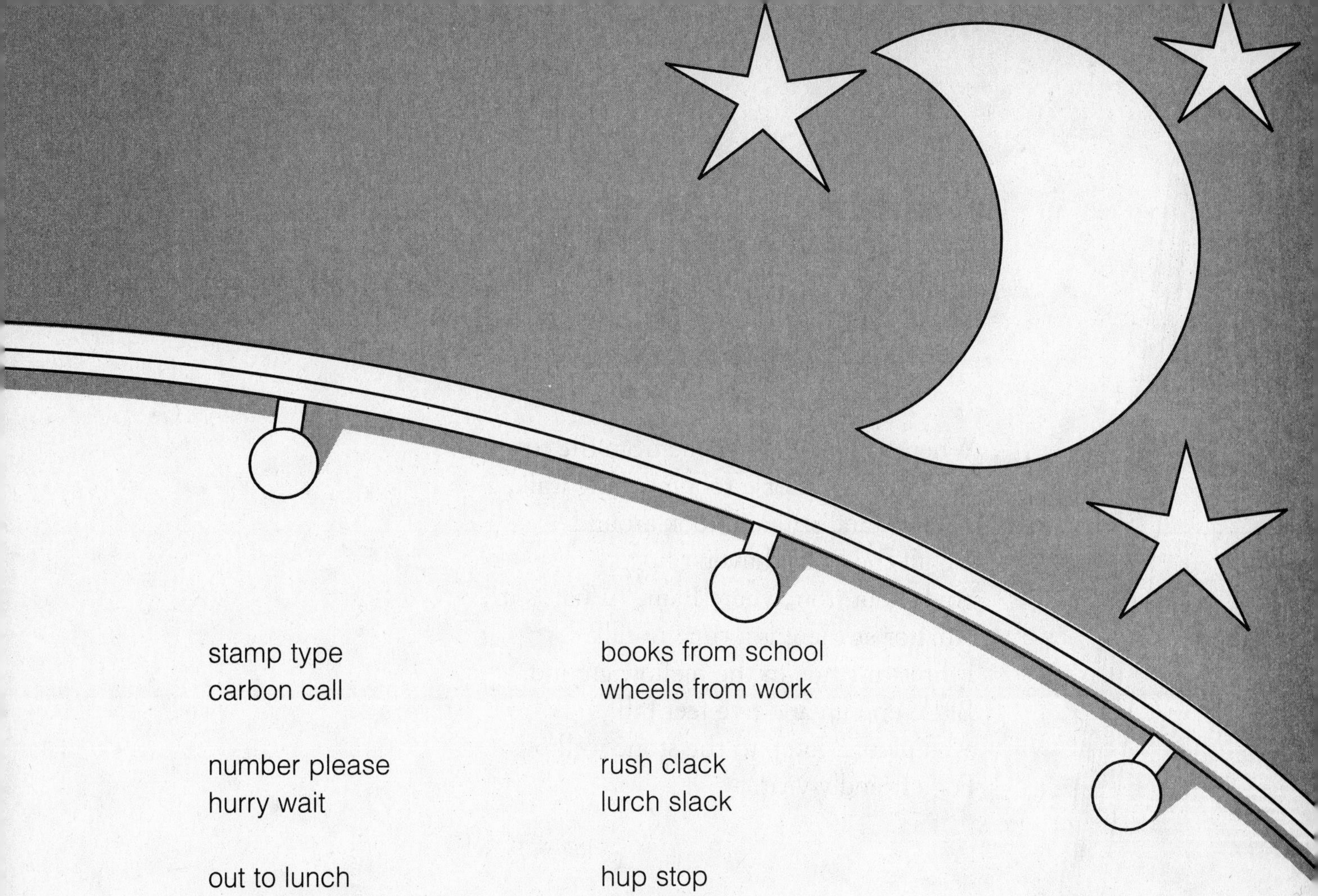

stamp type
carbon call

number please
hurry wait

out to lunch
sandwich bag

back inside
sun set

lights off
button press

going down
ground floor

out of the box
clip clop

books from school
wheels from work

rush clack
lurch slack

hup stop
out all out

walk the block
lock unlock

glass drain
plate scrape

teevee box
head to bed

tick tock
get up get up

—*Eve Merriam*

A Time to Talk

When a friend calls to me from the road
And slows his horse to a meaning walk,
I don't stand still and look around
On all the hills I haven't hoed,
And shout from where I am, "What is it?"
No, not as there is a time to talk.
I thrust my hoe in the mellow ground,
Blade-end up and five feet tall,
And plod: I go up to the stone wall
For a friendly visit.

—*Robert Frost*

To Miss Rápida

If you hurry so,
Time will fly ahead of you like a
Fleeing butterfly.

If you go slowly,
Time will walk behind you
Like a submissive ox.

—*Juan Ramón Jiménez*
Translated by H. R. Hays

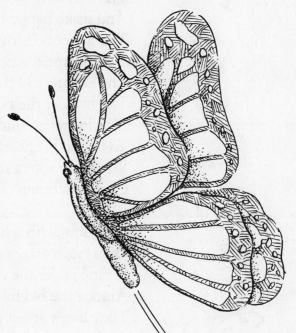

A Miss Rápida

Si vas de prisa,
el tiempo volará ante ti, como una
mariposilla esquiva.

   Si vas despacio,
el tiempo irá detrás de ti,
como un buey manso.

—*Juan Ramón Jiménez*

The Echoing Green

The Sun does arise,
And make happy the skies;
The merry bells ring
To welcome the Spring;
The skylark and thrush,
The birds of the bush,
Sing louder around
To the bells' cheerful sound
While our sports shall be seen
On the Echoing Green.

Old John, with white hair,
Does laugh away care,
Sitting under the oak,
Among the old folk.
They laugh at our play,
And soon they all say:
"Such, such were the joys
When we all, girls and boys,
In our youth time were seen
On the Echoing Green."

Till the little ones, weary,
No more can be merry;
The sun does descend,
And our sports have an end.
Round the laps of their mothers
Many sisters and brothers,
Like birds in their nest,
Are ready for rest,
And sport no more seen
On the darkening Green.

—*William Blake*

MY JOSÉ

When he see friends come home with me
he always says hello,
and if they're new friends
I'm supposed to tell their names and his name.
The problem is I don't know what to call him.

Stepfather is strange.

He's not my dad.

Mister is an uptight word.

I try to get outdoors to play
before he notices,
but if I can't I finally just say,

Hey guys, this is my José.

—*Martha Robinson*

The Delight Song of Tsoai-Talee

I am a feather in the bright sky.
I am the blue horse that runs in the plain.
I am the fish that rolls, shining, in the water.
I am the shadow that follows a child.
I am the evening light, the luster of meadows.
I am an eagle playing with the wind.
I am a cluster of bright beads.
I am the farthest star.
I am the cold of the dawn.
I am the roaring of the rain.
I am the glitter on the crust of the snow.
I am the long track of the moon in a lake.
I am a flame of four colors.
I am a deer standing away in the dusk.
I am a field of sumac and the pomme blanche.
I am an angle of geese upon the winter sky.
I am the hunger of a young wolf.
I am the whole dream of these things.

You see, I am alive, I am alive.
I stand in good relation to the earth.
I stand in good relation to the gods.
I stand in good relation to all that is beautiful.
I stand in good relation to the daughter of Tsen-tainte.

You see, I am alive, I am alive.

—*N. Scott Momaday*

I Ask My Mother to Sing

She begins, and my grandmother joins her.
Mother and daughter sing like young girls.
If my father were alive, he would play
his accordion and sway like a boat.

I've never been in Peking, or the Summer Palace,
nor stood on the great Stone Boat to watch
the rain begin on Kuen Ming Lake, the picnickers
running away in the grass.

But I love to hear it sung;
how the waterlilies fill with rain until
they overturn, spilling water into water,
then rock back, and fill with more.

Both women have begun to cry.
But neither stops her song.

—*Li-Young Lee*

ENCHANTMENT

On warm summer nights
the porch becomes our living room
where Mama takes her reading
and Dad and I play games
in the patch of brightness
the lamp scatters on the floor.
From the darkness, others come - -
small round bodies
clinging to the screens
which separate us
from the yard beyond.
Drawn to our light,
the June bugs watch our games
and listen to our talk till bedtime
when Mama darkens the porch
and breaks the spell
that holds them close to us.

—Joanne Ryder

Morning Horses

O look!
See the horses
In the morning snow!

—*Bashō*

Mother Horse

A mother horse
Keeps watch
While her child
Drinks.

—*Issa*

In the Mist

In the depths of the mist
The horses nuzzle
Each other.

—*Seisensui*

GOLD MEDALIST

In all my endeavor
I wish to be ever
A straight arrow spearing
Just past the possible.

—*Lillian Morrison*

Sea Calm

How still,
How strangely still
The water is today.
It is not good
For water
To be so still that way.

—*Langston Hughes*

The Courage That My *Mother* Had

The courage that my mother had
Went with her, and is with her still:
Rock from New England quarried;
Now granite in a granite hill.

The golden brooch my mother wore
She left behind for me to wear;
I have no thing I treasure more:
Yet, it is something I could spare.

Oh, if instead she'd left to me
The thing she took into the grave!—
That courage like a rock, which she
Has no more need of, and I have.

—*Edna St. Vincent Millay*

The Rescue

Running down the tracks one day,
thunder and lightning coming up on me,
and there a little girl crying
and walking,
looking at the sky.
Me scared to death of storms
crossing over:
You going home? Want me to walk with you?
And turning away from my house to walk her
through Beaver
to hers.
Lightning and thunder strong now.
So there's her mother on the porch,
waving, and she says bye to me then runs.
I turn around
and walk in the storm
slow and straight,
but inside,
a little girl crying.

—Cynthia Rylant

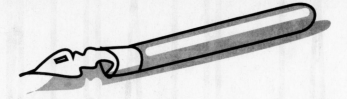

Señora X No More

Straight as a nun I sit.
My fingers foolish before paper and pen
hide in my palms. I hear the slow, accented echo
    How are yu? I ahm fine. How are yu?
of the other women who clutch notebooks and blush
at their stiff lips resting
sounds that float graceful as
bubbles from their children's mouths.
My teacher bends over me, gently squeezes
my shoulders, the squeeze I give my sons,
hands louder than words.
She slides her arms around me:
a warm shawl, lifts my left arm
onto the cold, lined paper.
"Señora, don't let it slip away," she says
and opens the ugly, soap-wrinkled fingers of my right hand
with a pen like I pry open the lips of a stubborn grandchild.
My hand cramps around the thin hardness.
"Let it breathe," says this woman who knows
my hand and tongue knot, but she guides
and I dig the tip of my pen into that white.
I carve my crooked name, and again at night
until my hand and arm are sore,
I carve my crooked name,
my name.

—*Pat Mora*

CHORAL READING ▶▶▶▶▶

Spelling Bee

group 1   group 2

solo   1   2   3

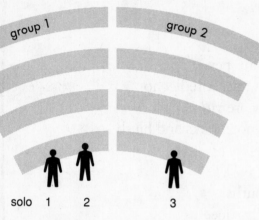

IT COULDN'T BE DONE
GET A TRANSFER

group 1   group 2   group 3

solo   1   2   3   4   5   6

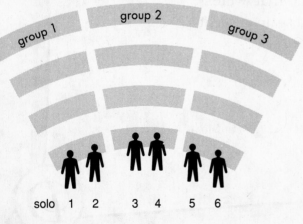

THUMBPRINT

group 1   group 2

solo   1   2   3   4   5   6   7

BOOKS FALL OPEN

boys   girls

Macmillan/McGraw-Hill

BLOCKING DIAGRAMS

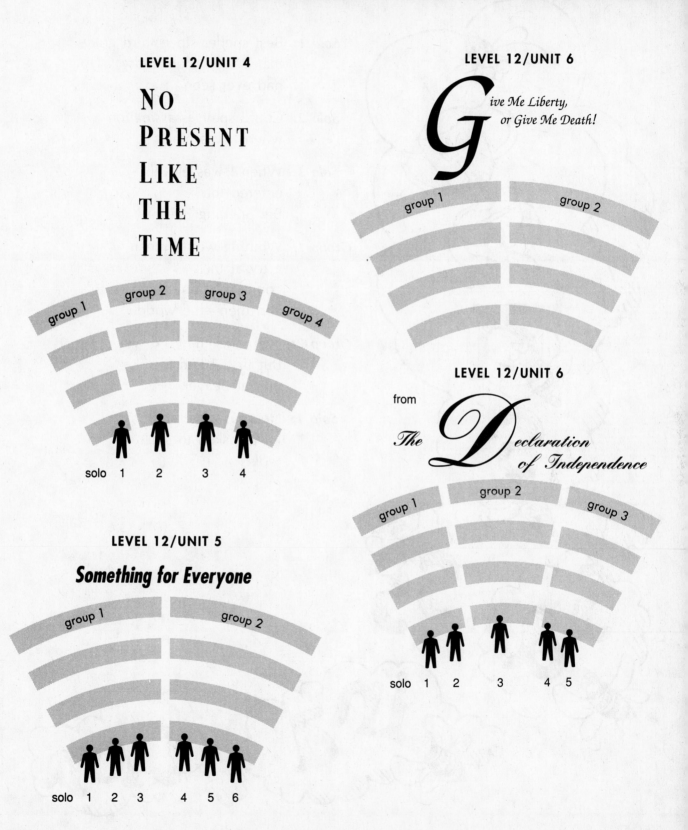

LEVEL 12/UNIT 4

NO
PRESENT
LIKE
THE
TIME

group 1 group 2 group 3 group 4

solo 1 2 3 4

LEVEL 12/UNIT 5

Something for Everyone

group 1 group 2

solo 1 2 3 4 5 6

LEVEL 12/UNIT 6

Give Me Liberty, or Give Me Death!

group 1 group 2

LEVEL 12/UNIT 6

from

The Declaration of Independence

group 1 group 2 group 3

solo 1 2 3 4 5

Spelling Bee

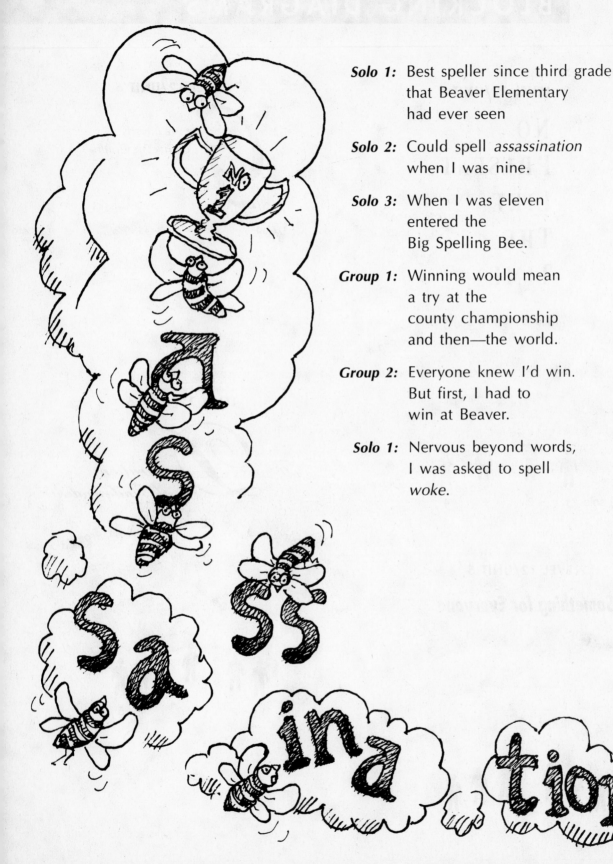

Solo 1: Best speller since third grade
that Beaver Elementary
had ever seen

Solo 2: Could spell *assassination*
when I was nine.

Solo 3: When I was eleven
entered the
Big Spelling Bee.

Group 1: Winning would mean
a try at the
county championship
and then—the world.

Group 2: Everyone knew I'd win.
But first, I had to
win at Beaver.

Solo 1: Nervous beyond words,
I was asked to spell
woke.

Solo 2: Sputtered W-O-A-K.

Solo 3: WOAK.

Group 1: Knew I'd blown it,
just nervous,
but made them check a
dictionary, anyway,
to save myself some
dignity

Group 2: and on the chance that
some stupid idiot
like me
had used it in a
spelling bee
and made it
a word.

All: It wasn't.

Cynthia Rylant

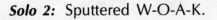

THUMBPRINT

All: In the heel of my thumb
are whorls, whirls, wheels
in a unique design:
mine alone.
What a treasure to own!

Group 1: My own flesh, my own feelings.
No other, however grand or base,
can ever contain the same.

Solo 1: My signature,
Solo 2: thumbing the pages of my time.
Solo 3: My universe key,
Solo 4: my singularity.
Solo 5: Impress, implant,
Solo 6: I am myself,
Solo 7: of all my atom parts I am the sum.

Group 2: And out of my blood and my brain
I make my own interior weather,
my own sun and rain.

All: Imprint my mark upon the world,
whatever I shall become.

Eve Merriam

BOOKS FALL OPEN

All: Books fall open,
you fall in,
delighted where
you've never been;

Girls: hear voices not once
heard before,
reach world on world
through door on door;

Boys: find unexpected
keys to things
locked up beyond
imaginings.

Girls: What *might* you be,
perhaps *become*,
because one book
is somewhere?

Boys: Some
wise delver into
wisdom, wit,
and wherewithal
has written it.

David McCord

IT COULDN'T BE DONE

Group 1: Somebody said that it couldn't be done,
But he with a chuckle replied
That "maybe it couldn't," but he would be one
Who wouldn't say so till he'd tried.
So he buckled right in with the trace of a grin
On his face. If he worried he hid it.
All: He started to sing as he tackled the thing
That couldn't be done, and he did it.

Group 2: Somebody scoffed: "Oh, you'll never do that;
At least no one ever has done it";
But he took off his coat and he took off his hat,
And the first thing we knew he'd begun it.
With a lift of his chin and a bit of a grin,
Without any doubting or quiddit,
All: He started to sing as he tackled the thing
That couldn't be done, and he did it.

Group 3: There are thousands to tell you it cannot be done,
There are thousands to prophesy failure;
There are thousands to point out to you, one by one,
The dangers that wait to assail you.
But just buckle in with a bit of a grin,
Just take off your coat and go to it;
All: Just start to sing as you tackle the thing
That "cannot be done," and you'll do it.

Edgar A. Guest

GET A TRANSFER

Solo 1: If you are on the Gloomy Line,
   All: Get a transfer.
Solo 2: If you're inclined to fret and pine,
   All: Get a transfer.
Group 1: Get off the track of doubt and gloom,
          Get on the sunshine Track—there's room—
   All: Get a transfer.

Solo 3: If you're on the Worry Train,
   All: Get a transfer.
Solo 4: You must not stay there and complain,
   All: Get a transfer.
Group 2: The Cheerful Cars are passing through,
          And there's lots of room for you—
   All: Get a transfer.

Solo 5: If you're on the Grouchy Track,
   All: Get a transfer.
Solo 6: Just take a Happy Special back,
   All: Get a transfer.
Group 3: Jump on the train and pull the rope,
          That lands you at the station Hope—
   All: Get a transfer.

Unknown

NO PRESENT LIKE THE TIME

All: "No time like the present," they always used to say,
Meaning—

Solo 1: Get Busy!

Solo 2: Do You Hear Me?

Solo 3: Don't Delay!

All: Much better in reverse (it doesn't have to rhyme):
Simply, simply,

Solo 4: No present like the time.

Group 1: Time, you agree, is everybody's gift,
But the packages aren't the same.
The lid of each is there to lift,
Yet only one package bears your name.

Macmillan/McGraw-Hill

Group 2: Lift the lid a little now each morning,
And what comes whistling out?
A day's supply of time. Almost a-borning
It dies with every breath as you go about
Your work or play.

Group 3: How much of it is in
That package? No one knows. You, least of all.
Time is indifferent to what we begin;
Indifferent also to whether we stand or fall.

All: Don't waste your time, they say. Waste time you will;
And such as you wish, of course, is yours to squander.

Group 4: Don't call it wasted when you climb a hill.
Through fields and woods to wander
Is to be young, and time belongs to the young.
It's when you're old that clocks begin to tick.

All: Play fair with time: his praise so rarely sung.
He is your snail. But oh, his pulse is quick.

David McCord

Something for Everyone

All: Something for everyone,
that's when a family's fun.
Group 1: There's lots of surprises,
with different sizes
and shapes to a family.
All: Something for sharing there,
with people caring there.
Group 2: It's a door you can go in,
a place you can grow in.
It's anything you need it to be.

Solo 1: Maybe it's your mother and your dad and you.
Solo 2: Maybe you have one place or divide it in two.
Solo 3: Maybe there's a brother or a sis who shares.
Solo 4: Maybe there's a grandma with a room upstairs.
Solo 5: Maybe there's an aunt with all her children grown.
Solo 6: Maybe there's a stepdad with kids of his own.
Group 1: Maybe there's a cousin, even three or four,
sleeping all together on one great big floor.

All: But there's
Something for everyone,
that's when a family's fun.
Group 1: There's lots of surprises,
with different sizes
and shapes to a family.
All: Something for sharing there,
with people caring there.

Group 2: It's a door you can go in,
a place you can grow in.
It's anything you need it to be.

Solo 1: Living in a castle or a riverboat,
Solo 2: living in a farmhouse with a billy goat,
Solo 3: living in an igloo or an Indian tent,
Solo 4: living in a small apartment—paying rent,
Solo 5: living on a mountain where the sky is blue,
Solo 6: living in a one-room with a window view....
Group 2: No, it's not the people or the place
they live.
It's more the kind of feeling and the
love they give.
All: But there's
Something for everyone,
that's when a family's fun.
Group 1: There's lots of surprises,
with different sizes
and shapes to a family.
All: Something for sharing there,
with people caring there.
Group 2: It's a door you can go in,
a place you can grow in.
It's anything you need it to be.

All: Something for everyone!

Carol Hall

Give Me Liberty, or Give Me Death!

All: Gentlemen may cry, Peace, Peace—
but there is no peace.

Group 1: The war is actually begun!
The next gale that sweeps from the north will bring
to our ears the clash of resounding arms!

Group 2: Our brethren are already in the field!
Why stand we here idle?

Group 1: What is it that gentlemen wish?
What would they have?

Group 2: Is life so dear, or peace so sweet,
as to be purchased at the price of chains and slavery?

All: Forbid it, Almighty God!
I know not what course others may take;
but as for me,

Group 1: give me liberty,

Group 2: or give me death!

Patrick Henry

—From *The Call to Arms,* a
speech delivered March 23,
1775, to the Virginia House of
Burgesses, Richmond, Virginia

Macmillan/McGraw-Hill

from The Declaration of Independence

July 4, 1776

Group 1: When in the Course of human events, it becomes necessary for one people to dissolve the political bands which have connected them with another,

Group 2: and to assume among the powers of the earth, the separate and equal station to which the Laws of Nature and of Nature's God entitle them,

Group 3: a decent respect to the opinions of mankind requires that they should declare the causes which impel them to the separation.

All: We hold these truths to be self-evident,

Solo 1: that all men are created equal,

Solo 2: that they are endowed by their Creator with certain unalienable Rights,

Solo 3: that among these are Life, Liberty, and the pursuit of Happiness.

Solo 4: That, to secure these rights, Governments are instituted among Men, deriving their just powers from the consent of the governed.

Solo 5: That whenever any form of Government becomes destructive of these ends, it is the Right of the People to alter or to abolish it, and to institute new Government,

All: laying its foundation on such principles and organizing its powers in such form, as to them shall seem most likely to effect their Safety and Happiness.

PERFORMANCE Evaluation

When you perform in a Readers Theater production, you may think of yourself primarily as a reader. Yet in Readers Theater, you are also a listener and a team member. Your performance in all three areas contributes to the success of the production.

Use this sheet to help you evaluate your performance in each area.

Oral-Reading Skills

	ALWAYS	MOST OF THE TIME	SOMETIMES	ALMOST NEVER	NEVER
Did I read my lines fluently?	1	2	3	4	5
Did I check for pronunciation of unfamiliar words?	1	2	3	4	5
Did I mark my script for pauses and for special emphasis?	1	2	3	4	5
Did I observe punctuation marks and pause marks in my script?	1	2	3	4	5
Did I read with expression?	1	2	3	4	5
Did I vary my reading rate depending on the meaning?	1	2	3	4	5
Did I vary my pitch, according to the mood of the play?	1	2	3	4	5
Did I work on my diction, pronouncing beginnings and endings of words carefully and clearly?					
Did I project my voice so I could be heard?	1	2	3	4	5
Did I familiarize myself with my script so I could use on-stage and off-stage focus?	1	2	3	4	5

Listening Skills

	ALWAYS	MOST OF THE TIME	SOMETIMES	ALMOST NEVER	NEVER
Did I listen attentively for my cues and come in on time?	1	2	3	4	5
Did I listen to myself as I read, making adjustments in rate, pitch, or diction as necessary?	1	2	3	4	5
Did I listen attentively as others read, avoiding any distracting sounds and movements?	1	2	3	4	5
Did I listen to the audience and allow time for their reactions?	1	2	3	4	5
Did I visualize the action and the setting of the play?	1	2	3	4	5

Teamwork Skills

	ALWAYS	MOST OF THE TIME	SOMETIMES	ALMOST NEVER	NEVER
Did I come to my Readers Theater team prepared to contribute?	1	2	3	4	5
Did I allow others to express themselves in discussions?	1	2	3	4	5
Did I show respect for the opinions of others?	1	2	3	4	5
Did I make my suggestions to others constructive?	1	2	3	4	5
Did I consider the suggestions of my teammates?	1	2	3	4	5

List two or three suggestions you received from teammates.

Explain how one of these suggestions helped you improve your performance.

Select a personal goal for your next production and write about it.

Select a team goal for your next production and write about it.

Macmillan/McGraw-Hill

ACKNOWLEDGMENTS

The Publisher gratefully acknowledges permission to reprint the following copyrighted material:

"About the Teeth of Sharks" by John Ciardi from YOU READ ME, I'LL READ YOU. Published by Lippincott. Copyright © 1962 by Curtis Publishing Co. Reprinted by permission.

"Another Mountain" by Abiodun Oyewole from ROOTED IN THE SOIL. Copyright © 1983 by Abiodun Oyewole. Reprinted by permission.

"At the Top of My Voice" by Felice Holman. Reprinted by permission.

"Books Fall Open" and "No Present Like the Time" from ONE AT A TIME by David McCord. Copyright © 1965, 1966, 1970 by David McCord. Reprinted by permission of Little, Brown and Company.

"The Clock Ticks" from A SKY FULL OF POEMS by Eve Merriam. Copyright © 1964, 1970, 1973 by Eve Merriam. Used by permission of Marian Reiner for the author.

"The Courage That My Mother Had" by Edna St. Vincent Millay from COLLECTED POEMS, HarperCollins. Copyright © 1954, 1982 by Norma Millay Ellis. Reprinted by permission of Elizabeth Barnett, literary executor.

"The Delight Song of Tsoai-Talee" from ANGLE OF GEESE AND OTHERS POEMS by N. Scott Momaday. Reprinted by permission of David R. Godine, Publisher, Inc. Copyright © 1974 by N. Scott Momaday.

"En vez de Humanos Dulces" by Carlos Germán Belli. Reprinted by permission.

"Enchantment" by Joanne Ryder. Copyright © 1990 by Joanne Ryder. Used by permission of the author.

"From the Most Distant Time by Emperor Wu of Han" by Kenneth Rexroth from ONE HUNDRED MORE POEMS FROM THE CHINESE. Copyright © 1970 by Kenneth Rexroth. Reprinted by permission of New Directions Publishing Corp.—WORLD RIGHTS.

"From Whitman" by Consuelo Posloncec from HAPPY NEW YEAR published by Teachers & Writers Collaborative. Copyright © 1991 by Teachers & Writers Collaborative, 5 Union Square West, New York, NY 10003.

"Gold Medalist" from THE BREAK DANCE KIDS by Lillian Morrison. Copyright © 1985 by Lillian Morrison. Reprinted by permission of Marian Reiner for the author.

"He ate and drank" by Emily Dickinson. Reprinted by permission.

LI-YOUNG LEE: "I Ask My Mother to Sing," copyright © 1986 by Li-Young Lee. Reprinted from ROSE, by Li-Young Lee, with the permission of BOA Editions, Ltd., 92 Park Ave., Brockport, NY 14420.

"In the Mist" by Seisensui from IN THE EYES OF THE CAT by Demi, translated by Tze-si Huang. Copyright © 1992 by Demi. Reprinted by permission of Henry Holt and Co., Inc.

"Instead of Gentle Human Beings" reprinted with the permission of Simon & Schuster Books for Young Readers from THE YELLOW CANARY WHOSE EYE IS SO BLACK: Poems of Spanish-Speaking Latin America edited and translated by Cheli Durán. English translation copyright © 1977 by Cheli Durán Ryan.

"It Couldn't Be Done" from THE PATH TO HOME by Edgar A. Guest. Copyright © 1919. Published by The Reilly and Lee Company.

"Ithaca" by C. P. Cavafy from THE COMPLETE POEMS OF CAVAFY, copyright © 1961 and renewed 1989 by Rae Dalven, reprinted by permission of Harcourt Brace & Company.

"Manners" by Elizabeth Bishop from THE COMPLETE POEMS OF ELIZABETH BISHOP. Published by Farrar, Straus & Giroux. Copyright © 1955, 1969 by Elizabeth Bishop. Reprinted by permission.

"Morning Horses" by Bashō from IN THE EYES OF THE CAT by Demi, translated by Tze-si Huang. Copyright © 1992 by Demi. Reprinted by permission of Henry Holt and Co., Inc.

"Mother Horse" by Issa from IN THE EYES OF THE CAT by Demi, translated by Tze-si Huang. Copyright © 1992 by Demi. Reprinted by permission of Henry Holt and Co., Inc.

"Mummy" from THE WAYS THINGS ARE AND OTHER POEMS by Myra Cohn Livingston. Copyright © 1974 by Myra Cohn Livingston. Reprinted by permission of Marian Reiner for the author.

"My Horse, Fly Like a Bird" by Virginia Driving Hawk Sneve. Copyright © 1989 by Virginia Driving Hawk Sneve. All rights reserved. Reprinted from DANCING TEEPEES: POEMS OF AMERICAN INDIAN YOUTH by permission of Holiday House.

"My José" by Martha Robinson. Copyright © 1989 by Martha Robinson. This appeared originally in POEMS FOR FATHERS selected by Myra Cohn Livingston. Used by permission of the author. Reprinted by permission.

"A Queen's Promise" by Hatshepsut from WOMEN POETS OF THE WORLD. Published by Macmillan Publishing Co. Copyright © 1983 by Macmillan Publishing Co. Reprinted by permission.

"The Rescue" reprinted with the permission of Simon & Schuster Books for Young Readers from WAITING TO WALTZ by Cynthia Rylant. Copyright © 1984 by Cynthia Rylant.

"Sea Calm" from SELECTED POEMS by Langston Hughes. Copyright 1926 Alfred A. Knopf, Inc., and renewed 1954 by Langston Hughes. Reprinted by permission of the publisher.

"Señora X No More" by Pat Mora. Copyright © 1990 by Pat Mora. Reprinted by permission.

"Something for Everyone" by Carol Hall from FREE TO BE . . . A FAMILY conceived by Marlo Thomas. Copyright © 1987 by Free to Be Foundation, Inc. Reprinted by permission of Carol Hall.

"The Song of Wandering Aengus" by William Butler Yeats from SELECTED POEMS AND TWO PLAYS OF WILLIAM BUTLER YEATS. Published by Collier Books. Copyright © 1962 by The Macmillan Company. Reprinted by permission.

"Spelling Bee" reprinted with the permission of Simon & Schuster Books for Young Readers from WAITING TO WALTZ by Cynthia Rylant. Copyright © 1984 by Cynthia Rylant.

"Thumbprint" from A SKY FULL OF POEMS by Eve Merriam. Copyright © 1964, 1970, 1973 by Eve Merriam. Reprinted by permission of Marian Reiner for the author.

"A Time to Talk" by Robert Frost from THE POETRY OF ROBERT FROST edited by Edward Connery Lathem. Copyright 1944 by Robert Frost. Copyright 1916 © 1969 by Henry Holt and Co., Inc. Reprinted by permission of Henry Holt and Co., Inc.

"To Miss Rápida/A Miss Rápida" by Juan Ramón Jiménez (translated by H. R. Hayes) from SELECTED WRITINGS OF JUAN RAMÓN JIMÉNEZ. Published by Farrar, Straus & Giroux. Copyright © 1957 by Juan Ramón Jiménez. Reprinted by permission.

"The Treasure Seekers" from TREASURE OF THE ATOCHA by R. Duncan Mathewson III. Copyright © 1987 by Gulf Publishing Company, Houston, TX. Used with permission. All rights reserved.

"The Wall of China" by Padraic Colum from A GREEN PLACE. Published by Delacorte Press. Reprinted by permission.

"Young Soul" by Imamu Amiri Baraka (Leroi Jones) from BLACK MAGIC POETRY 1961–1967. Copyright © 1990 by Imamu Amiri Baraka. Reprinted by permission.

ILLUSTRATION CREDITS

Pages 197–218, 366, 373, 375, 376, 378–380, 383, 386, 387, 390, 391 Alex Bloch; 364, 365, 370, 371, 374, 381, 382 Dan Cooper; 285–322 Neverne Covington; 165–196 John Dyess; 362 Rachel Geswaldo; 351 Scott Harvey Photograph; 394, 395, 398 Tom Huffman; 392, 393 Joe LeMonnier; 353, 355, 357–359 Judith Moncrieff; 363, 367–369, 372, 377, 384, 385, 388, 389 Julie Peterson; 396, 397, 404, 405 Bill Russell; 323–350 Dennis Schofield; 219–248 Sandra Speidel; 402, 403 Mary K. Thelen; 400, 401 Charles Waller; 249–284 Ron Zalme; 352, 354, 356, 358–361, 399 Jerry Zimmerman